FAMILY GUIDE TO SEX AND INTIMACY

Family Guide to Sex and Intimacy

Dr Trevor Stammers

Hodder & Stoughton
LONDON SYDNEY AUCKLAND

First published in 1994 by Hodder & Stoughton Ltd.
A Division of Hodder Headline PLC.

10 9 8 7 6 5 4 3 2 1

British Library Cataloguing in Publication Data

Stammers, Trevor
Family Guide to Sex and Intimacy
I. Title
613.9

ISBN 0-340-60816-1

Typeset by Phoenix Typesetting, Ilkley, West Yorkshire

Printed and bound in Great Britain by Cox & Wyman Ltd, Reading, Berks,

Hodder and Stoughton Ltd
A Division of Hodder Headline PLC
338 Euston Road
London NW1 3BH

To
Gordon and June, my parents
Bill and Dorothy, my friends,
and
Rachel, my wife
who have given me so much love through my own ages of
intimacy

CONTENTS

II Adolescence – The Turbulent Age

III Marriage and Parenthood – The Nurturing Age

FOREWORD

When I was a junior doctor in Oxford, one of my teachers was wont to say 'sex is not the most important thing in life: but it is one of the most important *less* important things'!

Down the ages society has both underestimated and overestimated its importance, and with disastrous results. Underestimation of sex led to classical Victorian prudery, the notion that shutting our eyes would make all its problems go away; exaggerating its importance, from St Augustine onwards, led to the notion that the worst kind of sin was sexual sin.

There are some who believe, either consciously or subconsciously, that when all's said and done God really does not approve of sexual intercourse – especially if the couple are doing it for mutual enjoyment and/or are preventing sperm meeting egg. The best rebuttal to this view that I know is a simple anatomical lesson followed by a simple question. Women possess a little organ of their very own, the clitoris, whose only function ever discovered is the production of sexual pleasure: primarily for her, though her lover may receive much vicarious delight through it as well. What is more, fertility is perfectly possible without it.

So these people should consider the question how can the God who created the clitoris disapprove of lovemaking? My answer is this: so long as it takes place within marriage, God doesn't disapprove of sex at all, and we should enjoy it to the full.

It gives me great pleasure to write a Foreword to this book, whose jokey headings display a light touch throughout. There is a lot of very serious stuff, of course, and I was pleased to find the author up-to-date, unabashed and accepting in dealing with controversial areas of particular uncertainty today. A good example is his approach in chapter twelve, 'It is amazing how many couples who may have been married for years have never even talked about oral sex. Perhaps if there was more "oral sex" of this kind, involving the talking through of sexual issues together, the other type of oral sex would not be such a sensitive subject.'

Much grief lies behind the modern statistics of divorce, abortions, sexually transmitted diseases and psychosexual ill health. Readers who do not share all Dr Stammers's conclusions will still find much on which to ponder and much from which a truly open mind might learn. With so many broken and hurting people in society today, there is much in this book to help put them back together again. It is a positive, practical and authoritative guide to enjoying relationships as originally intended.

John Guillebaud MA FRCSE FRCOG
Professor of Family Planning and Reproductive Health
Medical Director of Margaret Pyke Centre for Study
and Training in Family Planning
Honorary Consultant Gynaecologist, University College
Hospitals, London

ACKNOWLEDGMENTS

Many friends, colleagues and patients have contributed to this book.

There are three people in particular without whom it would never have been written at all. My wife, Rachel, not only read and suggested improvements on the initial draft, but also demonstrated great sacrificial love in remaining a word-processor widow for far more weeks than we had originally envisaged. She and my children also missed out on many weekends together with me as a family. I owe them a great debt of thanks.

I am also indebted to my friend, Dr Andrew Fergusson, for first suggesting that I write this book and for his helpful comments on the text. James Catford, my editor, patiently persuaded me finally to undertake the task and has also been an indispensable source of encouragement and advice throughout.

There are many others who have helped by both providing resources for and commenting upon individual chapters. I thank Prof. John Guillebaud particularly in this regard, and for writing the Foreword. I also thank Sgt Carol Abbott, Jeremy Booth, Margaret Cuthill, Barbara Davidson, Dr Patrick Dixon, Dr Angela Field, Margaret Finn, Ann Holt, Colin and Ruth Matthews, Paul Monger, Norman and Margaret Moss, Valerie Riches, Carmal Spreadborough, Ron Trickey and Dr Martyn Wake.

Finally, I thank Anna Bailey and Janet Grimes of Merton Library Services, Edward George of the Hirson Library, St Helier Hospital, Carshalton, and Susan Gilbert of the Medical School Library, St George's Hospital, for their tireless efforts in obtaining reference material and original papers for me.

INTRODUCTION

Yes this **is** yet another book about sex. But it's not just another book about sex. In fact, I guarantee that you will not find any volume on sex as controversial as this one in the whole bookstore. So what makes it so different?

First, it takes a holistic view of sex. There is plenty of biology in these pages, but the personal and symbolic meanings of our sexual nature are also considered in depth. This wider approach is not just concerned with the genital plumbing, but also with the architecture of the relationship in which the pipes are installed! It is a book about sex **and** intimacy. So for example, you will not only discover how to handle sexual organs sensitively, but how to handle conflict in your relationship as well.

Next I have written this book with the emphasis on the family. From the cradle to the grave, the normal development of intimate relationships is discussed in a family context in the first four parts of the book, while some of the many enemies of intimacy that erode close family relationships are explored in Part V.

The family context has determined my choice of subjects throughout so I have written only about those things that ordinary families are most likely to meet. Such subjects as transexualism or celibacy, fascinating though they are, have been omitted because they concern only a very small proportion of families personally. However all the major joys and difficulties of family life are included here – falling in love and falling out of it, having a row and making up, getting married and getting divorced, intimate intercourse and sexual problems, having children and being unable to have them.

Where highly controversial matters are discussed, I have again dealt only with those areas most relevant to families. Thus, in looking at homosexuality, the focus is on helping parents and their homosexual teenagers relate to each other, rather than, for instance, on what gay men and women do in bed.

Third, I write as a family doctor with over ten years experience in general practice, and several years in medical research. Though many doctors have written books about sex before, the wealth of research findings collected together in this volume is unique. I have deliberately quoted from such a wide range of original references because many of their conclusions are so surprising. Some are so contrary to the conventional creeds of many sexologists that they are utterly dumbfounded when confronted with the details.

What other book on sex has a whole chapter on premarital virginity for example? Yet this is a crucial topic, as you will see. In the autumn of 1988 I presented the substance of this chapter as the opening lecture at the National Conference of the Association of Sexual and Marital Therapists in Birmingham, England. I anticipated a great flurry of opposition from the wide-ranging and erudite audience present, but at the conclusion of my presentation you could have heard a pin drop. Though not everyone agreed with my views, there was not one scrap of dissenting scientific evidence put forward to cast any doubt on their validity. You will find many of the sacred cows of sexology are similarly challenged here, so prepare yourself for a few surprises.

Finally, I write as a Christian utterly convinced of the rationality and contemporary relevance of biblical teaching on sexual intimacy. Contrary to popular opinion, the Bible is not anti-sex. In fact, its teaching is well summarised by one sexologist who writes '... our maleness and femaleness is gorgeous. It is God-given, and we need to love that in each other'.[1] Sex and religion are inextricably bound since sex is God's idea, so it is no surprise to me that most writers on sex, whether Christian or not, quote directly from the Bible, or at least make religious allusions at some point. Even Alex Comfort refers several times to what he calls 'the divine gift of lechery'!

I am convinced however that if the biblical Christian understanding of sex is at all valid for the end of the twentieth century, and if it truly shows us the best way to fulfil our sexual potential, then some evidence for this must be demonstrable from scientific research. It is for this reason that you will find no biblical quotations at all in this book, though you will find some of the books suggested in the further reading sections can help you explore this area in greater depth.

It is my hope that you will be prompted to do so, and that as you discover how you can develop a deeper human intimacy, so you may also develop a longing for intimacy with the One from whom our capacity to love derives.

I

INFANCY AND CHILDHOOD –
THE ENQUIRING AGE

1

BOYS AND GIRLS COME OUT TO PLAY: GENDER IDENTITY

What are little boys made of?
Frogs and snails and puppy-dogs' tails...

Robert Southey
What all the World is Made of

It's a startling thought that our sexual experience begins even before we are born. Erections of the penis, for example, can clearly be seen on ultrasound scanning of baby boys when still inside the womb.

Our sex education also often starts before we have uttered our first cry. 'It's a boy!' or 'It's a girl!' is the first thing our parents say about us. Our sexual identity is of primary importance.

A mere glance at the external sex organs of a baby is all that is usually required to determine whether it is a boy or girl. The actual process of becoming male or female is however an extremely complex one, and still further factors come into play to determine our sense of gender identity – that is whether we are masculine or feminine. In this chapter we shall examine the main elements which determine our pathway through the winding labyrinth of sex differentiation.

The most fundamental difference between the sexes lies in the sex chromosomes. The chromosomes are rodlike bundles of genetic material contained within the nucleus of every cell in our bodies. With the exception of the sperms and eggs, every cell contains forty-six chromosomes joined in pairs. Forty-four determine our physical features such as eye colour, body build and height. The remaining pair – the sex chromosomes, determine whether we are male or female.

A woman's cells have two X chromosomes, and a man's have one X and one Y. It is the Y chromosome which confers maleness in humans, though for some other creatures such as birds, it is the female who has both X and Y.

The adult organs which produce the germ-cells – the testes in men and the ovaries in women – both have a common origin in the developing embryo. This is called the primitive gonad. In the presence of the male-determining factor programmed on the Y chromosome, the centre of the primitive gonad develops into a testis, starting at about the sixth week of fetal life. If the male factor is absent, the outer rim of the primitive gonad will start developing into an ovary at around the twelfth week after conception.

DEVELOPMENT OF SEXUAL ORGANS

In early fetal life, the external genitalia are the same regardless of sex. The origins of the internal sexual organs of both sexes are present in the form of the Wolffian and Mullerian ducts. The fetal testes produce two types of hormone, one of which stifles the growth of the Mullerian ducts, while the other stimulates the development of the Wolffian ducts to form the spermatic cord, seminal vesicles and ejaculatory mechanism in the male. In the absence of testicular hormones, the Mullerian ducts automatically develop into a uterus, Fallopian tubes and upper vagina in the female (p.25).

Similarly the development of penis and scrotum depends on the continuing presence of male hormones. In their absence a clitoris and labia will develop instead.

Occasionally the process of formation of the sex organs goes wrong because of faults in the genetic material. The birth of a child of indeterminate sex with ambiguous external sex organs is always a traumatic event for the parents concerned. Expert advice will be needed to determine the cause of the problem, the genetic sex, and what gender would best be assigned to the child.

DEVELOPMENT OF MALE AND FEMALE SEXUAL ORGANS

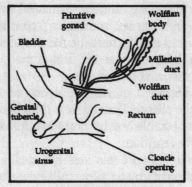

Undifferentiated 8 - 10 weeks

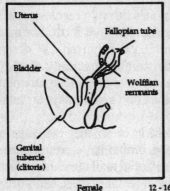

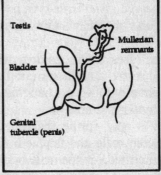

Female   12 - 16 weeks   Male

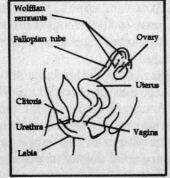

Female   At birth   Male

SEX DIFFERENCES IN THE BRAIN

In some species there are obvious structural differences in the brains of males and females, some of which can easily be seen even with the naked eye. In humans the situation is much more complicated, and here we enter the first of many a controversial territory to be traversed in this book.

Prof. Milton Diamond of Hawaii is one of the best-known proponents of the theory that all sex differences, behavioural and physical, are established by hormonal influences acting on the brain in early fetal life.

The evidence to support this idea includes, for example, the universal exhibition of greater physical aggression in boys, quite irrespective of any cultural differences involved. Further support is provided by the observation that the daughters of women who were given male-type hormones during pregnancy, showed not only masculinisation of their genitalia at birth, but marked tomboyish behaviour during childhood. Diamond also describes some cases where children who were anatomically of one sex, were reared as if they were the opposite sex. These attempts all apparently failed in changing the child's masculine or feminine behaviour patterns.[1]

It is only during the last decade or so that the differences between male and female human brains have been intensively documented.[2] In the male brain, spatial skills tend to be focused in the right hemisphere whereas, in females, these skills are controlled by both sides. Verbal skills, however, are focused in the left hemisphere in female brains. In practice these differences mean that men are likely to excel in areas such as maths, astronomy and musical composition, whereas women excel more in writing literature and mastering languages.

De Lacoste-Utamsing first described a further brain sex difference – that the neural jump-leads (the corpus callosum) which connect the two sides of the brain are thicker in the female brain.[3] This means that more information can be exchanged between the right and left hemispheres in the female brain. This may also explain the greater verbal fluency in women and may possibly be part of the explanation of the famous 'female intuition'. Recently though Byne and Parsons[4] have cautioned against an uncritical acceptance of such 'explanations', pointing out that some twenty or more recent studies have failed to confirm De Lacoste-Utamsing's original work.

GENDER ASSIGNMENT AND SOCIAL INFLUENCES

The way in which we treat our children is undoubtedly greatly influenced by our awareness of their sex. From the moment of birth, baby girls tend to be handled slightly more gently than boys. Other differences soon follow – girls are dressed in pink, boys in blue, girls have bows in their hair, boys have bows (and arrows!) in their toy-boxes, and so on. As children grow, the games that we play with them, and even the tone of voice we adopt in speaking to them, all provide them with subtle social clues about their gender identity.

At around the age of three or four, most children will have reached a critical stage where their belief that 'I am a boy' or 'I am a girl' becomes fixed. Stoller[5] calls this the 'core gender identity'. After this stage attempts to change gender identity are generally considered unlikely to succeed. Before this identity is established, however, some experts have argued that there is potential for change.

Prof. John Money of the John Hopkins Hospital, Baltimore, describes a case of a male twin whose penis was totally burnt off when he was seven months old.[6] After taking medical advice, his parents decided that he should be brought up as a girl, and surgery was performed to construct female genitals. He was given a girl's name and reared accordingly. By the age of four, there was no mistaking the child's girlish behaviour, which was in total contrast to that of his twin brother.

It will have already struck some readers that the findings of Diamond and Money are in conflict. Is gender identity biologically predetermined, or is it the influence of our environment and upbringing?

Research documented in a classic text of the 1970s, *The Psychology of Sex Differences* by Maccoby and Jacklin suggested that many differences between the sexes are either illusory or else socially determined.[7] For example, these researchers could find no evidence to support the commonly held suppositions that girls are more sociable, more suggestible, more helpful, more dependent or have lower self-esteem than boys. Neither could they find any difference in overall intelligence.

There were a few differences between the sexes confirmed by their studies however. Boys' mathematical skills develop faster than those of girls. Boys are also physically and verbally more aggressive.

Glenn Wilson comments on this work that, 'Maccoby and Jacklin succeed better than most in producing a book worthy of scientific consideration, but it is unfortunate that so many books on topics of sex differences are written by dedicated feminists whose political aims take precedence over objective facts.'[8]

This touches on an important point. Gender identity and the factors which influence it, are likely to remain a source of great interest and debate because they lie at the heart of strong political forces – not just those of feminism but also of gay rights, for example. Whether or not sex roles are biologically determined is for many campaigners – both for and against – a fundamental issue. Unfortunately scientific objectivity often evaporates in the heat of the controversy.

Most of the work on sex differentiation in the brain has only been documented relatively recently, and it now seems that the pendulum is currently swinging away from social learning theory towards a more genetic and hormonal explanation. One psychology lecturer, who for years believed and taught only the socialisation theory, writes, 'After reviewing a pile of journal articles that stood several feet high ... I changed my mind. The data collected within the last few years provide a convincing case for the importance of biological variables'.[9]

In this complex and highly active field of research, however, further new discoveries may yet cause the pendulum to swing again. John Bancroft is surely wise in his cautious observation that, 'It seems unlikely that this nature-nurture issue will ever be finally resolved and perhaps this is just as well.

'There would seem to be an inherent advantage in assuming that nature and nurture are both fundamental and that we cannot shape our children's destinies completely by controlling their environment. The importance of social learning is nevertheless crucial and a matter for concern, and it is undoubtedly desirable to reappraise continually the influences to which our children are subjected.'[10]

HELPING OUR CHILDREN

How then, can we best help our children develop a strong sense of gender identity?

●   First we need to have a strong sense of gender identity ourselves. If as parents we have an uncertain view of what it means to be a man or woman, this will be communicated to our children either directly or indirectly. This can be every bit as damaging as those attitudes which stem from an unbalanced sense of sexual superiority and result in parents' being very abusive about the opposite sex.

●   Model a good example to our children of what it means to be a man or woman. Spending time with them and sharing tasks together is very important. Fathers in particular need to give time to being involved with their young children. For single-parent families a suitable contact with an appropriate sex-role model should be encouraged. This could be either a relative or a family friend. Teachers at school may also exert an important influence in this area, but it should be remembered that very few in infants' schools are male.

●   Affirm and encourage gender-appropriate behaviour. Personal interpretations of this will of course vary enormously from one family to another. It does not mean every girl always has to play with her doll and never ride her brother's go-cart, but it does mean, for example, thinking twice about letting young boys wear lipstick.

The tragedy of a blind conformity to ill-considered sexual stereotypes is poignantly described by Le Sourd:

The pattern is depressingly familiar. A boy discovers he likes birds or music, but is pulled away from such interests to engage in sports he does not like at all. He cries when his dog dies and is told tears are not manly. He puts his arm affectionately around his good friend only to be admonished sternly that 'boys don't hug other boys'...

If he is honest about his shortcomings, he will be rebuked and told a man covers up such things. By the time he reaches manhood many of the genuine discoveries he's made about himself have been discarded on the advice of family and friends. In place of the real self is a plastic person moulded and shaped to 'make it' in the hard tough world.

These are the men who remain frozen-faced while listening to an impassioned speech.[11]

● Teach children at an early age, sensible defence guidelines against abuse by adults. Whatever uncertainties may surround some of the determinants of gender identity considered above, there is no doubt about the damage inflicted by early sexual abuse. A child who has been hurt in this way may face tremendous conflicts concerning gender identity in later life. This subject is discussed further in Chapter 23.

FURTHER READING

Anne Moir and David Jessel, *Brain Sex* (Mandarin, 1991).

Mary Stewart van Leeuwen, *Gender and Grace* (IVP, 1990).

2

SHOW ME YOURS! SEXUAL ANATOMY

An understanding of the anatomy and physiology of sex does not automatically confer any depth of understanding of its emotional burdens.

Paul Vaughan
The Pill on trial

As soon as children become aware of their sexual parts they
will want to explore them. They will then soon start comparing
their own anatomy with that of other children; 'Show me yours',
and 'doctors and nurses' are all a part of this natural stage of
exploration.

A working knowledge of sexual anatomy is therefore necessary
to answer children's questions about what they have got and
whether it's normal or not. This chapter will give straightforward
details of adult sexual anatomy and is deliberately clinical in
its approach. Practical aspects of sex education of children,
including an evaluation of the appropriate language to use, are
considered in the following chapter.

FEMALE ANATOMY

The anatomical name for a woman's external sexual organs is
the vulva. At the top of the vulva is a fleshy mound – the
mons pubis or mount of Venus. This is covered with variable
amounts of curly pubic hair after puberty. Some women have
a lot, in others such hair is scanty. Both are normal variations
and the hair is distributed in the shape of an inverted triangle,
the base running across the mons in a straight line.

Below the mons are the folds of the labia majora which

have hair on the outer surface and sweat glands on the inner aspect. These are usually the only externally visible features in a woman who has not had children.

Parting of the labia majora will expose the labia minora – another pair of skin folds but much more delicate. They have a generous blood supply, and during pregnancy and childbirth they engorge with blood and may remain permanently enlarged following delivery. They may then be visible, protruding through the labia majora.

EXTERNAL SEXUAL ANATOMY OF THE FEMALE

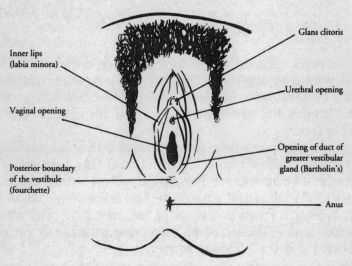

At the back, the labia minora are joined behind the vaginal opening by a fold of skin called the fourchette. At the front, they fork to enclose the clitoris. The moist area demarcated by the labia minora, fourchette and clitoris is known as the vestibule.

The visible part of the clitoris (the glans) is a pinkish bud, the size of a pea, and has a rich sensory nerve supply. There is also an extensive deeper component to the clitoris consisting of erectile structures (corpora cavernosa and spongiosum), which extend either side of the vaginal entrance to form the vestibular bulbs beneath the vestibule.

Just behind the clitoris is the opening of the urinary system – the urethra. To the rear of this is the vaginal opening. In virgins this is partially covered by a thin fold of skin – the hymen or maidenhead. This becomes torn or stretched during first intercourse or with the insertion of tampons. Just outside the attachment of the hymen are the openings of the Bartholin's glands which secrete lubrication during sexual arousal.

The vagina is an 8–14cm-long tube which in its non-aroused state is collapsed with a cross-section like the letter H. When distended it has a shape like an inverted flask from a chemistry set. This shape occurs because the lower third of the vagina – the 'neck' of the flask – is closely surrounded by the strong muscles which form the pelvic floor.

Goldberg[1] and others have claimed the existence of a specially sensitive area on the front wall of the vagina – the Grafenberg or G-spot. This is said to be responsible for female orgasms even in the absence of clitoral stimulation, though this concept is not universally accepted.

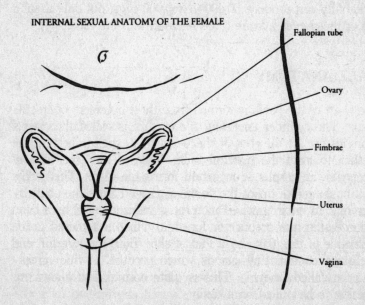

INTERNAL SEXUAL ANATOMY OF THE FEMALE

Fallopian tube

Ovary

Fimbrae

Uterus

Vagina

The womb, or uterus, is shaped like an inverted pear, and has a very thick muscular wall. The narrow neck of the womb, the cervix, protrudes into the top of the vagina. In the middle of the cervix is a small hole called the external os which opens into the cavity of the uterus.

In most women the uterus tilts forward and is said to be anteverted. In around 15 per cent of women, however, the uterus is retroverted and tilts backward towards the rectum. Both positions are quite normal.

The cervix, and the upper part of the vagina are anchored to the side walls of the pelvis by a mesh of tissue rather like a double fold of clingfilm. This is called the parametrium.

At either side of the top of the uterus the two Fallopian tubes, or oviducts, extend out towards the ovaries. These thin-walled tubes are lined with tiny hairs which maintain a sweeping movement towards the uterus, which facilitates egg transportation. The ends of the tubes fan out into seaweed-like fronds (the fimbriae) around the ovaries to 'catch' the egg cells at ovulation.

The two ovaries themselves are walnut-sized organs which potentially can produce 50,000 to 250,000 eggs, but only around 500 of these ever mature to be released into the tubes.

MALE ANATOMY

The shaft of the penis is formed from three cylinders of erectile tissue. The cylinder enclosing the urethra is called the corpus spongiosum. At the root of the penis this expands around the urethra to form the urethral bulb, while at the other end of the penis the corpus spongiosum forms the glans. This is the pink cushion-like tip of the penis, separated from the shaft by a groove. In uncircumcised men the glans is covered by a hood of loose skin (the prepuce or foreskin) which is tethered to the underside of the glans by a fold of skin. Both the foreskin and the glans contain tiny glands which produce a white greasy material called smegma. This is quite normal, and allows the foreskin to be pulled back easily.

Over the corpus spongiosum lie the two fused cylinders of the corpora cavernosa. These consist of a tough outer layer around a spongelike lattice of tissue which can engorge with blood and make the penis stiffen during an erection. At the root of the penis, the corpora cavernosa spread out to attach firmly on the pelvic bones.

There is so much mythology associated with the penis, that it is worth commenting here that penile size has nothing to do with a man's height, body build, race or virility. The length of the flaccid penis normally ranges from 8–11cm. When erect the penis is usually about 16cm long, irrespective of length in the non-aroused state. The erect penis may be straight or slightly curved. It may point nearly vertically upwards or just out at a right-angle to the body. All these are normal variants.

At the root of the penis is the pubic hair, which has the characteristic distribution in the shape of a rhomboid with the hair growing up the abdomen to the navel.

The testes are two oval balls about 5cm by 2cm, which are

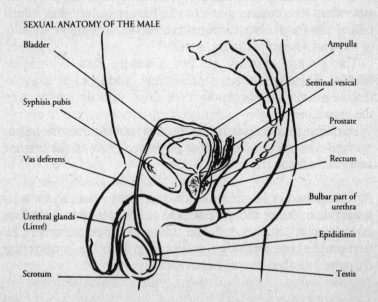

SEXUAL ANATOMY OF THE MALE

Bladder

Syphisis pubis

Vas deferens

Urethral glands
(Littré)

Scrotum

Ampulla

Seminal vesical

Prostate

Rectum

Bulbar part of
urethra

Epididimis

Testis

held in a sack of skin and muscle, the scrotum. The testes manufacture sperm and a male hormone (testosterone). Sperm production takes place only when the testes are about 2°C lower than body temperature. Muscles in the wall of the scrotum help maintain the correct temperature by moving the testes towards and away from the body.

There are about 500 sperm-producing tubes (the seminiferous tubules) coiled up within each testis. They make 200 million sperm a day, and join up to form a smaller number of convoluted tubes forming the epididymis which perches on top of the testis. This is where the sperms mature.

The prostate gland is a firm fibrous organ, chestnut-shaped, which sits under the bladder above the bulb of the urethra, the prostatic part of the urethra continuing up through the centre of the gland to the bladder base. The prostate gland contributes fluid to the semen during ejaculation.

The epididymis of the testis is linked to the urethra by a long tube called the vas deferens. This is the tube that is cut and tied off in a vasectomy (sterilising) operation. Within the pelvis the vas enters the prostate gland to join the ejaculatory duct which passes into the urethra. It widens at this point to form the ampulla of the vas where sperm are stored.

The seminal vesicles are two elongated sacs behind the bladder. They secrete the seminal fluid which passes along to discharge into the ejaculatory duct along with the sperm from the ampullae.

During sexual arousal, further fluid is secreted from the bulbourethral (Cowper's) glands situated on each side of the urethra near the bulbous part.

As the quotation heading this chapter rightly points out, anatomical knowledge, though essential, is not sufficient in itself to provide an adequate foundation for sexual understanding. The next chapter considers other aspects of sexual education of young children, and their sexual behaviour.

3

BEYOND THE GOOSEBERRY BUSH: SEXUAL BEHAVIOUR AND SEX EDUCATION

Ideals are like stars; they cannot be reached, but they chart our course.

ANON.

It was Sigmund Freud who first drew attention to the sexuality of infants and young children in his 'Three Essays on The Theory of Sexuality' published in 1905. While few psychiatrists today would give unqualified acceptance to Freud's theory of sexual development through oral, anal, genital, latent and pubertal phases, there can be little doubt about both the occurrence and developmental importance of sexual responses in young children.

SEXUAL BEHAVIOUR OF INFANTS AND CHILDREN

Erections can be easily seen in little boys within minutes of birth, and there are usually between three and eleven each day in the first few months of life. Though in infant girls it is much more difficult to be sure of sexual responses, the appearance of vulval lubrication in the first few days after birth may be one such outward indicator.

Most boys discover genital play at around six months of age and girls a little later at ten months – perhaps because their genitals are a little harder to find! No parent observing the smiling, chuckling and cooing that accompanies such play can have much doubt that infants find it pleasurable.

This infant genital play evolves into more obvious masturbation by sixteen months, though masturbation to orgasm has been reported to occur in children as young as six months. Girls have less tendency to engage in masturbation, and more frequently use indirect methods of applying pressure such as rocking to and fro.

Children of three or four are full of curiosity about one another's genitals, and bathtime can on occasions be used by siblings for mutual exploration and showing off their differences.

With increasing awareness of the prevalence of child sexual abuse (see Chap. 23) and the harm resulting from it, it is more important than ever that parents are not driven to the opposite extreme of denial of their children's sexuality. It is important to understand that genital play, exploration and masturbation at this age have only a tenuous, if any, connection with sex. They may be classed as similar sensual pleasures to thumb-sucking. Orgasms may occur from a whole variety of stimuli such as riding on a bus or sliding down a rope.

It is not until the age of eight or nine that children connect their sexual parts with sexual feelings or become aware that this anatomy is for making babies as well as going to the toilet. This fact does not of course preclude parents from undertaking the vital preparatory work indicated later in this chapter. It also has other important implications for dealing with expressions of 'sexual' behaviour in childhood. For example, it is unwise to be overly negative and repressive in dealing with masturbation in this age group.

SEX EDUCATION OF YOUNG CHILDREN AT HOME

As indicated earlier, sex education starts at birth, and as parents we only have the option of whether we educate our children about sex knowingly or unknowingly.

Infants first begin to be aware of the sexual identity from the touch that they receive. The warmth of closeness and intimacy that results from being cuddled and hugged will affirm a child's sense of feeling good about their bodily sensations, and provide a positive foundation for later sexual development. Where such early feeling is absent problems easily follow.

Alongside positive affirmation, we should seek to provide a good model for our children. When children can see that parents enjoy openly holding and cuddling each other, this builds their security and reinforces a positive view of sexual intimacy in marriage.

When we turn from providing a good general environment of affection, to giving specific information and teaching on sexual matters to young children, there is a wide divergence of opinion about when is the best age to start.

Children all differ in their individual rate of development and it is important not to give too much information too soon. This can cause confusion or even alarm, and certainly the information will not be absorbed. On the other hand, this understandable and proper concern about violation of a child's 'inner world' must not be used as an excuse for endless prevarication. I believe it to be a mistake to follow the philosophy that when the child is ready to learn about sex, he or she will ask. As Lynda Madaras points out, 'We don't wait until our children ask before we teach them how to cross the road safely. Or if we're religious people, we don't wait until they ask about God before we give them religious instruction.'[1] Why then make an exception about sex?

SCHOOLS AND SEX EDUCATION

Increasing concern about both the spread of AIDS and rising rates of teenage pregnancies has fuelled demands for compulsory sex education programmes to be introduced into all schools, including primary schools.

Controversy rages however concerning the effectiveness of such programmes. One professor of education states: 'Cause and effect are difficult to determine, but systematic introduction to the "facts of life" would appear to protect children from so-called temptation rather than encourage sexual activity'[2] while a report on unplanned pregnancy by the Royal College of Obstetricians and Gynaecologists maintains: 'Practically nothing is known about the effects of sex education programmes, either in regard to the future health and happiness of the individual or in relation to unplanned pregnancy. It was suggested that wrongly orientated sex education could be having a result which was the exact opposite of what it was desired to achieve, in that it was arousing curiosity and the desire to experiment. The rapidly rising incidence of unplanned pregnancies in the young age group gives some support to this idea.'[3]

Superimposed on such fundamental uncertainty is the attribution of hidden motives to those on opposite sides of the debate. Thomas Szasz, a professor of child psychiatry has gone so far as to state:

The term 'sex education' conceals far more than it reveals. It conceals the specific social, educational and economic policies used to implement sex education, the moral values secretly encouraged and discouraged; and last but not least, the problems that derive inexorably from involving the school system – and hence the government – in defining what constitutes education in human sexuality. The upshot is that many thoughtful and well-meaning people now endorse sex education (especially in schools) as a good thing. They should instead, oppose it as one of the most deplorable consequences of the combination of 'liberal' policies with medicalised morals.[4]

Szasz however is pointing out the dangers of a hidden agenda in sex education. These may (and do) exist, for sex is a readily exploitable commodity. But in rightly opposing the possible sexual manipulation of our children, we must not fall into the trap of leaving them in ignorance. There is another view that it is because we have not had proper sex education programmes in the UK that our teen pregnancy rates are so high. I consider the sex education of our children as an opportunity to be grasped eagerly.

OPPORTUNITY FOR PARENTS

At the very least, all parents should be aware of the sex education policy adopted by the schools their children attend. The 1987 UK Department of Education and Science guidelines to schools on sex education states that 'Teaching about the physical aspects of sexual behaviour should be set within a clear moral framework in which pupils are encouraged to consider the importance of self-restraint, dignity and respect for themselves and others, and helped to recognise the physical, emotional and moral risks of casual and promiscuous sexual behaviour.' If sex education follows such advice, it should present few problems, although the 1993 Education Act does give parents the right to withdraw their children from sex education.

Supplementation at home of any such school provision is essential in any case. The ideal that formal sex education should not just be left to schools is one that unites liberal and conservative alike. Kolodny, Masters and Johnson in their classic *Textbook of Sexual Medicine* agree that '...school instruction alone cannot be an effective substitute for sex education in the home; the role is complementary rather than exclusionary'.[5] Children are much more affected by what they are told – or not told – at home, and by the general parental attitude to sexual matters than by any programme of sex education at school. There is evidence from research in the USA which shows that where parents do play an active role in the sex education of their children those children are less likely to engage in early intercourse.[6]

There are also other advantages. Tuition by a parent at home, tackling the subject in stages over a period of time, can allow for far greater flexibility in understanding than is possible in the classroom. How then can parents go about providing teaching on sexual matters for their children?

A FRAMEWORK

Chances to talk about sex are not difficult to come by in everyday life. McDowell tells an instructive story about his eight-year-old son, Sean, getting into an argument with his little sister and saying 'F— you!'[7] Instead of becoming angry and telling Sean never use language like that again, McDowell wisely asked him if he knew what the word meant. When the child confessed his ignorance, his father enlightened him and used the situation for some sensitive sex education.

With a little thought, opportunities can be easily created. My wife and I recently had a very good sex education book for young children on our bedside cabinet. It wasn't long before my five-year-old son picked it up and said 'What's this about?' We then spent time explaining some aspects of sex to him.

The story is well known of the father who proceeded to give a lecture on sex to his son who had asked, 'Where did I come from, Dad?' On concluding his monologue the father enquired, 'Why did you ask?' 'Well my friend Tommy says he comes from Liverpool,' replied the boy.

We may well need to clarify with young children just exactly what they mean when for example they ask, 'Where do babies come from?' This may not require a twenty-minute homily on reproduction in reply; 'Out of mummy's tummy' may suffice.

Answers referring to storks and gooseberry bushes will not do. Some parents will obviously feel more comfortable than others in talking over sexual matters with their children. If you do find it difficult, there is no shame in saying so, but you should still attempt it as best you can. If you do not know the answer to a particular question, you should say so, and look it up later for future reference.

Coyness on sexual matters even affects some professionals, so you are in good company. I once received a letter from an eminent gynaecologist in which he stated he was quite sure the reason my six-year-old patient had a sore vulva was because she was masturbating. However he didn't like to mention this to the parents, so asked me if I would do it!

My wife and I well remember that feeling of pride when our first son learnt to name the parts of his body. 'Nose' was the first, then 'eye'. Having mastered these, there was no stopping him, and eventually of course 'willie' entered his vocabulary as well.

Some sex educators feel it is wrong to use euphemisms like this ('willie' for a penis, and 'minnie' for a vulva are the most common I encounter in my paediatric clinical practice) in naming the genitals. They reason that such terms may reinforce the view that genitals are unmentionable. I do not think this is necessarily the case. It is very common for married couples to have pet names for their genitals as adults, and they may actually convey the idea that the genitals are special rather than unmentionable.

While some maintain that the anatomical terms penis and vagina should always be used, other sex educationalists go to the opposite extreme. Many seem to take a real delight in listing every vulgar word and obscenity they can think of for the genitals. While openness and freedom in communication is the pretext for doing this, little thought seems to be given to *what* is being communicated. Many (though not all) of these words, far from being the language of love, are the barbs of bitterness and hate. When young children overhear angry exchanges on television or in the street where 'You cunt' and 'You prick' are flung around in verbal abuse, how are they to reconcile this with intimacy and closeness? There is some terminology which our children should know only in order to avoid it. Madaras, to her credit, does point out that sexual language can sometimes be offensive.[8] I maintain that some sexual slang words are *always* inappropriate for children.

Having made clear that I do not think using euphemisms like 'John Thomas' is 'wrong' in speaking with young children, I do consider it essential that children are taught the correct anatomical names well before they reach the age of seven. It was not until dissecting the rat in biology class at high school that I innocently asked, 'Please sir, what is the penis?' Well, I survived the gales of laughter and have proved that it's never too late to learn, but I think it would have helped if I had known the answer earlier on.

Peer influence at school usually conveys the impression that sex is dirty and needs to be kept secret. An open, unashamed attitude at home towards such things as nudity (both of parents and children) on appropriate occasions such as bathtime, will help to develop healthy sexual self-acceptance in young children.

A positive approach can be taken even when setting necessary limits. As already mentioned, young children do not generally link masturbation with sex, and dealing punitively with such activity can be harmful. Most parents, however, want to restrict their children from masturbation in public, for example. If they find their children doing so, my suggested approach would be, 'I know that playing with your penis feels nice and it is very important that you get to know your own body, but just as Mum and Dad don't like you to clean your nose in front of other people, we would prefer you not to fiddle with your penis.'

It's little use having a five-minute session on sex education, and then breathing a huge sigh of relief and thinking it's all done with. Sex education is an ongoing process throughout childhood, and the same answers may need to be reinforced or expanded many times in order to give our children a firm foundation for building their sexual lives.

FURTHER READING

Young Children

Malcolm and Meryl Doney, *Who Made Me?* (Marshall Pickering, 1993).

Claire Rayner, *The Body Book* (Piccolo, 1979).

Older Children

Nancy Kohner, *What Shall We Tell the Children* (BBC, 1993).

Michael Lawson and David Skipp, *Sex and That* (Lion, 1992).

Lynda Madaras, *What's Happening to my Body? A Growing-Up Guide for Parents and Sons* (Penguin, 1984).

Lynda Madaras, *What's Happening to my Body? A Growing-Up Guide for Parents and Daughters* (Penguin, 1989).

Jack and Angela Wingfield, *Growing Up Now* (Lion, 1992).

II

ADOLESCENCE –
THE TURBULENT AGE

4

ALL CHANGE! PUBERTY AND ADOLESCENCE

Until I was fifteen I was more familiar with Africa than my own body.

Joe Orton

Rob knocked on the door of his eleven-year-old daughter's bedroom before entering. It was only later that day he realised he'd

STAGES OF BREAST DEVELOPMENT

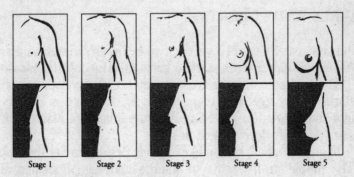

Stage 1   Stage 2   Stage 3   Stage 4   Stage 5

Stage 1: Pre-adolescent : elevation of papilla only.

Stage 2: Breast bud stage.

Stage 3: Further enlargement of breast and areola.

Stage 4: Projection of areola and papilla above level of breast.

Stage 5: Mature stage, areola has recesses, papilla projects.

never done that before. She was no longer a child but a young woman, and Rob had recognised the fact quite subconsciously in not entering without asking.

Our children seem to grow up all too quickly and indeed there is evidence that they are maturing at an earlier age. In the Western world the average age for the breaking of a boy's voice is thirteen, and for a girl the average age at onset of her first period is twelve years. It is important to understand the meaning of these figures. They suggest, for example, that a half of all girls will have started menstruation by the age of twelve. In fact 2.2 per cent will have started by ten years and a further 15 per cent by eleven.[1] These statistics have important implications for preparing children at an early enough stage for the changes that will overtake them at puberty.

Many adolescents become confused and even scared by the rapid pace of change in their bodies and emotions at puberty, and thoughts of 'Am I normal?' are very common. This chapter looks at the normal stages of pubertal development.

GIRLS AND PUBERTY

Puberty usually starts a year or two earlier in girls than in boys. At around eleven girls start to grow taller at a faster rate.

The first sign of puberty is usually breast development. This starts at any age from eight to eleven, and doctors classify it into five stages (p. 47). Stage 1 is the immature state with no signs of adult development at all.

In stage 2 small, button-like mounds develop under the nipple. The nipple itself begins to enlarge and the pigmented area around it (the areola) widens and darkens in colour. The mound of the breast gradually begins to swell and stand out from the chest wall. At this stage the sensitivity of the breasts increases greatly, and they may become quite tender or even painful.

In stage 3 the areola and nipple continue to darken and enlarge and the whole breast becomes rounder and swells out more. The breasts are often conical in shape at this stage.

Not every girl has a distinct stage 4 in which the areola and nipple form a separate mound which protrudes above the general contour of the breast.

Stage 5 is the adult state with the smooth round contour of a fully developed breast.

As there can be great variation with the age of onset of puberty, so the actual rate of breast development varies. Some girls may reach stage 5 within a year; others may take six years or more. The average time is about two and a half years. The age of onset of breast development bears no relationship to the eventual size of the breasts in adult life.

Many girls worry about the size of their breasts fearing that only large breasts are truly feminine or sexy. In our 'page-three'-oriented culture this fear is as understandable as it is groundless. Small breasts will both produce as much milk for a baby, and as much excitement for a husband as large ones.

At the same time as the breasts are developing, the contour of the rest of the body will be adopting a more feminine shape. The hips get wider, and fatty tissue is laid down around the buttocks and thighs.

Growth of pubic hair usually starts a few months after breast development, but it can start before. Once again doctors use a five-stage classification. Stage 1 is the childhood state with a total absence of pubic hair. In stage 2 the first dark curly hairs begin to grow on the mons pubis. In stage 3 the hairs increase in number and darken further. In stage 4 they form the adult pattern but cover a more limited area than in stage 5 which is the fully developed adult pattern in shape and extent.

As with underarm and leg hair, the final amount of pubic hair varies widely.

During puberty both the mons and the labia become fleshier. In addition the labia darken and wrinkle. The oil-secreting glands on the underside of the labia become more active, and most girls will become aware of the moist feeling this produces.

The hymen becomes thicker and more noticeable, but some girls may have such a small hymen that it is hard to see it even during puberty. Very rarely the hymen may be congenitally absent. At the other extreme, it may be so thick and impermeable that when menstruation starts the blood cannot escape through it at all. This causes the menstrual flow to be trapped in the vagina. This very rare condition called haematocolpos can cause severe abdominal pain, and usually requires surgical incision of the hymen.

The vagina, like the rest of a girl's body, also has a growth spurt during puberty, and reaches the adult length of 8–13cm. The vaginal glands also secrete more fluid which may give rise to a clear milky-white discharge which leaves a stain on underwear when it dries. This discharge is perfectly normal and does not itch or smell offensive.

The uterus not only grows to its adult size during puberty but usually changes its position from being almost vertical in childhood to leaning forward over the bladder in the adult woman. Sometimes the uterus may tilt the other way – a retroverted uterus. This too is a normal variation.

HORMONAL CHANGES, OVULATION AND MENSTRUATION

The onset of periods, called the menarche, usually occurs between eleven and fifteen, some two and a half years after the start of breast development. Although it is possible to conceive even before onset of the first period, the early cycles are usually infertile. Menstruation results from a complex set of hormonal interactions controlled by the pituitary gland and the closely-associated area in the brain called the hypothalamus. At the onset of puberty, there is a surge in the pituitary output of hormones called gonadotrophins. The main gonadotrophins are follicle stimulating hormone (FSH), and luteinising hormone (LH).

FSH, as its name suggests, stimulates some of the follicles containing egg-cells, to start growing in the ovary. It also stimulates the follicle to produce a female hormone called oestrogen which causes many of the changes of puberty considered above, such as breast development.

As the follicles in the ovary grow larger, more oestrogen is produced. The rise in oestrogen triggers the pituitary gland to reduce FSH secretion and to produce LH. LH causes the largest ovarian follicle to burst and shed its egg into the fimbriae of the Fallopian tube. This process is called ovulation.

The remnant of the follicle in the ovary turns into a structure called a corpus luteum (meaning yellow body). LH then stimulates the corpus luteum to produce yet another hormone, progesterone, which thickens the endometrial lining of the uterus. This is in preparation for the fertilised egg to implant in the lining. If however the egg remains unfertilised, the corpus luteum shrivels up within a few days and stops making progesterone. Without progesterone the lining of the uterus disintegrates and falls off and trickles into the vagina and forms the menstrual flow of a period.

BOYS AND PUBERTY

In boys, the growth spurt takes place on average a year or two

STAGES OF MALE GENITAL DEVELOPMENT

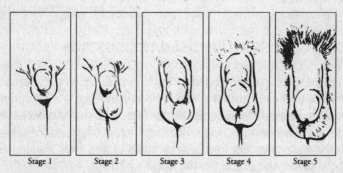

| Stage 1 | Stage 2 | Stage 3 | Stage 4 | Stage 5 |

Stage 1: Pre-adolescent

Stage 2: Enlargement of scrotum and testes

Stage 3: Lengthening of penis

Stage 4: increase in breadth of penis and development of glans. Testes continue to enlarge. Scrotum darkens

Stage 5: Adult. By this time pubic hair has spread to medial surface of thighs later than in girls, and not usually until the genitalia have already begun to grow. Thus most boys will notice that they are growing taller more rapidly at around the age of twelve to thirteen.

In boys the first sign of the start of puberty is growth of their sex organs, which usually starts in the age range of ten to fourteen years. Doctors again classify this growth into five stages, which take between three and five years to complete.

Stage 1 is the childhood stage. There is no pubic hair and the scrotum is drawn up closely to the body.

In stage 2 the scrotum becomes reddened and wrinkly. It also enlarges and begins to hang lower. The testes inside it enlarge.

At stage 3 the penis enlarges, and by this time one testis (usually the left one) is noticeably hanging lower than the other. Pubic hair begins to grow around the base of the penis. This may be pale at first, but gradually darkens and becomes more curly. The oil-secreting glands on the scrotum start functioning fully, and the surface of the scrotal skin feels and smells differently.

The penis is wider and longer with a more developed glans in stage 4. Both penis and scrotum deepen in colour and the pubic hair becomes coarser, darker and more widespread.

Stage 5 is the fully developed adult stage. The penis and testes have completed their growth and the pubic hair forms the adult pattern (p. 51).

SECONDARY SEXUAL CHARACTERISTICS

This is the technical term used by doctors to describe the changes in the body during puberty which do not involve the genitalia.

In boys, hair starts to grow on the face, and shaving becomes necessary. This usually occurs during stage 4 of genital development, between fourteen and sixteen years of age. Hair also starts to grow under the arms, on the chest and legs.

The other major change that occurs in boys at this age is lowering of the voice. The vocal cords in the larynx grow thicker and longer, and the pitch of the voice consequently drops.

Breast changes do occur in boys, and can often be a cause of great anxiety. During puberty the nipple and surrounding areola darken and enlarge and may be sore.

The appearance of a button-like mound under one or both nipples is very common, and between a third and a half of all boys will get some actual swelling of one or both breasts (called gynaecomastia). This may be markedly noticeable and lead to considerable embarrassment. It is, however, quite normal and, in nearly all cases, will regress with time.

HORMONAL CHANGES

In boys, the surge in LH (also called interstitial cell stimulating hormone in the male) from the pituitary gland, stimulates cells in the testis called Leydig cells to produce testosterone. It is testosterone which causes the development of the sex organs and the changes in voice and body hair. Other effects include increased sweating and the awakening of sexual desire.

FSH in boys stimulates the growth of the sperm-producing mechanism in the testis.

EMOTIONAL ASPECTS

Change is usually stressful, and most adolescents view puberty with a mixture of excitement and apprehension. Hormonal surges give rise to new urges, and the awakening consciousness of a newly-found sexuality often produces uncertainty and questioning.

During this time of fluctuation, adolescents need both parental stability and flexibility. They should be instructed in advance to expect and prepare for the changes that will occur, and parents must give them sufficient time and attention at this vital phase. Although personal parental values should be discussed and limits suggested, attempts to dominate or impose too many restrictions may simply provoke rebellion. Most adolescents do in fact get on well with their parents, however, and acceptance, affirmation and praise are especially important at a time when negative values can so easily be absorbed. Menstruation for example need not be viewed as 'The Curse', but as an important milestone of developing maturity.

Some further specific aspects of adolescent sexual behaviour will be considered in the following chapters in this section.

FURTHER READING

Dr Roger Hurding, *Understanding Adolescence* (Hodder & Stoughton, 1989).

Lynda Madaras, *What's Happening to my Body? A Growing-up Guide for Parents and Sons* (Penguin, 1984).

Lynda Madaras, *What's Happening to my Body? A Growing-Up Guide for Parents and Daughters* (Penguin, 1989).

Dr Laurence Steinberg and Ann Levine, *You and Your Adolescent* (Vermilion, 1992).

5

ALL BY MYSELF: SOLO SEXUALITY

No other form of sexual activity has been so frequently discussed, so roundly condemned, and more universally practised, than masturbation.

-L. Dearborn
The Encyclopaedia of Sexual Behaviour

If, in childhood, genital stimulation is rarely associated with sex, puberty soon changes that situation. With the hormonal awakening of the testis or ovary, comes the awareness of the association between orgasms and sexual stimuli. This is a normal part of adolescent development, but can provoke great anxiety, particularly in those who have not been prepared for these new experiences.

For girls the principal changes to prepare for are breast development and menstruation (pp. 48–51) and bras, sanitary pads and tampons are topics which need to be considered in advance. In boys, ejaculation is the main functional change to occur.

EJACULATIONS AND WET DREAMS

For most boys their first ejaculation happens about a year after penile growth begins, the age ranging from eleven to fifteen years. Though the first ejaculation may occur following masturbation, it may equally occur during sleep – a nocturnal emission or wet dream. This can be an alarming experience for the uninitiated. Some boys may think they have urinated or even bled if they awaken with a wet patch on their pyjamas or sheets. There may or may not be conscious recollection of the sexual content of the accompanying dream.

Wet dreams are a natural physiological mechanism whereby the body drains the ejaculatory system and makes way for new sperm. On no account should guilt about them be engendered or reinforced.

Spontaneous erections may become more frequent during puberty, and though they may be triggered by sexy thoughts or sights, they can also result from travelling over a bumpy road, or simply feeling nervous. Boys who in infancy have been given the impression that the genitals are 'dirty' often have real problems in coming to terms with the literally increasing prominence of their penis. If, however, good channels of communication on sexual matters have been established early on, parents can be of great help in allaying their teenagers' common fears about their developing sexual capacity.

MASTURBATION

Masturbation is the self-stimulation of the penis or clitoris. It is such an accessible and successful means of achieving sexual pleasure that most adolescents, particularly boys, will soon discover it and make regular use of it. It is a topic that arouses both much interest and a great deal of controversy even today.

Myths about masturbation are still rampant, the only difference from a hundred years ago being that a permissive mythology is replacing the old repressive one. We shall examine some statistics about masturbation and look at various historical and contemporary attitudes towards it. This will provide a broad perspective from which we can help our teenagers to think through their own solo sex-life.

How prevalent is masturbation? The old joke that 'ninety-nine out of a hundred boys will admit to having masturbated and the remaining boy is a liar,' does seem to be near the mark.

In various surveys the incidence of masturbation to orgasm at some time in their lives is consistently around 94 per cent for men. The peak frequency of masturbation is in the early teens at an average of three times a week.[1]

In girls the picture is less clear. In one study between 25 and 30 per cent of girls between sixteen and twenty-five were masturbating,[2] whereas in another survey 60 per cent of the same age group reported doing so.[3] These wide variations may possibly be accounted for by the time span between the studies, and confounding differences in the populations surveyed. For example, it seems clear that masturbation is less frequent in those with strong religious beliefs.

It is interesting to see how the high incidence of masturbation is often used as a reason for promoting unquestioningly positive attitudes towards it. In one popular sex manual, the authors use a third of their chapter on masturbation attempting to prove that 'it is true to say that virtually everyone masturbates in some way or another'.[4] They suggest that the 50 per cent or so of girls who claim in some surveys they do not masturbate are just not aware that they are doing it!

This suggestion of the universality of masturbation in adolescent girls needs to be seriously questioned. It runs contrary to the evidence from much published research, and in my view is an example of one of the modern myths of masturbation.

'Your brain is full of grey matter, a kind of jelly. Touch yourself in that evil way and this jelly will leak down your spine and go to waste.'[5]

That solemn warning from a Victorian father still has its counterpart in present-day fears such as this example:

I regularly stood on the same spot outside our house and tried to read the road sign 50 metres down it. I could always read it which was a relief, but once I did wake up in a panic because I could not see. After much yelling and gentle reassurance from my mother it transpired that my eyelids had stuck together with sleepies. That was a close call, and it made me stop masturbating for at least a month. Amazing what fear can do![6]

The repressive myths that masturbation makes you blind, stunts

your growth, or drives you mad, die hard. Doctors have unfortunately played a part in perpetuating them. 'This rubbish
was propagated particularly by numbers of sour medical men
in Queen Victoria's reign, and it is as much rubbish now as it
was then.'[7]

Agreed, but have the sweeter medical men of the permissive
society's reign merely substituted another myth in its place? Far
from being harmful, masturbation is now considered an essential
experience. 'Learning to masturbate bears the same relation to
intercourse as does learning to speak to conversation.'[8]

Many sexologists now share this view that masturbation is a
necessary rehearsal for adult love-making. Thus the old myth is
paradoxically reversed and it is now those who do *not* masturbate
who are told they are being harmed. Llewellyn-Jones even claims
that people who don't masturbate are more likely to have sexual
problems when they marry,[9] though reliable evidence for this
assertion is singularly lacking.

These views require careful dissection. First, if as some surveys
suggest, up to a half of all adolescent girls do not masturbate, how
can it possibly be an essential prerequisite for successful marital
intercourse? Or is it essential only for boys?

Second, as we shall see in the next chapter, it is *not* sexual
experience but premarital virginity that is positively associated
with a stable and successful marriage (including its sexual aspects). Could it be that with masturbation as with premarital
sex, what is often advocated as a 'necessary rehearsal', may
actually prove to be counter-productive? Bancroft[10] and Kroll,[11]
for instance, give some interesting examples of clinical cases
where masturbation worked against a good sexual relationship.
Some of my own case-examples are discussed on pages 288–91
in connection with pornography.

Third, the frequency and depth of guilt associated with
adolescent masturbation is in my view inadequately explained. 'When people masturbated they neither passed go
nor collected 200 dollars, but went straight to hell and
often died of guilt on the way.'[12]

In Hite's survey many of her subjects described masturbation
as 'lonely, guilty, unwanted, selfish, silly and generally bad'.[13]

Hite explained this purely as a manifestation of the negative attitude of society generally towards masturbation, but this is a rather circular argument. What is then the root cause of these guilt feelings which affect individuals and society alike?

The usual explanations for the negative attitudes of most societies towards masturbation focus on two main factors – the threat to health (which, as we have seen is simply non-existent – merely a repressive myth) and the supposed immorality of non-procreative sex.

It is easy to see how the idea of the immorality of any sexual act not intended for reproduction had political advantages in a society struggling to maintain its population size. There seems to be no support within our sexual nature for such a notion, however. For example, the fact that individual human capacity for sexual pleasure far exceeds our reproductive life-span by several decades, goes against the idea that non-procreative sex is immoral per se. Why then should self-stimulation continue to give such bad psychological vibrations?

I think the primary reason is that sexual intercourse is essentially inter-personal. It is the most intimate way in which I can communicate with another. Masturbation, however, is lonely love. It arouses all the pent-up yearning within me to love and be loved, and yet releases it in total isolation – often as not down the lavatory pan. What was intended to consolidate intimate communion, merely intensifies solitary confinement. As one psychiatrist writes, 'It frustrates the very instinct it gratifies'.[14]

Yet there is more to it than just the question of self-centredness. Seeking self-satisfaction in sex is not necessarily wrong (pp. 150, 161). Which of us does not seek pleasure from it for ourselves, even in the midst of our self-giving to our partner? It is only when this self-seeking excludes or violates the needs of others that it becomes morally suspect. Thus the feeling of dissatisfaction which follows solo sex may not be so much actual guilt about its self-centredness, as a sense of the intrinsic incompleteness of the act.

This still does not explain though why so many adolescent boys in particular, become compulsive masturbators. This situation is potentially much more serious than the occasional act of self-pleasuring. Prof. Lewis Smedes comments:

> ... compulsive masturbation is a form of self-punishment. We used to call it self-abuse, but we meant only physical abuse. Nobody calls it that any more. But it may just be a form of self-abuse – not of one's body but of the soul. Let me explain what I mean. Many youngsters bear a heavy load of vague unattached guilt. They cannot locate any concrete horrendous evil in their lives, but they still feel vaguely guilty. They need something specific on which to fasten their feelings, and since their guilt feelings are already fuzzily related to uneasiness about their sexuality, what better peg is there to hang their guilt feelings on than masturbation?[15]

Thus for many adolescents, masturbatory guilt can act as an emotional life-belt in the turbulent sea of their own insecurity. The problem is this life-belt ultimately sinks. Compulsive masturbation is not normal; it is a cry for help which should not go unheeded.

SEXUAL FANTASIES

So far we have considered masturbation in isolation from pornography and sexual fantasy, but they are in fact inextricably linked. 'Pornography is for masturbation; that is its use'[16] and most boys and many girls will indeed use it.

Though sexologists rightly assure us that everybody has sexual fantasies and they are in this sense 'normal', it is worth considering how much sexual fantasising is purely (or more often impurely!) a product of media influence and in this sense 'abnormal'. Would we fantasise about owning a Porsche or travelling to Hawaii if communication technology had not given to us the raw material on which to base such fantasies? I believe that much sexual fantasising is similarly artificially induced.

Like masturbation, fantasy in itself need not necessarily be wrong, but is often treacherous in practice. This issue is considered further in Chapter 22.

FINDING THE ANSWERS

What then should be our approach to masturbation? In young children it is not associated with sexual ideas and should never be dealt with punitively (p. 38). Attempts to do so may paradoxically stimulate even more interest in masturbation, which is often a comforting habit in childhood. If young children are seen to be masturbating a lot, parents should consider if too little stimulation is being provided in other areas. Is the child bored or not receiving enough in the way of physical affection?

In adolescence, masturbation will increasingly be consciously associated with sexual climax and there is much that parents can do to help their children prepare for this phase.

● Talk about it

If we don't talk about masturbation with our children, they will learn about it from others anyway. If they receive instruction mainly from their peers, they are likely to take on board many of the masturbatory myths we have considered previously. Nearly all boys will masturbate sooner or later and the topic should be discussed with them around the age of eleven or even earlier.

Masturbation is not always such a key issue for girls, though this is changing with the increasing promotion of pornography marketed specifically for women.

● Recognise that its significance can vary

For the boy or girl who, without using pornography, masturbates occasionally to relieve an ache in the testicles or ease period pains, there is, in my view, no case against it.

● Emphasise its transitional nature

It is important to stress however that masturbation is not an essential preparation for adult sexual life, but more like a 'Portakabin' in which to accommodate our sexual urges temporarily, before moving into a real home. It is totally 'unrealistic to suppose that we can try to teach youngsters to accept masturbation the same way they accept little league baseball'.[17] It is not a junior version of adult sex, and in today's pressured sexual climate, teenagers need strong reassurance that even if they never masturbate at all, they are perfectly normal and can still enjoy a full and satisfying sexual experience after marriage.

● Encourage alternative channels

There is no doubt that the sexual energy released in masturbation can be channelled more creatively in other directions. Sport and physical recreation in particular can be a great asset in this process of sublimation.

Such sublimation is quite different from denial or repression. In sublimation, the reality of sexual drive is freely acknowledged and consciously controlled.

● Be alert to the dangers of pornography and associated compulsive masturbation

The compulsive masturbator is, if you'll pardon the pun, in a totally different ball-game. Addictive behaviour patterns are by definition very difficult to break and those related to pornography are no exception. If your teenager is caught in this trap, expert help may be required but, in the first instance, take a non-condemnatory stance and keep the channels of communication open. Most teenagers value at least being able to speak to parents about such deeply personal matters and feeling free to ask for help is the first step to getting it.

FURTHER READING

Joyce Huggett, *Just Good Friends?* (IVP, 1990).

Thomas Szasz, *Sex: Facts, Frauds and Follies* (Blackwell, 1981).

6

VIRGIN TERRITORY:
GROUND WORTH DEFENDING

(One) destructive myth in our lives is that sexual activity is natural, while sexual inactivity is not.

Celia Haddon
The Limits of Sex

Rebecca, aged twenty-one, was a stunningly attractive girl. A few months before her forthcoming marriage, she went along to the local family-planning clinic to see about going on the pill.

'What does your fiance do?' asked the nurse.

'He's a tennis coach.'

'And what contraception have you been using up to now?'

Rebecca looked slightly annoyed at the underlying assumption.

'We haven't been using any contraception,' she replied.

'Isn't that rather risky?' asked the nurse earnestly.

'No, I don't think you understand me, we haven't needed any contraception.'

The nurse now moved into a much more authoritative mode. This poor girl was obviously clueless.

'You wouldn't be the first girl to come in here pregnant thinking she didn't have any need of contraception. Haven't you even thought of using a condom?'

'You still haven't grasped it, have you?' countered Rebecca getting rather exasperated by now. 'We don't believe in sex outside of marriage. We are both virgins!'

We usually regard the loss of something irreplaceable as a misfortune, but with virginity there seems to be a remarkable exception. Most teenagers today are more interested in being chased than chaste, and most family-planning clinic doctors automatically assume their clients have not only been chased but caught well before the aisle!

There is good reason for such an assumption with statistics from virtually every Western society showing a marked increase in teenage sexual activity and a decrease in age at first coitus.

Michael Schofield's survey of British teenagers in the early 1960s showed an incidence of adolescent sexual activity which paralleled that of white Americans in the monumental Kinsey surveys carried out fifteen years earlier. By the age of eighteen, 17 per cent of girls and 34 per cent of boys interviewed said they had experienced intercourse.[1]

Ten years later, in another British survey, Farrell noted a dramatic increase in these figures, with 55 per cent of girls and 69 per cent of boys reporting experience of coitus by the age of eighteen.[2]

In the 1990s this trend has continued. A recent textbook on adolescent medicine claimed that in the USA '6 per cent of girls and 14 per cent of boys start sexual intercourse between the ages of 10 and 11'[3] while in Britain, the 1990 Health Education Authority report on teenage sexual behaviour stated that 65 per cent of those interviewed between sixteen and nineteen, reported that they were sexually active.[4] Similarly, Phillips commenting in 1992 on a survey for the South Western Regional Health Authority, noted that researchers found a 'culture in which premarital sexual intercourse was universally condoned', and 'a half of the 16-year-olds were non-virgins and virtually 100 per cent by their early 20s.'[5]

As we noted earlier in connection with masturbation (p. 57), statements such as 'virtually 100 per cent' need closer examination. Phillips, for example, gives no information on how many of the sample were married by their early twenties.

Even allowing for a degree of overstatement in Phillips's remarks, however, there is no doubt that virgin territory, like the tropical rain-forest, is seriously threatened with extinction. Let us look at the factors which have contributed to this situation.

REASONS FOR THE RARITY OF VIRGINS

● The Naturalness and Fun of Sex

Sexual passion is a natural part of the range of human emotions and most teenagers, not surprisingly find it exhilarating. The rapture of the sexually-experienced enthusiast is highly infectious. As one of them quips, 'Friends of mine used to preach joyful promiscuity, and since they were both joyful and promiscuous, I didn't argue.'[6]

By contrast, many who advocate premarital chastity appear rather dull and boring. As Gerhard Hauer writes, 'Our society lacks not only tender and loving married couples, but also attractive models of how young people can treat each other openly and affectionately without being caught in a sexual relationship.'[7]

I consider one of the greatest needs of our day is for more role-models who both practise and preach joyful chastity. One of the reasons why I am such a passionate advocate of premarital chastity myself is that I saw in my teens such a good example of its power to produce an intimate marriage that I wanted such a relationship for myself. This proved a powerful incentive throughout many struggles in my adolescence.

● The Instant Society

Today the emphasis is on the instant. We live in a world of speed. Instant coffee, fast food, express photos, Swiftair mail – all vie for our approval and patronage on the basis of their quick delivery. In the age of the microwave oven and Fax machine we are encouraged to be impatient. To have to wait for anything is usually considered a disadvantage.

In such an environment, it is not surprising that appeals to wait for sex are likely to fall on deaf ears.

In a society which is consumer orientated and dependent on the immediate satisfaction of as many personal needs as possible, there is no area of need which is left unexploited or used sparingly. This means that sexual liberalisation can be seen as a socially conforming ... process, and this conformity is the very reason why liberalisation has met with so little resistance.[8]

● Marital Breakdown

The increasing incidence of marital breakdown and divorce (considered in chap. 19) threatens the value placed on premarital virginity in at least two ways. First it raises the question that if marriage is so likely to end in disaster what point is there in preserving virginity until your wedding night? Second it means that many more adolescents will be brought up in single-parent families, usually, though not always, with an absent father. There is some evidence that premarital sex occurs less frequently among teenagers in families which are headed by their natural fathers.[9]

● Media Influence

There can be little doubt about the powerful effect of advertisements, magazines, films and television in promoting early sex as 'a good thing'. Little wonder, since sex boosts sales and viewing figures, the earlier you're hooked the better.

Even Prof. Ronald Goldman, who is not exactly noted for his conservative approach to sexual matters, writes, 'It is factors such as external influences of a sexy, sex-obsessed and sexually-stimulating society which arouse the young.'[10] The media inevitably must constitute a large part of such 'external influences' and they mould sexual attitudes by various means:

(a) *Inaccurate Reporting* A good example of this was the misrepresentation of statistical data about teenage sex in a national newspaper headline in 1992, which ran, 'Nearly half of young people lose virginity before 16.'[11]

This headline was in fact untrue, the data being reported actually confirming that most teenagers (actually two-thirds) are *not* sexually active before their sixteenth birthday, the legal age of consent in the UK.

In a most illuminating commentary on this particular piece of media misinformation, several consultant paediatricians wrote to the *British Medical Journal* to point out:

Society's view of what is normal has an important influence on individual behaviour. 'Everyone's doing it' is a common myth among teenagers ... If teenagers are led, by both the medical and the general press to believe that most of their peers are sexually active this will increase pressure on them in their relationships still further. Those under 16 who are virgins may be labelled a minority group, with an implication of abnormality ... There is enough heat within teenage relationships without the medical profession stoking the fire.[12]

The same comment could be made of the mass media.

(b) *Sex Saturation*   The media give teenagers the impression that sex is the one and only thing in life that matters. One American author estimates that in the course of a year the average viewer in the States watches approximately 9,230 sex acts portrayed on TV. Of these, more than 80 per cent will be outside of marriage.[13] Is it any surprise that teenagers who are not indulging in the delights so incessantly portrayed will begin to think that they have something the matter with them?

(c) *Role-modelling*   Examples of this are legion, but I focus on one which I find particularly sad. Phillip Schofield is a highly talented and deservedly popular children's TV presenter, looked up to and admired by countless teenagers. In a 1992 newspaper feature he stated: 'No one forgets their first time, do they? For me it was in the sand dunes in Newquay – I was about 15. I took my flip-flops off as a boy and put them on again as a man.'[14]

Such a lead can only encourage his many admirers to follow in his flip-flops, and such a statement perpetuates the popular myth that it is having sex that makes you an adult. In fact saying 'No' is a much surer proof of your maturity in the midst of social pressure like this.

● Moral Uncertainty

Morality is out of fashion, especially when it comes to sex. 'Moral attitudes are irrelevant as a basis for judging the reasons for going to bed, still less for condemning them.'[15]

Even among those who do not think morality is totally irrelevant, many would none the less agree with Ernest Hemingway that it is relative: 'What is moral is what you feel good after, and what is immoral is what you feel bad after.'[16]

The problem with this definition, of course, is that the very thing you feel good about today you may feel bad about tomorrow. Tears of regret are never planned in advance.

● Spiritual Decline

As I mentioned in the Introduction, sex and religion are inextricably connected. Many popular books on sex quote from the Bible or refer to its teaching, usually in order to assure readers that they can safely ignore it! The declining influence of Christian belief in Western society generally has inevitably led to a corresponding decrease in motivation to abstain from premarital sexual activity.

Ira Reiss cites a programme screened as far back as 1965 entitled 'The Playboy and The Christian' in which a theologian, Harvey Cox, stated that there was nothing necessarily wrong with premarital coitus. Reiss wryly comments 'This is rather a major change from the traditional Christian position on abstinence from sex before marriage!'[17]

● The 'Sexperts'

In 1948 the era of systematic research in human sexuality really took off with the publication of Alfred Kinsey's *Sexual Behaviour in the Human Male*. This was soon followed by Masters' and Johnson's research into how sexual responses occur. Their work relied heavily on a behavioural framework which concentrated on the mechanism of sex rather than its meaning.

Such an approach has revolutionised sex therapy and can be of great value, but behaviourism has tended to reduce sexual desire to the level of a basic instinct which must be gratified. 'Sexual desire and extreme hunger for food have much in common. Hungry and lusty individuals are restless, urgently searching the means of gratification.'[18]

Most sexperts today would agree with this view and in this

context, virginity, far from being virtuous, seems foolish. Thus Alex Comfort, the doyen of contemporary sexologists asserts his own belief that, 'Chastity is no more a virtue than malnutrition'[19] – a view which sounds very plausible until one considers the alternative that, 'Unchastity is no more a virtue than obesity.'

Of course the problem is that such alternatives are rarely considered. The pronouncements of the sexperts are swallowed without question, and the possible values of maintaining pre-marital virginity are never given serious thought.

● The Contraceptive Revolution

The introduction of reliable contraception, and especially the advent of 'the pill' in 1961, is often indicted as the principal 'virgin-killer' of the century, I question the validity of this charge, however. In my view the pill's role was that of an 'accessory after the fact'. It seems highly likely to me that the increase in premarital sexual activity would have occurred even without the pill, fuelled by the factors already considered.

The pill did, however, exert a powerful influence on sexual attitudes. As one young girl confessed, 'Although I went on it purely for the sake of my boyfriend it became increasingly easy to stray from the path due to the total lack of inhibition. Promiscuity becomes as easy as another cigarette. In this respect the pill *to the addict* is as morally dangerous as heroin is physically'[20] (my italics).

Society in the early sixties was already addicted to the heady wine of sexual liberalisation; the pill arrived on cue to make the existing craving easier to satisfy.

Contraception is often an irrelevance anyway to those looking for sexual experience. In a recent survey of 315 16–17-year-olds, 54 per cent were sexually active, and of these a half said they had unprotected sex.[21] First intercourse is often a spontaneous event, whereas contraception requires foresight. If teenagers are taught and believe that virginity doesn't matter, they will lose it 'in the heat of the moment' irrespective of the risks involved. 'The desire for this unity is so powerful that couples can find themselves having intercourse without taking any contraceptive precautions, hence the point that I have made repeatedly that the principal deterrent to premarital pregnancy is not to be found in contraceptives but in the will.'[22]

● The Contraceptive Industry

While I do not accept the view that effective contraception in itself has led to increased premarital sexual activity, the way in which that contraception is promoted and marketed is certainly culpable. The contraceptive industry is as keen as any other commercial enterprise to make profits, and advocating abstinence is not the way to boost its sales.

Thus, those involved in the marketing of contraceptives are likely to have a vested interest in encouraging a permissive approach to sexual relationships, regardless of the compelling considerations in favour of premarital chastity, to which we now turn.

THE VALUES OF CHASTITY

Before examining some of the many good reasons for maintaining premarital chastity I should stress that they are as equally valid for men as for women. The current double standard by which the bride is still expected (at least in theory!) to be a virgin on her wedding night, but it is considered perfectly all right for the groom to have had intercourse, is nothing less than rank hypocrisy.

● Chastity Accords With The Meaning of Sex

The fact is that sexual intercourse has a deeper meaning than merely the sum of the pleasures experienced by the participants. Just as the penetration of the sex act unites two people physically, there is also a simultaneous union on a different plane. Arthur Miller recognises something of this in his classic play *The Crucible*[23]:

> ELIZABETH   John – grant me this. You have a faulty under-
> standing of young girls. There is a promise made in any
> bed—

JOHN   What promise!

ELIZABETH   Spoken or silent, a promise is surely made.

In a deeper and more powerful language than any other, the sex act communicates the message that 'I am totally yours'. So, as Smedes succinctly puts it, sex before or outside of marriage is wrong because 'it violates the inner meaning of the act. It is wrong because unmarried people thereby engage in a life-uniting act without a life-uniting intent.'[24]

Though many today would argue that 'mutual epidermal stimulation'[25] provides a valid reason in itself for sex, this is not true. Sex though pleasurable is never for pleasure alone. Casual sex is only casual in the same sense as casual theft. They may both be casual in intent but not in their essential nature and they inevitably lead to casualties. This is because '...intrinsic in the sexual act is the tendency for attachment in and through the personal encounter, and when this dimension is ignored, then the meaning of the act is devalued.'[26]

● Chastity Promotes Marital Stability

There is a consistent body of research dating back as far as 1923 which clearly shows the positive association between premarital virginity and subsequent stability, mutual happiness and good sexual adjustment after marriage.[27-29] Even Reevy's study of just premarital petting (without actual intercourse having taken place) concluded that 'The group with unfavourable marital predictions can be characterized as being more active sexually than the group with favourable marital predictions.'[30]

These findings are a considerable embarrassment to permissive sexologists, and as a consequence are rarely even mentioned in contemporary writings, although Bancroft with his customary even-handedness with the facts is forced to admit, albeit reluctantly, that 'it seems that the statistical support for premarital "virtue" won't go away'.[31]

Such statistical support was in fact given a strong boost in 1992 when a survey published by the Office of Population Censuses and Surveys showed that couples who lived together before getting married were up to 60 per cent more likely to divorce than couples who did not.[32](p. 110).

Zelda West-Meads, a spokeswoman for Relate, commented, 'I am very surprised by these figures.'[33] They came as no surprise, however, to those already familiar with the positive association between premarital chastity and marital success. Though I agree it would be totally naïve to assume that all the couples in that survey who did not live together before marriage were virgins, certainly there were going to be more virgins in that group than in the group of cohabitees!

Athanasiou and Sarkin in an elegant and carefully-controlled research study in 1974 concluded that 'Generally speaking respondents who report extensive premarital sexual experience report extensive extra-marital activity.'[34] This association could well be a major factor in explaining the higher divorce rate of cohabitees.

It also gives the lie to those writers who propagate such popular nonsense as: 'To expect a girl to go into marriage a virgin is just folly. There is so much that can go wrong with the physical relationship that I have become quite clear in my mind that no girl should allow herself to become engaged till she has lain with her man and found joy, peace and release in it.'[35] Such advice is to put the cart before the horse. It will not travel very far that way.

In any case, the notion of a sexual 'test-drive' is totally unnecessary – 'after all, the sexual organs are not made of bones, but of muscles and soft tissues which adjust to each other during the course of marriage'.[36] As we shall see later, marital break-up is almost never caused by sexual problems. Indeed the very same experts who suggest the advisability of sexual experience before marriage also admit that marriage counsellors 'never accept sexual problems at face value because they are so rarely the cause of marital disharmony. Sex is usually the injured bystander . . .'[37] Why then do they put such emphasis on having sex before marriage in the first place?

My wife and I were both virgins when we married – a situation which arose not from the absence of opportunities to have sex, but from the presence of a mutual conviction that premarital virginity is the best way. We are both quite clear that this has contributed positively to our intimacy and security in marriage.

We are not alone in this view. Madaras, for example, quotes extensively the comments of another couple who interestingly have no religious beliefs:

> By being willing to wait until we were married, I felt I was showing her that it wasn't just sex I wanted from her but real, true love and lifelong commitment with her. And she was showing me the same thing, that we really mattered to each other as people, beyond just a physical, sexual wanting or desire. We really trusted each other ... This trusting and promising made us able to grow to be better lovers than we might have been otherwise.[38]

As Dominian so rightly asserts, 'Coitus is not a research tool for personal compatibility, but later completes the compatibility that has already been achieved.'[39]

● Chastity Protects:

While these reasons constitute the very positive values of premarital chastity, those which follow are often played down because of a laudable concern not to impose restrictions based on fear; but these reasons too can be viewed in a context of love, not fear. Is it really a loving thing to expose your partner or indeed yourself to these risks?

Dissenters may also argue that the following are reasons against early coitus, or multiple partners rather than actual loss of virginity, but who can doubt that these three factors are bound together? As one psychiatrist puts it 'after sexual relations have become common, a psychological wall has been broken down which makes future sexual relationships apart from marriage all the easier but no more right.'[40] Premarital sex predisposes to postmarital infidelity. This is considered further in Chapter 18.

(a) *From Unplanned pregnancy* This is a widespread and ever-increasing problem. Between 1977–9 and 1987–9, the UK conception and abortion rates increased for girls under sixteen, by 24 per cent and 30 per cent respectively.

Unplanned teenage pregnancy is usually a disaster for the individuals concerned. It entails increased risk for the girl herself and an increase in complications for her baby, such as premature delivery. The birth is often followed by what Fielding describes as the 'dismal pattern of lost educational opportunity, unstable family life, poor employability and welfare dependence'.[41]

Abortion is often advocated as the solution to this problem, but there are few women who undergo this procedure without any pangs of regret, and a first abortion may well be the start of a dismal pattern of its own leading to unstable family life (chap. 14).

After twenty years of increasing contraceptive promotion in this country, the wiser sexologists are beginning to realise that 'contraceptive use among adolescents is far from being a straight-forward matter of availability and common sense.'[42]

Denial and a sense of invulnerability both characterise adolescent thought. Shah, Kantner and Zelnik[43] report that an astonishing 70 per cent of teenage girls they interviewed thought that they could not become pregnant. Other studies have shown that teenagers who get pregnant are aware of the availability of contraception but haven't used that knowledge. The appalling double standard among teenage boys that contraception is a girl's business only contributes further to the problem.

Then there is the sad fact that contraception does not always work anyway. The heavily-promoted sheath, for example, has a failure rate of at least 15.7 pregnancies for every 100 women relying on that method each year, and this rate is higher among young unmarried women. Nearly every young girl with an unwanted pregnancy that I see in my own clinical practice has actually been using contraception. Contraceptives may indeed reduce the risk of pregnancy, but they cannot eliminate it.

(b) *From Sexually-transmitted Diseases* The devastation wrought by sexually-transmitted diseases (STDs) is often played down. For example, a popular text on adolescence makes light of the topic and mistakenly encourages its readers to believe that 'the figures do not support commonly prevailing mythology'[44] that STDs are increasing.

Yet this was published less than a year after experts at an international conference on STDs in New York declared that the 'situation was nearly out of control. The 70 per cent of people sexually active by age 19 may have been exposed, become infected and passed it on without ever feeling ill or knowing they were infected.' The same report on the conference lamented, 'Immunological virgins seem to be almost the only kind one finds among adolescents any more, and that fact may account for the tremendous increase in STDs in the US.'[45]

The situation is not quite so critical at present in the UK, but nevertheless, Prof. Michael Adler, one of Britain's leading authorities on STDs, states that the number of cases in the UK has quadrupled over the past fifteen years and now totals 700,000 a year,[46] with diseases such as non-specific genital infection (146,636 cases in 1989) and genital warts (84,615 cases in 1989) leading the field currently. In the UK each year there are over 20,000 cases of sexually-transmitted diseases among teenagers.

It is true that many of these STDs are curable but some, such as herpes, are not (pp. 279–81). All are unpleasant and can lead to complications such as infertility, or may be associated with an increased risk of serious disease such as cancer of the cervix or AIDS.

(c) *From Cancer of the Cervix*   Over 2,000 women in Britain die each year of cancer of the neck of the womb. The age of girls at first intercourse is one of the most important risk factors. In girls who first engage in coitus at sixteen or less, the risk of getting cervical cancer is doubled.

The positive association between cervical cancer risk and the total number of sexual partners is also well established. As we have seen, an early sexual debut is likely to be associated with a pattern of sexual behaviour involving more than one partner, thus increasing the risk further for those girls who lose their virginity at an early age.

Boys are not exempt from responsibility, however, in decreasing the risk. Unfortunately, there is still widespread ignorance concerning the so-called 'male factor'[47] in increasing cervical cancer risk. In women with cervical cancer who have had no sexual partner other than their husband, the number of previous sexual partners of the husband is, in its own right, a risk factor for cervical cancer. Thus early loss of virginity and subsequent multiple sexual partners for a boy will increase the risk of any future spouse for cervical cancer.

(d) *From AIDS* AIDS is considered in detail in Chapter 24, and I almost hesitate to mention it at all in the present context because I believed in the value of premarital chastity long before the advent of AIDS, and will continue to do so should a cure for AIDS eventually be found.

In 1991, however, the World Health Organisation issued the following guidance: 'The most effective way to prevent the spread of HIV virus is to abstain from sexual intercourse or for two uninfected partners to remain faithful to each other'.[48] In order for this advice to be followed, it is obvious that premarital chastity must inevitably play an important role.

As I hope I have amply demonstrated, there are better reasons than AIDS for defending virgin territory but none more deadly.

(e) *From Psychological Harm* David Weis's[49] study of the emotional reaction of female college students to their first intercourse showed only one third actually had positive feelings about it. The majority had a mixture of negative emotions including guilt, anxiety and a feeling of being exploited. Hardly the wonderful experience promised by the sexperts!

The third of Weis's women who did enjoy first coitus nevertheless open themselves up to other psychological harm. The pain of abandonment, the fear of comparison, the pressure of performance-based sex are far more common outside of marriage than within it.

For men the situation is slightly different in that a much higher percentage enjoy first coitus, but at what cost to their girlfriends?

A young girl already involved with her sixth sexual partner once told me of a dream which haunted her. In this dream she awoke in terror to see Marilyn Monroe standing at the foot of her bed smiling seductively. Then the bed began to enlarge and fold up and swallowed the girl alive into a suffocating blackness while Monroe laughed.

I claim no particular expertise as an interpreter of dreams, but it was easy to see how this patient's premarital sexual experience was coming back to torment her in her sleep. She is certainly not alone in that. Even such a liberal authority as Dr Mary Calderone, the founder of the Sex Information and Education Council of the United States, admits that 'No-one knows what effect sex precociously experienced, will have ... Sex experience before confidentiality, empathy and trust have been established can hinder and may destroy the possibility of a solid permanent relationship.'[50]

The validity of such a warning is further borne out by a recent American research study which showed that girls of sixteen and under who had lost their virginity were more likely to report feeling lonely and were six times more likely to have attempted suicide than their virgin classmates. Non-virgin boys and girls alike were also much more likely to have engaged in alcohol and drug abuse than their virgin counterparts. The authors of the study conclude that 'early sexual experience among adolescents is associated with other potentially health-endangering behaviours'.[51]

BRIDGING THE GAP

Communicating to our children the value of premarital virginity is not an easy task in today's world. To do it meaningfully involves entering into their culture and understanding the pressures on them to engage in early sex.

It may mean, for example, reading a copy of a teen magazine with your daughter, or watching a popular children's TV programme with your son and then discussing their underlying messages and values. Some of the books mentioned at the end of Chapter 3 are well worth getting for children and teenagers to read for themselves.

As in so many areas of life, what you are will speak more powerfully than what you say. If you have an intimate and happy relationship without having had premarital sex, you will provide a model worth striving for. If on the other hand you have been through the experience of premarital sex and lived to regret it, sharing this with your children may also help them in their own struggles.

FURTHER READING

Liz Hodgkinson, *Sex Is Not Compulsory* (Columbus, 1988).

Joyce Huggett, *Life In A Sex Mad Society* (IVP, 1988).

WHEN THEY SAY THAT THEY'RE GAY: HOMOSEXUALITY

> Unlike Sleeping Beauty, real life children have no built-in mechanism ready to spring into operation the moment the first Prince comes along.
>
> Donald J. West
> *Homosexuality Re-examined*

In writing on intimacy and sex within a family context, I have not automatically made the assumption that every family member is heterosexual.

This mistake is often made, however. Many parents feel that homosexuality is something that only exists in other people's families. As child and adolescent psychiatrist, Prof. Peter Hill, points out, 'There are possibly more grounds for counselling parents than teenagers' when it comes to the subject of homosexuality.[1]

David is a homosexual who has had to cope with rejection for much of his life. His dad died when he was nine, and he left home in his early teens because his mother could not cope with his gay lifestyle which became increasingly apparent during his teens. Of David's large family network only his aunt showed him any sort of understanding, and eventually he went to live with her.

One gay rights publication understandably laments, 'Many parents lack even a basic understanding of homosexuality. The onus is too frequently on the young lesbian or gay man to inform and educate the parents. This added responsibility is not often seen in other areas of the parent/child relationship.'[2]

I sympathise with this view, but would add that a 'basic understanding of homosexuality' is not easy to come by. The whole subject is surrounded by such prejudice and conflicting expert opinion that getting to the truth of even the most elementary issues connected with homosexuality is not at all easy, as we shall see.

It is essential that parents should have some knowledge about homosexuality so that they can answer their own children's questions, and also engage more effectively with its wider social implications.

HOW COMMON IS HOMOSEXUALITY?

The incidence of homosexuality, which may be defined as a strong preferential attraction to members of the same sex, has been difficult to determine precisely. This is because, until very recently, there was a dearth of accurate research data. Also, any information collected is possibly skewed by the fact that homosexual acts between men in the UK are illegal under the age of twenty-one. Further imprecision arises because there is a spectrum of homosexual tendency. Kinsey[3] classified this range on a scale of 0–6, with 0 being exclusively heterosexual and 6 exclusively homosexual.

Most assessments of the incidence of homosexuality refer to Gagnon and Simon's[4] re-analysis of the original 1948 Kinsey data. This shows that 30 per cent of men surveyed had at least one homosexual experience leading to orgasm for themselves or their partner and half of these experiences took place before they were fifteen. Only 3 per cent of adult men were exclusively homosexual, however, with a further 3 per cent being bisexual. In women, Kinsey found that 13 per cent had homosexual experience to the point of orgasm by the age of forty-five.

Very recent studies both in Britain[5] and in the USA[6] have consistently shown that the number of men having experienced homosexual intercourse is only around 1–2 per cent. Kenyon[7] estimates that only around 1 in 45 of the adult female population in the UK are persistently and exclusively homosexual. These and other recent findings have given rise to considerable doubt about the validity of Kinsey's work. 'It is known that Kinsey's high homosexuality rates were no accident.'[8] In his group of 5,300 men, he had around 25 per cent prisoners, an additional high percentage of sex offenders, and several hundred male prostitutes.[9] Hardly a representative sample of the general population! Similarly 58 per cent of his female survey-group consisted of unmarried women, which would give a greater bias towards lesbianism than in a more representative random sample of the population. Kinsey's bibliographer comments, 'Kinsey's purpose was to "validate" types of behaviour previously thought to be deviant by showing how common they were.'[10]

Nevertheless even if, as seems likely, the true incidence of homosexuality is less than 2 per cent, we are still talking about millions of people. Moreover, anxieties about homosexual feelings are much more common among adolescents than actual homosexual practice. The issue is therefore an important one in many families.

Donald West, after a professional lifetime in examining homosexuality, reached the conclusion that 'Research into the causes of homosexuality has left a lot of mysteries unsolved.'[11] Perhaps this is not so surprising when we consider how little we know about the causes of heterosexuality either!

The very mention of the causes of homosexuality is seen as offensive by many sections of the gay community. I once attended a meeting in London at which an eminent professor of medicine was due to give a lecture on the possible genetic influences on homosexual orientation. He never got a chance to speak, however, because of the persistent heckling of a vociferous minority in the audience and the lecture had to be abandoned.

Not all homosexuals are so opposed to such discussion however. John Hart,[12] for example, considers that it is important at least to consider the question of causation because it crops up so frequently in conversation with the family and friends of gay people.

Before we turn to look at some of the causes that have been suggested, it is important to note that the overwhelming majority of such research and writing has been about male homosexuality. Hart may well be right when he suggests that this reflects the predominant focus of Western society on masculinity, and the general neglect of women's relationships except in relation to men.[13] I would emphasise, therefore, that the theories considered below apply equally to both sexes.

BIOLOGICAL FACTORS

● Genetic

One of the first studies suggesting that homosexuality has a genetic component is that of Kallman,[14] published in 1952. This was a study of what is technically known as concordance rates in twins. This needs a brief explanation. Identical (monozygotic) twins develop from the same genetic material which divides in two very early on in fetal development. Non-identical (dizygotic) twins develop from two separate eggs and sperms. Both identical and non-identical twins share the same prenatal environment, but only identical twins share the same genes. Thus for any condition with a genetic basis, one would expect a higher presence or absence of that condition in *both* twins (i.e. a higher concordance rate) when the twins are identical, than when they are not.

Kallman reported a 100 per cent concordance rate for homosexuality in thirty-seven identical twins, and only 12 per cent in twenty-six non-identical twins. The problem though was that Kallman's sample was highly selective and included a large number of psychotic patients. He himself later admitted to his critics that his results were a statistical artefact.

Two more recent studies, however, have again shown a higher concordance rate for homosexuality in male[15] and female[16] identical twins. A genetic component does therefore appear to be implicated. This suggestion however needs to be seen in perspective. For example, twin studies have recently shown that identical male twins have higher concordance rates for smoking than non-identical twins. Most people would agree, however, that smoking is not entirely a matter of genetic predisposition!

It is very difficult in studies of twins brought up in the same home, to eliminate completely the influence of subtle environmental factors affecting identical and non-identical twins differently. Both the studies mentioned above have been criticised on these and other grounds.[17] Furthermore some recent UK research by King and McDonald[18] showed a striking absence of concordance for male and female homosexuality among both the identical and non-identical twins in their study. They concluded that genetic factors are an insufficient explanation of sexual orientation.

The discovery of a 'gay gene', however, was given much media hype when first reported in 1993.[19] Though at the time of writing it is thought that an area on the X chromosome, present in around two-thirds of male homosexuals, may influence homosexual orientation, this research has been highly criticised and will certainly need to be confirmed by other studies before too much weight can be given to it.

● Neuro-Hormonal

Research in animals has shown that hormonal manipulation can produce changes in sexual behaviour that seem to parallel homosexual behaviour in humans, but it does take quite a leap of faith to equate the mounting of male rats by other males, or female rats by other females, with the homosexual situation in humans, in which psychological features predominate over any physical act.

Work on hormones in humans has centred on two main areas.
(a) It has been shown that blood and urine levels of testosterone are significantly lower in male homosexuals and higher in female homosexuals.
(b) Girls affected by male hormones during fetal development show tomboyish behaviour (see p. 26).

It is difficult to know what to make of these findings. One of the testosterone studies, for example, included many cannabis smokers in the homosexual group. Cannabis is known to lower testosterone concentrations.

Furthermore the administration of sex hormones to adults certainly has no effect whatsoever on sexual orientation, and tomboyish behaviour in girls is generally considered to be independent of lesbianism anyway.

Sadly, as with the 'gay gene', such research findings have often been sensationalised by the popular press to the detriment of scientists and homosexuals alike. One notable example occurred in *The Times*: 'The cause of homosexuality has been discovered and it will soon be possible to prevent "congenital homosexuality" by means of injections during fetal development.'[20] The undeniable influence of hormonal factors on human sexual behaviour is more subtle than this.

If hormonal factors do play a part in determining sexual orientation, they would be expected to exert such effects on the brain. In 1991 Simon LeVay broke new ground with the publication of his finding that a cluster of neurones in the brain known as INAH 3 (third interstitial nucleus of the anterior hypothalamus) was only half the size in homosexual males than in heterosexual males.[21] This again gave considerable impetus to the neuro-hormonal explanation of male homosexuality, but once again this is far from straightforward. Kenneth Klivington draws attention, for example, to evidence that the networks of nerves in the brain restructure themselves in response to learned experiences. 'Once the individual is born, the story gets more complex because of the interplay between the brain and experience. It's a feedback loop: the brain influences behaviour, behaviour shapes experience, experience affects the organisation of the brain.'[22]

In a comprehensive and thought-provoking review of biological theories of sexual orientation, Byne and Parsons conclude, 'There is no evidence at present to substantiate a biologic theory ... the appeal of current biological explanations may derive more from dissatisfaction with the present status of psychosocial explanations than from a substantial body of experimental data.'[23]

PSYCHOSOCIAL FACTORS

Biological theories of homosexuality are controversial because of their moral implication. Dr Richard Pillard puts it neatly, 'A genetic component in sexual orientation says, "This is not a fault, and it's not your fault".'[24] On the other hand psychological explanations of homosexual behaviour are often controversial because they can so easily imply blame and induce guilt in parents and children alike. These theories, like biological ones, may sometimes say as much about their proponents as about homosexuality.

● Early seduction

It is still a popular belief that children are seduced into a gay or lesbian lifestyle by older homosexuals. This does not appear to be a common pattern however.

Kenyon[25] for instance, found seduction to be a factor in only 8 per cent of the female homosexuals he studied, and a very recent paper[26] examining the lifestyle of homosexual men found that their first sexual experience was usually with a man of similar age. There was no convincing evidence that young men were seduced by older ones. It is also worth mentioning here that the seduction of young children is a very real problem in the heterosexual community.

● Disordered Parent-Child Relationship

Classical psychoanalytic thought, from Freud onwards, has always considered homosexuality as a disruption of normal development. The difficulty with psychoanalytical explanations is that they are based on clinical impressions and speculation rather than more objective scientific study. Explanations based upon such impressions are so widespread, however, that they are worth examining in a little more detail.

Irving Bieber's[27] examination by questionnaires into the family background of 106 homosexuals and 100 heterosexuals popularised the idea that male homosexuals came from families with a close-binding, 'seductive', over-indulgent mother dominating the family over the head of a detached, ambivalent or hostile father.

Bieber's work has since been heavily criticised on the grounds that his homosexual sample consisted of men who were already into analytical 'treatment'. Furthermore, later studies such as that of Siegelman[28] have shown that many male homosexuals have good, dominant and generous fathers.

There can, however, be little doubt that early sex education and role-models must influence a child's own sexual development to some degree. If heterosexual activity is portrayed by parents as something dirty, then aversion to it may well be encouraged in their children. If sex isn't mentioned at all in the family, the absence of factual information may predispose to various distortions and fears. In such a situation it is easy to see how, driven by fear of the unknown, a child may 'direct or have drawn what libido they have towards a member of their own sex'.[29]

Recently, the theory of disordered parent-child relationships has been modified and expanded by the work of the Cambridge psychologist, Elizabeth Moberly.[30] Her central thesis is that both male and female homosexuality is a condition of 'same-sex ambivalence', rather than just a love for the same sex.

Moberly understands the primary problem in homosexuality to be a disruption of the child's attachment to the parents of the same sex. This leads to a defensive detachment and distancing of the child from the same-sex parent. Such a disruption and detachment may be obvious to an external observer, or it may be a totally unconscious process. Homosexual love is then considered as an attempt to repair the disruption. 'The homosexual condition does not involve abnormal needs, but normal needs that have, abnormally, been left unmet in the ordinary process of growth.'[31] Some further implications of this approach will be considered later.

In conclusion, there seems to be no single determinative cause for homosexual orientation in the individual case. Homosexuality is multiply determined by psychological, sociocultural, biological and situational factors.

WHATEVER WILL YOUR DAD SAY? – ACTION FOR PARENTS

How should parents deal with a teenager who 'comes out' and tells them about his or her homosexuality?

● Affirm their personhood

Always remember that even if your child is homosexual, he or she does not cease to be your son or daughter. Homosexuality, whatever its cause, is about people. The stereotypes of the effeminate gay or the butch lesbian which abound in our society are largely unhelpful and should be firmly rejected. Homosexuals constitute as diverse a group of men and women as heterosexuals in terms of physical appearance, occupation, personality, and ability. So even if this revelation comes to you as an unwelcome shock, as it does in most families, remember your child is still the same person in these other respects.

There are two other important points to hold in mind. First, it has almost certainly taken a great deal of courage to speak to you in the first place about what is, after all, a deeply personal matter. It would have been much easier to have let you hear about it from a third party, or else to go on pretending that nothing was the matter. A personal revelation is always better than continuing deception. This should not go unacknowledged. To say 'I'm very glad that you told me yourself' is one positive goal that all parents should aim for in this situation.

Second, this will be one of the most crucial moments in your teenager's whole emotional experience, and will make a lasting impression. So your response should be made in the light of the probability that the youngster may often be asked subsequently, 'How did your folks take it? Do they still love you?'

● Put personal disappointments into perspective

Part of the grief that many parents feel in this situation is the shattering of expectations of their child's courtship and marriage. In addition, grandchildren are one of the few things in life that bring many joys and few responsibilities, and the potential loss of them may also be part of the felt disappointment.

You should clearly recognise however that teenagers don't have to be homosexual to inflict such heartaches. Not all 'straight' teenagers will fulfil all their parents' dreams. It is also worth mentioning here that 'what the neighbours think' is entirely up to them.

● Don't Apportion Blame

Any parent in this situation is tempted to blame either their son or daughter – 'She's doing this deliberately to hurt us', or themselves – 'Where did we go wrong for him to end up like this?' Neither of these reactions is helpful.

For most homosexuals, the awareness that they are different gradually dawns during late childhood and adolescence, and as Hill correctly indicates, 'This is not a decision but a realisation.'[32]

Richard was around the age of fourteen when he first became aware of the thrill of sexual arousal and excitement on entering the school changing rooms when the sixth form were showering. He noticed this same feeling was triggered off by watching wrestling on TV with his father on Saturday afternoons. One day his father noticed that Richard's excitement was about more than a half-nelson or a fall, and when he asked him about it, Richard told him about his homosexual feelings.

If parents have knowingly neglected their children, either physically or emotionally, they may well deserve blame for it, whether their child turns out gay or not, but not all, or even most such overtly neglected children do develop homosexual tendencies, whereas children who are apparently well cared for may do so. As Moberly points out, 'No parent of a homosexual should necessarily blame himself or herself on account of this disruption of attachment ... The human situation is such that hurt may sometimes occur without it being a matter for blaming anyone.'[33]

● Recognise the Situation Can Change

As we have seen, homosexual feelings are much more common in adolescence than in adult life. Your teenager's feelings may change as they grow older. This cannot be assumed however, and to respond to their 'coming out' with an automatic 'We all go through that phase', may well be harmful, and will be counter-productive if the feelings persist.

'There is an obvious and understandable need for minority groups to maintain their numbers and one way of doing this is to reinforce the idea "once a homosexual, always a homosexual."'[34] This idea is certainly widely advocated today, but is it necessarily correct?

There is considerable evidence to the contrary. Psychoanalysts such as Socarides[35] have long maintained that homosexual orientation can be changed. More recently, Green and Miller[36] in their review of 'treatments' for homosexuality conclude that 'cure' is possible at least in some cases, although they also point out that most homosexuals request psychiatric help in adjusting to their homosexuality, rather than in seeking to change it.

One of many implications of Moberly's work discussed above is that change from homo- to heterosexual orientation is possible. Since, in her view, homosexuality results from legitimate needs for same-sex love, fulfilment of such needs, as opposed to the eroticisation of them, will result in change. 'It is the provision of good same-sex relationships that helps us to meet unmet same-sex needs, heals defects in the relational capacity, and in this way forwards the healing process'[37]. Dominian[38] makes the same point when he states that 'Within the context of such stable relationships, love as expressed in sustaining, healing and growth, can take place.'

It is interesting that, within such relationships – often in a Christian setting, increasing numbers of both men[39] and women[40] are claiming change from their homosexual inclination. Such anecdotal biography is also supported by research literature of a more academic nature.[41]

● Encourage Sexual Integrity

We have already seen that in most cases, homosexual orientation results from a growing awareness of what already is, rather than a conscious choice of what is to be. The same could be said of heterosexual inclination, however, and the fact that our sexual orientation is realised rather than selected does not absolve any of us, gay or straight, from the responsible choices we all have to make about our sexual behaviour.

A central thesis of this book is that marriage is the only context in which sexual intercourse has total integrity and can find its most appropriate expression. In encouraging teenagers to a virgin lifestyle outside of marriage, I do not discriminate on the basis of sexual orientation. I am acutely aware that in advocating homosexual teenagers to take this path, there are several specific areas which need to be considered.

(a) *'You can't possibly understand'* The majority of homosexual groups resent the suggestion of advice being given by heterosexuals. 'What do they know about us?' is a very common

sentiment expressed in gay literature. You cannot afford to
be ignorant about homosexuality if you have a teenager who
thinks he or she is gay. Buy, or borrow books from the library
to get yourself fully informed.

(b) *The War of the Worlds*   Sexual politics makes the personal
dilemma of homosexual teenagers and their families that much
harder. The following is a relatively mild example from gay literature of the sort of provocation you can expect: 'Finally remember
that if you ever bring pressure against a son or daughter for engaging in homosexual acts, you yourself are being unethical.'[42]

From the gay perspective, any criticism of homosexuality is
automatically immoral, and this viewpoint may make communication very difficult.

(c) *The Law*   The Sexual Offences Act 1967 sets the age of consent for male homosexual sex at twenty-one in the UK. The law
does not expressly set an age of consent for homosexual acts between women. Even though, as we have seen, there is no evidence
to substantiate early seduction as a widespread 'cause' of homosexuality, adolescent homosexual feelings are relatively common
and may often just disappear. 'Gradually over the course of many
years the sexual interest in male bodies has left me, evaporating
like an unhealthy cloud, so that at times were it not for memory
I would be puzzled as to how it could ever have been.'[43]

This fact alone is enough to discourage any change in the law,
even though many, gays and straights alike, see this differential
in the age of consent for homosexuals as an example of prejudice.

(d) *'A long obedience in the same direction'*   Alex Davidson in
The Returns of Love – a very moving account of his struggles
with life as a homosexual, writes, 'Isn't it one of the most wretched
things about this condition that when you look ahead the same
impossible road seems to continue indefinitely? You're driven to
rebellion when you think of there being no point in it and to
despair when you think of there being no limit to it.'[44]

He eloquently spells out the pain of an enduring dilemma.
Yet paradoxically at the same time he demonstrates that the
road of sexual integrity is not 'impossible' after all. He himself
has travelled it, and there are many others who share that same
journey.

(e) *Homosexual marriage?* In an attempt to ease the long obedience just considered, the concept of homosexual marriage is often put forward, and homosexual teenagers will be faced with this issue. There are two main problems that I can see with this concept. One relates to the nature of marriage, and the other to the nature of homosexuality.

Marriage unfolds at a personal level something that is true at a biological level, namely that human beings come into existence in two sexes clearly ordered towards heterosexual union. 'Other relationships, however important in themselves and however rich in intimacy and fidelity do not disclose the meaning of biological nature in this way. They float, as it were, like oil upon water, suspended upon bodily existence rather than growing out of it.'[45]

Second, if, as discussed earlier, the homosexual state is indeed one of striving after unmet same-sex needs, then, as Moberly suggests, 'a form of marriage to sanction the homosexual relationship would be inappropriate because the relationship is inherently self-limiting, and because marriage is not right for a relationship analogous to that between parent and child.'[46]

● Face Up to the Future Realistically

If your child does decide to pursue a gay lifestyle, he or she will undoubtedly face many problems in which your understanding and love will be needed. Such difficulties need to be pointed out and prepared for.

(a) *Rejection*   Homosexuality is more or less universally rejected by contemporary Western society. 'A very good case can be made out that the homosexual is the modern equivalent of the leper.'[47] Green and Miller[48] maintain that this attitude has been consistently reflected throughout history.

Homosexuality presents a threat to established social norms, and rejection of it stems from a variety of sources. These include suspicion of the unknown and alien, defence reactions against fear of homosexuality in oneself, and 'guilt by association' involving the linking of homosexuality with other socially unacceptable behaviour such as paedophilia.

Though on these and many other grounds such rejection is irrational, homosexuals will inevitably face relative separation from the mainstream of society.

A further unfortunate consequence of this rejection is sexual discrimination. Homosexuality may well prejudice the chances of getting such things as accommodation, employment or promotion.

(b) *Transient Relationships*   Moberly maintains that homosexual relationships are 'inherently self-limiting. There is no basis for permanence in the structure of the homosexual condition.'[49] This is borne out for men by Bell and Weinberg's[50] classic study of homosexual behaviour. They concluded that very few homosexual men were in stable faithful relationships (though those who were in that rare situation were reported as 'particularly happy').

But in general, 'sex in the homosexual world precedes relationships, often being quite detached from personal relationships of even the most transient kind.'[51] In gay steam baths men may pass from one partner to another in a succession of more than twenty or thirty in a single night. This kind of activity is unusual in even the most highly sexually-adventurous straight male.

Lesbian women have far fewer partners than their male counterparts, and are less likely to be involved in such brief sexual encounters. Even so one psychiatrist, after many years of experience, states his opinion that 'it is much more difficult for homosexual relations to become as stable, durable and unexploiting as a good heterosexual one can be.'[52]

(c) *Strains on Health*   Bell and Weinberg's[53] large-scale survey showed that gay men and women reported lower self-esteem than their straight counterparts, and that depression and suicide attempts were more common among homosexuals. In my experience many homosexuals are particularly prone to alcohol addiction with all its attendant health problems (chap. 21).

Although some sexually transmitted diseases, including AIDS, are especially common (though none exclusively so) in male homosexuals, this needs to be balanced against the fact that lesbians are probably in the lowest risk group of all in this regard.

Though homosexuality is compatible with good physical and mental health, the likelihood of problems is increased. I am sure I am not the first to draw attention to the irony of adopting the word 'gay' to describe the homosexual lifestyle. In practice this 'burning torment'[54] as Davidson describes it, can be anything but gay.

● Seek Professional Help

The best place to start may be your local branch of Relate or a local doctor with an interest in sexual problems. If your doctor is not helpful, he should be able to refer you on to an appropriate specialist.

By going directly to a gay counselling service teenagers run the considerable risk that their homosexuality will simply be endorsed and embraced. The agencies listed at the end of this chapter will take a sympathetic approach, yet without such automatic reinforcement.

FURTHER READING

Jeff Konrad, *You Don't Have To Be Gay* (Monarch, 1993).
Simon LeVay, *The Sexual Brain* (MTP, 1993).

CONTACT AGENCIES

Courage Trust, PO Box 338, Watford, WD1 3BQ. Tel 081-420 1066.

Turnabout, PO Box 592, London SE4 1EF.

True Freedom Trust, PO Box 3, Upton, Wirral, Merseyside, L49 6NY. Tel 051-653 0773; London office 081-314 5735.

8

ASPECTS OF LOVE: ROMANCE, ATTRACTION AND PARTNER CHOICE

Many a man has fallen in love with a girl in a light so dim he would not have chosen a suit by it.

Maurice Chevalier

Teenage sexuality involves so much more than just 'having sex', and the wider enjoyment of sexual attraction and the mysterious chemistry of romance are a wonderful part of adolescent experience. Such chemistry can produce some highly successful compounds spontaneously, but explosions are more likely to result if there is no understanding of some of the basic equations involved. An analysis of these underlying factors involved in sexual attraction and falling in love forms the basis of this chapter.

ROMANCE AND REALITY

There can be no mistaking it: that glance 'across a crowded room' which tells you that you've met the right one. The heart beats faster, the pupils dilate, the eyes glisten. Energy levels suddenly seem endlessly high and the whole world looks different somehow.

The search for intimacy is all a part of growing up, and romance is one of its most thrilling components. To deny the reality of romantic feelings is to impoverish our emotional experience. But to over-emphasise the importance of romantic feelings, or insist on their permanence is to arrest our emotional development. By definition 'falling in love' is an initiatory experience, and those who fail to progress beyond this stage into staying in love are bound to discover deep disappointment and hurt.

It is necessary to emphasise this point in a society in which romantic love is constantly portrayed as the whole and not just a part. Puerile paperbacks, sentimental soaps and vacuous videos all chorus in unison that it must be 'true love' if the lights are low and the violins are playing. In such an environment it seems almost brutal to remind ourselves that

> The glances over cocktails
>   That seemed to be so sweet
> Don't seem quite so amorous
>   Over the Shredded Wheat![1]

Such realism however is a necessary counterpoint to romanticism. Romantic love in all its intoxicating power should be enjoyed for what it is, but must be firmly put in its place when it attempts to be something more. Romance unchecked presents several potential dangers which need to be clearly recognised.

It is possible to be more in love with the state of 'being in love' than with the 'beloved'.

Girls are particularly prone to this danger though men are by no means immune from it.

Alexandra had never had a boyfriend before so when Roger, a trainee solicitor, asked her out, it was hard to say 'No'. He was good looking, dressed well, and the restaurant he chose was the most expensive place she had ever been to in her life. The bouquets of flowers, the chocolates, the theatre trips and lavish parties which followed were all too good to be true. He just had to be the right one for her.

It was only months later during a prearranged holiday away from Roger that Alexandra realised that she hardly knew him as a person at all. She was so overwhelmed with the happiness of romance that Roger himself had virtually become a secondary consideration.

Romance can lead into a fantasy world.

In the excitement of new-found love it is easy to project an unreal image of perfection on to your partner. Consequently those aspects of their personality which you would normally find irritating or even disturbing may be overlooked.

> ... love is blind and lovers cannot see
> The petty follies they themselves commit.[2]

Similarly, you do not want consciously to display those aspects of your own life that you consider less desirable either. So you may hide them, or pretend they don't exist. An amusing if rather basic example is that couples in the early stages of romance rarely release wind in each other's presence!

Romance is a poor indicator of compatibility

When the first flush of romance begins to wear off, it can lead to the mistaken idea that the relationship is finished. Some people cannot cope with the settling down of the initial turbulent excitement, and may abandon a relationship that still has much potential for happiness of a calmer and more committed kind.

There is good evidence that exciting and romantic events such as holidays, parties and dinner-dances form more than anything else the setting for the initial meeting of couples who subsequently marry. In such circumstances the initial attraction must inevitably be quite superficial, and 'something in addition of permanent power should be developed ... capable of holding the couple together "for better or worse"'.[3]

Let us now look at some of these sources of attraction.

MADE FOR EACH OTHER? – THE ANATOMY OF ATTRACTION

Physical Factors   Facial characteristics and body shape play an obvious role in initial attraction though even here psychological and social influences seem to be closely involved.

Height, for example, is linked with expectations of power, and women usually prefer men who are taller than themselves and men choose women who are shorter.

The low but positive correlation for height among spouses (tall women tend to marry tall men, and short women tend to marry short men) also applies to colour of skin and hair. Skin colour is also a reminder of the powerful influence that race still plays in the selection of a partner. In Hollingshead's examination of 2,063 couples in New Haven in 1950 there were no inter-racial marriages.[4] By 1970 still less than 10 per cent of American marriages were of mixed race.

There is some evidence that our partners do bear a physical resemblance to our parents or other close family members of the same sex as that partner. This only applies, however, if the emotional bonds between us and our parents were strong and positive.

More subtle physical features such as smell may also be involved in the process of sexual attraction! Chemicals called pheromones are produced by many animals to attract mates and influence their behaviour. Humans produce these substances too and it has been shown, for example, that telephone receivers sprayed with male pheromones were used more frequently by women than adjacent unsprayed ones.

PSYCHOLOGICAL AND SOCIAL FACTORS

These are far more important than physical features in influencing the selection of a partner. As indicated above, they may actually limit the range of choice that is made on the basis of physical attributes.

● Geographical Proximity
Even in this age of supersonic travel and the global village, people tend to marry others who live near by. In Clarke's[5] widely quoted American study, 50 per cent of the married couples he surveyed consisted of partners who had lived within thirteen blocks of each other prior to marriage.

● Social Similarity
Geographical closeness obviously operates as a decisive factor

only for those with scarce social contacts. Social proximity, however, is a more powerful influence which far outweighs the purely geographical.

There is a wealth of research showing that spouses tend to share such inter-linked social factors as social class, religion, race, age, educational background and intelligence.[6]

● Image of The Ideal

Such social similarity between partners is perhaps not surprising when one considers the psychological process involved in their selection.

Most people form a mental picture of the ideal characteristics they would like to have in a partner. This consists of physical attributes which as we have seen are important in initial attraction, but it also involves emotional factors such as leisure interests and personality type which exert a much more powerful bonding effect in the long term.

This ideal image will be strongly influenced by the parental image. If the childhood relationship with the parent of the opposite sex (or whoever substituted for that role) was good, then the developing temperament and opinions in particular will be shaped by that image, and similar features will be sought in a future spouse.

Of course, if parental relationships were poor the parental image will equally well have a negative effect. In the extreme case of psychological or sexual abuse by a parent, it may result in the child's having severe difficulties in forming any meaningful relationships in later life (see pp. 306–7).

● Homogamy

This refers to the overall tendency of people to marry those with like characteristics rather than differing traits.

Characteristics such as having a good sense of humour show themselves in physical features such as laughter lines in the face, upright posture, bright eyes and so on. This body language is quickly registered at a subconscious level by others who share such traits, and it excites a positive response in them. How homogamy works in detail is brilliantly and humorously described in the classic book by Robin Skynner and John Cleese, *Families and How To Survive Them*,[7] which I strongly recommend.

The contrary view to homogamy is that 'opposites attract' and was primarily championed by Winch[8] in 1959. However there is little evidence to support it. It does, however, draw attention to another important concept in partner selection called the 'marital fit'. The 'fit' is like that of a jig-saw puzzle (rather than of apoplexy!) and refers to how well the couple interlock emotionally with each other.

Two apparently dissimilar people may interlock well emotionally with each other in spite of their differences because they both supply something the other lacks. Thus a loud party-loving but volatile extrovert boy can make a good team with a shy, retiring girl who is very even-tempered. He brings excitement and spontaneity into her dull life, and she brings order and calm into his chaotic one. Thus they balance and help out each other's shortcomings. However the dynamics of such relationships make high demands which cannot easily be met by most people. If the areas of diversity are too great, there is little scope for respect for each other to develop.

LOVE FOR A LIFETIME?

An awareness of how the mechanics of partner selection operate in general can never be a substitute for personal knowledge of a particular potential marriage-partner. An inter-racial marriage can be sublimely happy, whereas marriage to 'the boy next door' may end in complete disaster. Are there then any helpful indicators as to whether love between two particular individuals will last a lifetime or not?

● Maturity

A psychiatrist colleague of mine maintains that males do not finish their adolescence until they are thirty. My friend may be biased (since he is over thirty!), but it is certainly true that emotional maturity is rarely complete in the teenage years.

You cannot choose a partner to match yourself until you know yourself. This is one reason why engagements and marriage in the under-twenties tend to flounder. Self-knowledge is rarely advanced enough, particularly in men, at this age.

Maturity in relationships is only learned through experience. Engagement to one's very first boy or girl friend can therefore be dangerous. 'It is a vital part of growing up and maturing psychosexually that we *do not* marry our first love object after puberty. It would usually be disastrous if we were to do so.'[9] Coping with the heartaches of broken teenage relationships can be a maturing process in preparation for subsequent marriage, especially if the factors which led to the break-up are understood and any problems identified are corrected.

● Time

While it is true that couples can be married for years and still not know each other well, you cannot usually get to know your partner really well in a matter of weeks. A brief acquaintance prior to engagement is usually a dangerous proposal!

As we have seen, romantic love can both blossom and wither very quickly, and rarely lasts more than two years at most. The vital thing is that your relationship is tested by seeing how you cope with difficulties together, and this is unlikely to be demonstrated substantially within a year of meeting.

● Laughter

If you love someone you can afford to laugh a lot. Failures and mistakes will often lead to laughter rather than rows in a relationship in which you unconditionally accept your partner and are accepted by them. Humour then doesn't put the relationship in jeopardy but rather puts things into perspective.

● Friendship

Never think about marrying anyone unless he or she is also your best friend. Falling in love, as we have seen, can be a very ambivalent business, and staying in love is so much easier if you actually like the person as well. If you truly enjoy each other's company and approve of each other's tastes and interests these will continue to produce an affinity long after the passion of early romance has settled.

● Respect

Erich Fromm defines respect as 'concern that the other person should grow and unfold as he is. Respect thus implies the absence of exploitation. I want the loved person to grow and unfold for his own sake, and in his own ways, and not for the purpose of serving me.'[10]

This means putting the other person before my own wants and desires. This may well involve as much restraint and self-sacrifice in the physical expression of sexual feelings as it does in other areas of the relationship. I have met plenty of couples who lost respect for each other by 'going too far' physically prior to marriage. I have yet to meet anyone who felt their relationship suffered premaritally by 'not going far enough' in that area.

● Forgiveness

When I was a teenager I used regularly to play Francis Lai's theme 'Love Story' on the piano. It was written for the film of Erich Segal's novel of the same name, and on the front of the music was quoted the classic line from the book – 'Love means never having to say you're sorry'!

This motto has a lot to answer for. In fact love means always saying you're sorry when you need to. If you are in the wrong and you know it, say so. And if you have been wronged, don't hold grudges. Keeping short accounts makes for longer happiness.

● Generosity

Giving to your partner is an important component of love. We all need rewards in life. Psychologists refer to such rewards as 'positive strokes'. The more cynical would say that we only ever give positive strokes in order to receive them back again, but as Fromm points out, giving can be its own reward. 'Giving is the highest expression of potency. In the very act of giving, I experience my strength, my wealth, my power ... Giving is more joyous than receiving, not because it is a deprivation, but because in the act of giving lies the expression of my aliveness...'[11]

Generosity sometimes means being willing to give way when agendas clash. For example it means not complaining unduly when your partner is unavoidably late. If a relationship is characterised by such generosity it is a good sign it will last.

● Commitment

This is the acid test. My psychiatrist colleague mentioned earlier has another saying concerning love. He maintains there are two sorts of love – '50/50' love and the '100 per cent both ways' love.

In the first sort of relationship, if one partner gives only 49 per cent, the other partner responds in kind. Such a mutual attitude soon whittles down each contribution to zero. In the other sort of relationship each partner has determined to give 100 per cent irrespective of how much the other gives. It's not so much a question of 'give and take' as of 'give and give'. Such a love involves true commitment. It is very costly because it can lead to total vulnerability, as well as to total security. In my view however no one should embark on getting engaged without it.

FURTHER READING

Joyce Huggett, *Just Good Friends?* (IVP, 1986).

MEANT FOR EACH OTHER? COURTSHIP AND ENGAGEMENT

LADY BRACKNELL   When you do become engaged to someone I, or your father, should his health permit him, will inform you of the fact. An engagement should come on a young girl as a surprise, pleasant or unpleasant as the case may be. It is hardly a matter that she could be allowed to arrange for herself...

Oscar Wilde
The Importance of Being Earnest

COURTSHIP

Courtship is rather a quaint word these days but there is really no substitute for it. It is the phase of a relationship in which there is a mutual awareness that marriage is a possible outcome. The purpose of courtship is to assess the potential of the relationship for long-term mutual happiness.

It is quite striking that authors who take a very different line from my own concerning sex in some other relationships, should take an equally cautious approach regarding sex in courtship. 'It is best to avoid intercourse ... Progress is best made out of bed ... Anyone can be happy in bed for a while'[1] are all typical examples of such caution. And with good reason. In a hundred hours of average married life less than five will be spent in actual intercourse. If preparation for marriage is the aim of courtship, it should centre on the wider aspects of 'making love' – not just genital contact.

Courtship is a time for discovery of what potential partners are really like. What are their likes and dislikes? How do they feel about important issues? What sort of temperament do they

106 Family Guide to Sex and Intimacy

have? Are they in good health, both physically and mentally?

It also gives an opportunity to discover what has shaped partners' lives thus far. Family is particularly important. Do you get on with them or not? Your opinion of the same-sex parent as your partner is often a helpful guide. If you can't abide them, ask yourself why? and do any reasons identified apply to your attitude towards your partner as well? If your partner's parents are divorced or separated, the causes for this need sensitive exploration. Research has shown that divorce rates are higher among couples with divorced parents themselves. This is especially so if both members of the couple come from such a family background.[2]

Other shaping factors to consider are the partner's social background, education, job and leisure activities, religious, philosophical or political beliefs, and previous serious relationships.

Plans and aspirations for the future also need exploration, particularly those relating to the planning of finances and starting a family. How partners view their future role and tasks within marriage are also very important.

In considering all these aspects of a prospective partner's life, similar questions will arise about yourself and a deepening self-awareness should be apparent. This will in turn enable your partner to get to know the real you more intimately as well.

The degree of physical intimacy should reflect the growing depth of the relationship in the areas outlined above and not run ahead of it. I have argued, in Chapter 6, that intercourse rightly belongs only within the context of the commitment of marriage. Therefore those practices which usually act as a prelude to intercourse should generally be avoided, even in the later stages of courtship. 'There are no moral mileposts on the slippery slope to detumescence.'[3] Thus the much advocated activities of mutual masturbation, or even the fondling of genitals or breasts should be approached with great caution before marriage. Couples need to ask themselves, 'Is this really an appropriate physical expression of the degree of our mutual self-giving on other levels, or is it just self-gratification?'

ENGAGEMENT

At some point the relationship will reach the stage where a decision will be made on whether to get married or not. Before popping the question (or answering it) there are some other essential questions to be considered.

● What is your motive for getting married?

The ideal motivation for marriage is a self-giving love for each other that has had time to reach the necessary depth of commitment, communication and assessment of compatibility.

In practice people marry for all sorts of reasons including:

Desire to escape from the parental home.
Means of obtaining a higher income and social status.
Avoidance of the law, e.g. to escape deportation.
Fear – e.g. of hurting one's fiancé(e), of being left on the shelf.
To act as a cover for minority sexual tendencies.
Unplanned pregnancy.
Romantic delirium.
Searching for a substitute for a lost love.
Pressure from parents or friends.

Such motives, although not automatically spelling disaster for every ensuing marriage, will inevitably put added strain on the relationship.

Anthony was eighteen when his younger handicapped sister, Lucy, died. She had cerebral palsy and Anthony, being her only sibling, had to make lots of personal sacrifices in order for the family to care for Lucy. In spite of the cost involved, he adored her and was heartbroken when Lucy died. He also felt inexplicably guilty, feeling that if he had done more, she might have lived longer.

Within a year he met and married Madeline, a rather simple, needy girl who reminded him in many ways of Lucy. It was only after a year or so of marriage that they both realised that he wanted to be a 'brother' to Madeline rather than a husband. Severe difficulties followed when this role could not be sustained within the marriage.

Broadly speaking, people marry for one of two reasons. Either they lack love and thus see marriage as an escape from their problems, or they see marriage as an exciting opportunity through which they can tackle their problems because the presence of love gives them the power to do so.

● What is the quality of your relationship now?

I have already discussed some of the qualities of a love that is likely to last (pp. 100–3). Are these present or absent? Has there been much conflict in the courtship thus far? Frequent rows are a bad sign, and physical violence indicates a very poor outlook for any future marriage (chap. 20).

'As now, so then' is a good maxim for couples contemplating marriage. The wishful thought that 'She/He'll change when I marry her/him' rarely comes true. The altar alters little as far as personality is concerned.

In order to make an adequate assessment of the quality of the relationship, you must have the necessary depth of knowledge concerning your future partner. Guesswork is out. In George Eliot's *Middlemarch*, Dorothea is about to marry Mr Casaubon, whom she hardly knows at all.

> She filled up all the blanks with unmanifested perfections, interpreting him as she interpreted the works of Providence and accounting for seeming discords by her own deafness to the higher harmonies. And there are many blanks left in the weeks of courtship which a loving faith fills with happy assurance.[4]

To embark upon marriage with a heart riddled with gaping holes of doubt plugged only with wishful fancies, is a highly dangerous venture.

● Is there realistic provision for the future?

This obviously has financial implications. What ideas are held about the future standard of living? Can they be met? How is the distribution of joint income going to be arranged?

There are other aspects too. Marriage is not independent of the wider family circle and friends. What are their feelings about the relationship? Is their support going to be available in the future if needed? On the other hand, have both partners made the necessary level of emotional separation from parents needed to make a separate family unit?

If honest and positive conclusions can be reached in answer to these questions then the marriage stands a good chance of success, but because no marriage can be guaranteed to bring lasting happiness, many couples today choose what they see as a safer alternative, or at least a prelude to it – living together.

LIVING TOGETHER – HITCHED WITHOUT THE HITCHES?

'Living together as a couple before you get married has much to recommend it.'[5] Such advice is commonplace today, and on the surface appears to make sense: hence its popularity. The number of couples who live together before marriage has increased dramatically from a few per cent in the mid-1960s to more than 50 per cent in the late 1980s.

The reasons why couples live together will vary. Some will do so simply for financial reasons – it is cheaper than getting married. For others who simply feel they are too young to make a lasting commitment, living together may seem an attractive compromise.

Those who regard living together as a kind of 'trial marriage', however, should be aware that it doesn't usually work out that way. It may well test the heat of the flames of passion with the cold water of domestic routine. But do couples really need to live together in order to realise that cooking, washing, cleaning, shopping need to be done and decisions must be made about who should do them? I doubt it.

What many look for in living together is the chance to test compatibility and build an intimate relationship that they can be sure of. Though this is a worthy goal, much research indicates that living together is not in fact the best way to achieve it.

The 1992 Office of Population Censuses and Surveys report on the 1989 UK Household Survey 'provided the first tentative evidence that in Great Britain, premarital cohabitation is associated with an increased probability of subsequent divorce'.[6] This confirms a trend already documented more substantially in Canada and the US.

Alfred DeMaris is one of the leading researchers into cohabitation and its effect on subsequent marriage. He concluded from one of his studies that those who cohabited prior to marriage 'scored significantly lower in both perceived quality of marital communication and marital satisfaction'.[7]

In general, couples living together are less likely to discuss issues deeply, and often fail to develop a close intimacy for fear that the discovery of differences may terminate the relationship. As Prof. Mansell Pattison describes it, 'There is a superficial sharing, but it does not extend to the core of the self that we spend so much time hiding from ourselves and others.'[8]

Sexual satisfaction does not seem to be ultimately helped by cohabitation either. 'There is no real pressure on the couple to try and work out their sexual problems together, and in this regard it is of interest that the leading cause for the breakup of cohabiting couples is sexual problems or dissatisfaction.'[9]

Living together, then, though it may have both economic advantages and a sense of romantic adventure attached to it, is certainly no substitute for the commitment of marriage and may actually be detrimental as a precursor to it. 'We might say that living together is a selfish enterprise. The nature of the personal relationship varies with different couples – but as an overall feature, it is striking that there is social intimacy and sexual intimacy, but not personal intimacy. Couples enact the social role of living together, but they are personally apart. They live the role but hide the self.'[10]

BROKEN ENGAGEMENT – BROKEN HEART?

Not every engagement leads to marriage and this is just as well. Sometimes it is only during the closeness of engagement that hidden problems may surface for the first time. If persistent uncertainties arise at this stage they must be faced. Better an engagement broken on the night before the wedding than separation proceedings starting the day after it. The photographer at our wedding told my wife's parents that he always requested payment in full before or on the wedding day as he had so many bad debts from couples whose marriage hadn't survived the honeymoon!

Breaking off an engagement is always painful. So much time, money, effort and expectation will have been put into the relationship by this time that it will seem hard to throw it all away. Besides, this romantic love is so often deaf to the cry of reason.

> Everyone knows that it is useless to try to separate lovers by proving to them that their marriage will be an unhappy one. This is not only because they will disbelieve you. They usually will no doubt. But even if they believed they would not be dissuaded. For it is the very mark of Eros that when he is in us we had rather share unhappiness with the Beloved than be happy on any other terms ... Eros never hesitates to say 'Better this than parting. Better to be miserable with her than happy without her. Let our hearts break provided they break together.'[11]

When only one partner realises the need for parting, the other may go to extraordinary lengths to try and maintain the relationship, but emotional blackmail and suicidal gestures only confirm the unsuitability of a partner who resorts to them.

The pain of parting may lead to a period of great vulnerability in both partners and, should clinical depression result, medical help may be required. There are usually positive aspects about such situations which can help to ease the pain. The trauma of divorce is a thousand times worse and you have escaped it. You are not to take all blame on to yourself; marriage is about relationship and it takes two to be incompatible. The lessons learned from this break-up may be invaluable in promoting personal growth, and in preventing the same problems from developing in future relationships.

FURTHER READING

Walter Trobisch, *I Married You* (IVP, 1991).

III

MARRIAGE AND PARENTHOOD – THE NURTURING AGE

10

FROM THIS DAY FORWARD: MARRIAGE

Marriage is popular because it combines the maximum of temptation with the maximum of opportunity.

George Bernard Shaw
Man and Superman

It was Mae West who boasted, 'Marriage is a great institution, but I'm not ready for an institution yet.' Not too many share this view, however. Marriage is still highly popular, despite all the rhetoric denouncing it periodically as unholy deadlock or legalised prostitution.

The number of marriages in the UK has remained remarkably constant over the past quarter of a century at around 350,000 per year, though the number has fallen quite steeply in recent years to under 307,000 currently. Both men and women are marrying at a later age than they did twenty years ago, but still nine of every ten people in Britain will marry at some point in their lives. Thus marriage today is statistically even more common than in the Victorian era. In 1990 the average age at first marriage was just over twenty-seven for men and just over twenty-five for women. These ages represent an increase of two years over the comparative figures for 1980.

Just over a half of weddings in England and Wales take place in church, though this may have little actual spiritual significance. It has been estimated that among couples who have a church wedding, only one in four of the brides and one in seven of the grooms do so for even vaguely religious reasons. The proportion of couples who marry in church because of a robust and relevant faith in the God before whom their marriage vows are made must be even smaller.

CONTEMPORARY MARRIAGE

Expectations from marriage are higher today than they have ever been. A UK study done in the 1950s and repeated twenty years later has suggested that there has been a shift away from 'instrumental' to a more 'companionship' model of marriage.[1]

In the 'instrumental' model the husband was regarded as the breadwinner, head of the house, the initiator in sexual activity and the one who represented his family to the outside world. The wife was expected to be at home, cooking and cleaning, looking after the children and being the initiator of affection in the family. If such a couple had well-behaved children, remained faithful to each other and kept their expected roles they were said to have a good marriage. Such criteria for success are insufficient in today's world. What sort of love is needed, then, in contemporary marriage to realise the expectations of the 'companionship model'?

● Sustaining Love

The greater number of women at work now, combined with their increasing ability to control their own fertility has inevitably led towards a model of marriage incorporating a greater measure of equality between the sexes. Instead of just monetary provision, pychological sustenance is expected of both partners. In a society where even friendship, let alone intimacy, is increasingly hard to find, there is a rising expectance for marriage to meet our longing to love and be loved more deeply.

> There are essentially four kinds of love. The infantile type of love, 'I love me'. The next state, 'I love the me in you. I love you because you are my brother, my mother, my father, my sister, my dog. The me in you.' Then the adolescent love, 'I love you because your dancing pleases me, and because your brains please me.' And the adult stage of love wherein, 'I want to love you and cherish you because I find my happiness in your happiness. The happier you are, the happier I will be. I'll find my happiness in yours.' So the mature love is the capacity to find enjoyment of the other person's enjoyment.[2]

● Healing Love

The breakdown of wider family networks, and the increase in leisure time available to couples to be together from reduced working hours have led to a greater expectancy of psychological closeness from the marriage relationship. It is within such intimacy however that our wounds are exposed.

All of us undergo some psychological and spiritual hurts on our journey through life, and 'these wounds are particularly relevant in marriage because they affect our capacity to relate'.[3] Such wounds can either destroy a marriage or the marriage can provide healing for them – the shy can find encouragement, the rejected can find acceptance, the anxious can find security.

The greater freedom in our society to discuss and promote a whole variety of new sexual norms has led to an increased expectation from the physical intimacies of marriage too. Many people come to marriage feeling sexually bruised or even broken and expect to find a measure of healing in sexual intercourse in addition to physical pleasure. This aspect of marital sexuality is considered on page 145.

● Adapting Love

The average age at death is currently around seventy-three for men and seventy-eight for women. With such a high and increasing life expectancy, one new feature of contemporary marriage is that it lasts so much longer than before. It is not uncommon now for a marriage to have to last for fifty years or more before death separates the partners. Those who ridicule the idea of marriage, see this long duration as an insuperable obstacle to permanency.

Such an objection is only valid, however, if marriage is viewed as a static arrangement. In fact, growth and adaptation are essential ingredients of a healthy marriage. It is possible to learn to take pleasure and delight in the emotional and intellectual growth of your partner rather than becoming jealous or critical. This in turn can enhance your own development.

This companionship model of marriage is admittedly full of expectations which are hard to live up to. One social anthropologist has described the overladen marital union of today's world as the 'pressure-cooker marriage'.[4] In spite of such pressure, the wonder and enduring power of marriage continues to triumph: two out of every three marriages still remain intact until the demise of one of the couple. In many of these marriages, both partners will engage emotionally to their mutual joy and satisfaction, and will experience a growing, fulfilling love until death finally parts them.

ANYTHING TO DECLARE? – EMOTIONAL CONTRABAND

No matter how much a couple may wish their marriage to remain a purely private, inter-personal relationship, it is inevitably to some degree a social affair as well.

> The frequency with which people still choose to underpin their personal promises with public vows emphasises the social significance with which marriage is imbued. It makes no sense to separate the personal from the social when thinking about marriage because each dimension affects the other. Marriage, in essence, contains and expresses the personal and the collective.[5]

As well as the overt social aspects of marriage, such as the public ceremony and the couple's relationships with both families and friends, there is also a hidden dimension of further involvement which can surface at the most inconvenient of moments.

Each partner will unknowingly smuggle into the marriage a measure of emotional contraband from their relationship with their own parents. This extra unseen luggage may work for better or for worse, but it is always there. The healthiest of marriages are often between two people who have the privilege of coming from truly loving homes. As Stephenson expresses it, 'We love in as much as love was present in the first great affair of our lives!'[6] namely the relationship with our parents. Of course, this does not mean that those who had a bad start in life will never make a go of marriage – indeed, as we considered above, marriage has the very potential within it to heal our childhood hurts. What it does mean is that the experience of being loved as a child helps us in taking the risks of loving as an adult.

The capacity to love or hate ourselves and others is not the only emotional contraband that will enter the marriage relationship. We also bring models of partnership learned from our parents – an inheritance of expectations of how to behave in intimate relationships. From direct observation of our parents we see how a marriage operates. Are they ever intimate in public? Do they have rows? If not, how do they handle conflict? What roles and tasks do they undertake in the partnership? How our own family did things will influence the way we do them too.

One further item of emotional contraband of vital importance in marriage is how we react to crises. Some couples will weather a major family catastrophe – such as the birth of a severely disabled child – with comparative harmony together, while other couples will threaten divorce every time they take a wrong turn in the car because one of them read the map wrongly!

> It is not so much what happens to people that is important as what they think has happened to them. It is less the events which matter than the interpretation placed on the events. And the framework people use to make sense of their experiences developed over time and so has strong connections with the past.[7]

Although it is obvious to look at marital stress in terms of a couple's current difficulties, the connections with emotional contraband from the past may be more relevant than we first think.

THE PHASES OF MARRIAGE

Jack Dominian, the Director of the Marriage Research Centre (now renamed One plus One), which he established in 1941, has written much about the phases through which a marriage passes.[8,9] This section summarises his pioneering work in this area.

● Phase 1

This first phase is from the average age at marriage (around twenty-seven for men and twenty-five for women for first marriages) to thirty and usually covers the time until the arrival of children. These years are particularly crucial for the development of intimacy, because up to 40 per cent of the marriages that run aground do so during this time; moreover, at whatever stage a marriage eventually breaks down, the principal source of conflict usually materialises in these early years.

There are several important areas to be negotiated in the early years of marriage.

Parental Separation The support and goodwill of the couple's parents is invaluable in making a good start to married life and perhaps, not surprisingly, there is evidence that where the marriage is actively opposed by one or more of the parents involved, the couple are more likely to run into marital difficulties at an early stage.

After marriage each partner should be the most significant person in the other's life. If there is over-involvement with a parent and a failure of emotional separation from them then the development of intimacy between the couple will be severely impaired.

Ruth always felt that John had never really left his parents' home when they got married. He was always round there, and hardly a day went by without his ringing Betty, his mother, to check something with her.

After about eighteen months, John's father died suddenly, and, much against Ruth's better judgment, she allowed John to have his way when he suggested that his mother moved in with them. Betty soon became totally overbearing, making constant demands on the couple that they felt guilty about being unable to meet. A crisis developed when Betty insisted that John and Ruth should not go out for a meal to celebrate their wedding anniversary unless they took her along too!

At the opposite extreme from such over-identification with a parent, lies the problem of overt hostility towards parents. If a couple have married in order deliberately to spite one or both sets of parents, there may be little in the way of positive emotional support for each partner once the deed is done. Feelings of guilt may creep in, leading to tension and moodiness with which either spouse finds it difficult to cope. Insecurity is thus added to anxiety.

The majority of couples do, however, report good relationships with both their parents and in-laws, who can all provide invaluable emotional and financial support at the start of married life.

Setting Up Home Intimacy requires some degree of privacy in order to flourish, and so couples ideally need a home of their own, if at all possible, in which to start their married life. Those who are forced by economic constraints to live with parents are more likely to encounter problems in their relationships

Even with 'a place of your own', it can still be difficult enough sorting out the tasks of everyday living. There needs to be an agreed division of work within the home, and it is essential that promises once made are kept. Half-finished fireplaces will not warm a home but may fuel resentment for years.

Financial Arrangements Though the love of money is the root of all evil, lack of money can certainly imperil intimacy, especially where one partner holds the other responsible for financial debts.

Even when there is sufficient income, its distribution can often be a cause for complaint among couples. It is important to decide early on whether a joint account or separate ones will be used after marriage. In the early years both husband and wife are likely to be earning. If one of them loses or leaves that job, then the financial arrangements may need further negotiation.

Many wives still complain that their husbands keep them inadequately informed about family finances. This has important consequences, not least because money has psychological as well as financial significance. The wife who is kept on a tight allowance is often emotionally short-changed as well. Money easily becomes a tool with which to exercise power over a spouse rather than a means of demonstrating love.

Employment and Recreation Work has many implications apart from the financial ones. It can impose undue constraints on the time available for developing intimacy together. If both spouses are shift-workers on different rotas, for example, they may find that some months they have no time together at all. The husband or wife married to work and who regularly leaves the school, office or factory late because of 'essential' business, will sooner or later find the partner expressing understandable discontent.

Increasingly, the strains of unemployment are being placed on marriages. Those who marry for the status conferred by their spouse's occupation are in for a particularly stormy time if redundancy threatens.

Whether they are employed or not, most people in Western society have an increasing amount of leisure time available. Many women still complain that husbands carry on with their leisure activities as if they were still single. The weekend fishing trips, soccer or rugby games with the lads, and late nights at the pub leave many wives feeling neglected. Shared leisure activity is an important asset to intimacy.

Work and leisure are both important means of regulating the degree of intimacy in a marriage. Too much work and couples become strangers to each other. Too much leisure and they can get under each other's feet.

Sex For most first-time newly-married couples, sex is both frequent and enjoyable. Thornes and Collard[10] reported that among such couples they surveyed 94 per cent of men and 85 per cent of women expressed good sexual satisfaction in early married life. Among those newly-married, but who had been through at least one previous divorce, these figures fell to 84 per cent of men and 76 per cent of women.

This study also showed that among those previously divorced, there was an increased tendency to put the blame for any sexual difficulties onto the spouse, whereas first-timers were more likely to accept mutual responsibility. Such problems occurring in the first phase of marriage include non-consummation, premature ejaculation and failure to experience or enjoy orgasm. The joys and the problems of sex are discussed in chapters 12 and 13.

● **Phase 2**

The second phase of marriage spans the years from thirty to fifty. During this time there are three crucial factors which have a powerful effect on the depth of intimacy within a marriage. First, of course, the children, if any, grow up and eventually leave home, but second, the couple themselves also grow up. These are often the years during which extensive psychological transformations occur, and spouses may shift in both their sense of identity and purpose in life. This new self-discovery may result in profound changes with which the spouse then has to negotiate and adapt. Third, women will enter the menopause during their late forties.

Not unexpectedly during this phase, marital satisfaction often declines and does not tend to rise again until the children reach their late teens. Even then, studies such as that of Walker[11] show that satisfaction does not quite go back to the same level as at the beginning of marriage. Satisfaction tends to reach its lowest level when the children are still at home and waiting to start school.

Changes in self-awareness and direction can cause stress in any of the areas already discussed in the section on the first phase of marriage, and they will compound any other difficulties arising in the second phase. Two areas are, however, particularly significant.

Employment To be in paid work is one of the signs of worth in our society, and it is not surprising that in this second phase of marriage many women discover a psychological need to find fulfilment in a job once the children have started to grow up. Long gone are the days of 'Man for the field and woman for the hearth'.[12] As the wife advances in her chosen occupation, her husband can become jealous of her success and begin to feel insecure.

In fact, the ascent of either partner up the career ladder can pose potential threats to intimacy. The dizzy heights of promotion may for example necessitate geographical relocation which the spouse resists. Alternatively, the increasingly affluent social life involved may alienate a spouse who cannot relate emotionally or intellectually to a different circle of friends. In such a situation they may feel they are losing their partner.

In times of increasing job uncertainty, social descent may sadly be equally as likely as promotion. Redundancy or dismissal may lead to severe depression or other ill health. Even without these complications, the spouse may be unsympathetic and blame the other partner for the loss of job. Intimacy may also be jeopardised if one partner leaves work to fulfil a longing in a different direction – to be involved in charity or church work, for example. Unless such a major upheaval is a mutually agreed venture, trouble is likely to result from it.

Sex Attitudes towards sex may change dramatically in this phase. When problems have arisen in the earlier phase of marriage they often relate to a perceived 'selfish' or 'cruel' husband and a 'cold' or 'disinterested' wife. In the second phase of marriage, wives often become interested in more frequent sex as they relax and enjoy intercourse more. At the same time husbands, increasingly involved with other demands, become less interested in sex and considerable tension may result.

At the opposite extreme, some women become relatively turned off sexually following childbirth, and such a wife may even resent her husband's just touching her. Similarly, menopausal changes may result in declining sexual interest. This is discussed further on pages 215–16.

With such sexual flux in the marital relationship, it is in this phase of marriage that many affairs find their beginnings (chap. 18).

Though these problems are all too common, they should not be regarded as expectations. Rather an ever-deepening sexual intimacy and fulfilment should be the norm. We will look in Chapters 12 and 13 at some of the ways in which this can be achieved.

● Phase 3

This lasts from the age of fifty to the death of one of the pair. It spans the time when the children leave home and the relationship becomes one-to-one again. The menopause and retirement from work are other critical life-events in this phase.

Generally marital satisfaction tends to increase again during this time, but the sobering fact that a quarter of all divorces in the UK take place in marriages lasting twenty or more years leaves no room for complacency.

Empty Nest Syndrome It is only when the children have all left home that many mothers discover all too late that they had relied totally on them for affirmation and support, and when they have gone she is left with a husband who is a total stranger to her.

Similarly, the husband who has retired finds hours on his hands with a wife with whom he has not communicated directly for years. All interchange has occurred through the children until then – 'Tell Mum I'll be late for dinner tonight.' Now the go-betweens have gone, a barrier of silence takes their place.

This sudden revelation of absent intimacy usually comes at a time when real closeness is most needed. It is during this period that the couple's own parents will often be at their most frail and in need of support. The practical and emotional strains of caring for a sick or dying parent can be highly stressful. In addition, the spouse may be faced with fearful reflections of his or her own mortality, and echoes of past relationship with the parent, whether good or bad, can contribute to development of anxiety or depression.

The budding romances and love-life of the couple's children can also resurrect painful memories of past hurts as well as being a source of joyful reminiscence. If the children's choice of partner is not approved of by one spouse, this can spark further conflict.

These difficulties only serve to emphasise the importance of giving the marital relationship top priority even after the arrival of children. By putting your partner first, your children gain the benefit of a united and loving partnership. This is also a good preparation for your own future together, and does not mean you love your children less.

Sex Many married couples will continue with an active sex life into their seventies and eighties, though the frequency of intercourse usually declines.

Impotence in men becomes an increasing problem with age, however, and post-menopausal women are more prone to a variety of diseases which may cause sexual problems. These topics are discussed in Chapters 16 and 17.

The decline in self-esteem accompanying such sexual difficulties may precipitate involvement on an extra-marital affair in an attempt to boost morale. This will ultimately contribute to a further erosion of intimacy between husband and wife.

For other couples, however, old age brings new and legitimate freedoms of its own – freedom from fear of pregnancy, from interruption by the children, from the time-constraints of work responsibilities. Such factors may enable the development of new heights of intimacy. The formidable heights of attachment reached by some older couples can be an inspiration to younger climbers.

MEN SHOULD . . . WOMEN SHOULD . . . PATTERNS AND ROLES WITHIN MARRIAGE

Within every marriage, couples have to evolve a pattern of life to accommodate their different personalities, abilities and roles as husband and wife. This must take sex differences into account. 'There are no human beings; there are just men and women, and when they deny their divergent sexuality, they reject the deepest sources of identity and love.'[13]

Patterns of marriage are highly variable but may be conveniently classified as:

Traditional In this pattern the husband is the leader, main provider and decision-maker, with the wife taking a relatively passive role at home.

Democratic Here decision-making is by joint discussion. Tasks are done by whoever is most suited.

Equal Opportunities Tasks and roles are performed on an inter-changeable basis as much as possible.

Reverse Traditional The wife is the principal breadwinner and the husband looks after the home and children.

Some of these patterns, especially the reverse traditional, involve much more stress as a way of life than others. A healthy marriage will, however, be able to accommodate some change from one pattern to another. For instance, in a traditional pattern marriage if the husband becomes ill for a long period, it may be necessary for his wife to go out to work and take a more active role in decision-making.

Whichever pattern is adopted, intimacy within marriage is enhanced if there is a mutual acceptance of equality of worth irrespective of role. Men and women are different – 'Still in every society men are by and large bigger than women, and by and large stronger than women.'[14] This does not, however, make them either superior or inferior. As Betty Friedan, one of the founders of the American women's movement points out, 'There is a danger today for men and women who may try to get out of their own binds by reversing roles. Exchanging one obsolete model of a half-life for another, they may copy the worst aspects of the old feminine or masculine mystique . . .'[15]

In the intimate marriage both partners delight in the otherness of the beloved, rather than seeking to deny it on the one hand or exploit it on the other.

FURTHER READING

Jack Dominian, *Marriage: Making or Breaking* (Family Doctor, 1982).

Paul Tournier, *Marriage Difficulties* (Highland, 1984).

ARE YOU RECEIVING ME? INTIMATE COMMUNICATION

He draweth out the thread of his verbosity finer than the staple of his argument.

William Shakespeare
Love's Labour's Lost

In the first episode of Roy Clarke's classic television comedy series, *Keeping Up Appearances*, Daisy turns to her husband, Onslow, and wistfully muses, 'You don't talk to me any more, not even when we're making love. *Especially* when we're making love.' Onslow pauses for a moment, then without looking up, replies, 'Do you mean that if I concentrate on doing two different things at once, I shall do both of them better?'!

Poor Onslow is not alone in thinking that talking has no connection with making love. In fact the two are closely intertwined. Some counselling agencies such as Relate, for example, lay such importance on this fact that they will not refer a couple for sexual counselling until any other possible areas of breakdown in communication have already been thoroughly explored. This makes good sense. Both verbal and sexual intercourse involve reception and penetration to be optimally fruitful. Both are forms of communication, and as such, both can be enhanced by the development of good communication skills.

EMOTIONAL AND SEXUAL INTIMACY

The American psychotherapist Stephen Levine in his essay

entitled 'Psychological Intimacy',[1] indicates that it is psychological or emotional intimacy which lays the groundwork for people to become lovers, and ultimately to discover their full sexual potential with each other over the years.

For many people, however, having sex has become a widely adopted scheme for bypassing the time-consuming and tender growth of emotional intimacy. This is very understandable, as busy people can so easily rely on actual coitus to try and create closeness. But does it sustain sexual intimacy for a couple for a lifetime? 'No!' is Levine's answer. 'It may be, in fact, an enormous fallacy that costs the couple their ability to be sexually active together for a lifetime.'[2]

He goes on to state that sex as a substitute for psychological intimacy works best only during early adulthood. As men and women age, they need better psychological conditions to make love which can only be achieved and maintained by deepening emotional intimacy.

Such intimacy develops when you share your inner experiences with another who listens, hears and understands the significance of what you share and unconditionally accepts you.

It is far from easy for such intimate exchanges to occur. They require the presence of:

(a) self-awareness of what you truly feel and think.

(b) the openness to make the disclosure which in turn will expose your vulnerability.

(c) the communication skills either to express or to receive and understand the disclosure.

This makes intimacy a particularly difficult goal for men to achieve. 'Big boys don't cry' is the masculine social convention of Western culture. Vulnerability doesn't have much of a macho image, and yet it actually takes a great deal of courage to choose to be vulnerable.

Moreover, most women appreciate and admire men who have the strength to share with such openness. In Shere Hite's famous survey of 4,500 women, 98 per cent said they wanted more emotional intimacy with the men they loved – they want the men in their lives to talk more about their personal thoughts, feelings and plans, and questions, and to ask them about theirs.[3] With this in mind, we shall explore in this chapter some important aspects of how such communication can be established in marriage.

THE COMPONENTS OF COMMUNICATION

● Let Me Hear Your Body Talk – Non-Verbal Communication

Getting our message across involves much more than words alone. There are some occasions where powerful communication takes place in total silence. Who has not experienced, for example, the withering glare of disapproval that says it all? At other times words, though actually spoken, are drowned out by other contradictory messages.

Alex and Candace had been married for several years when Alex gradually became aware that something was wrong between them. Whenever he approached Candace about it, she always smiled sweetly, and said that everything was fine. But her whole appearance told a different story. She rarely laughed spontaneously these days, and avoided looking directly at him. Even her posture had changed; she had become slightly more stooped, and moved more slowly. She kept sighing a lot too. No matter how much Candace denied it, Alex knew there was a problem. He was right. Unbeknown to him, Candace had been involved in an affair which she had just terminated.

Alex had discovered the power of non-verbal communication to cancel out what was actually being said. If a 'mixed message' is delivered in this way, it is the non-verbal component that is usually conveying the truth. This is why I have started our consideration of the mechanics of communication at this often neglected point.

There are three basic elements of non-verbal communication:

BODY LANGUAGE

This was what gave Alex the most clues that something was wrong. It is a common indicator of people's attitudes and emotions and is displayed in five principal ways.

Facial Expression   This is the easiest aspect of body language to read accurately, with the eyes and the mouth being the most sensitive indicator of a person's thoughts. For example, if someone looks at you a lot, they probably like you. Conversely poor eye contact means there may be a problem between the two of you.

Gesture This refers to the way in which we use our limbs, particularly our arms and hands, but even our feet may betray our intentions! Just watch, for example, someone in a meeting who is getting bored. Their feet will soon start tapping or wagging – in their minds they are already walking out.

Posture The way in which we hold our bodies says a lot to others. For example, the person in love with life walks with bold, confident steps, head held high, and looks straight ahead or slightly upwards.

Body Space If someone we do not know well gets too physically close to us, it often makes us feel uncomfortable. We like to have a certain amount of space around us. As intimacy develops, however, we feel more comfortable with that person drawing closer. Sexual intercourse is perhaps the ultimate expression of moving into intimate body space!

Touch Touch, 'the wordless language of intimacy'[4] is so often either underused or abused in contemporary society, and yet its proper expression desperately needs to be rediscovered. The British are notorious for being one of the least 'touching' nations in the world. Part of the problem is that for many people, touch equates only with having sex. Touch, however, can be a powerful affirmation of love quite independently of sex.

● Dress and Appearance

These can also speak volumes. If a man stops washing or shaving regularly, and dresses up in his best clothes only when he goes out without his wife, little else need be said.

● Paralanguage

This refers to uttered but non-verbal signs which accompany our words – sighs and chuckles for example. It also encompasses the way in which the words themselves are expressed. Identical words can have very different meanings depending on the paralanguage used.

This is well illustrated by the story of the bishop who was visiting New York for the first time. The press were waiting in force at the airport, and one of them, hoping to catch out the cleric asked, 'Bishop, will you be visiting any night clubs while in New York?' The bishop paused for a moment, aware of the trap, and replied as innocently as he could manage, 'Are there any night clubs in New York?' Imagine then his horror the next morning when, stripped of his paralanguage, the headlines read. 'Bishop's first question on landing – "Are there any night clubs in New York?"'!

Even such a simple remark as, 'You'll be here at eight then' could be a question, a command, an expression of delight or a cry of anxiety. The correct interpretation depends upon the paralanguage – the music behind the lyrics.

Being more aware of all these aspects of your partner's non-verbal communications and learning to interpret them correctly deepens intimacy in a way that few other things can match. As one husband expressed it, 'It's quite amazing how Diane sometimes knows exactly what I'm about to say, even before I open my mouth. I often think she knows me better than I know myself.'

TALK TO ME SLOW, LIKE I'M FROM NORWAY – SPEECH AND LANGUAGE

We have seen that inter-personal communication involves so much more than the mere speaking and hearing of words. Having stressed this point, we must now turn to the actual words themselves.

We all tend to take words for granted. They are, however, a highly complex code of sound signs which we learn over a long period of time. Effective communication with those learned words is influenced in a number of ways:

Any man who has called his wife a witch instead of an enchantress, will know that although two words may share the same definition, they can nevertheless convey entirely different messages.

Some friends of mine were expecting for dinner an Asian

student who was visiting England for the first time. When he arrived, after the usual introductions they asked 'Would you like to use the bathroom?' He said 'Yes' and went upstairs. A few minutes later my friends were rather surprised to hear the taps running, followed a few minutes later by loud splashing. They later discovered that in the student's home land it was the custom to offer guests a bath before eating!

I think it was a politician's wife who complained that her husband always addressed her as if she were a public meeting! Politicians are not the only such offenders, however. Direct and informal speech is usually the most appropriate in intimate relationships. If a policeman's wife asked him where he went the previous night and he replied, 'I was proceeding in an easterly direction...' then she might be forgiven for thinking his mind was still on the job!

SAY IT WITH FLOWERS – IMPROVING YOUR COMMUNICATION

There are many ways in which our outgoing messages can be improved.

Tune In To Your Non-Verbal Communication   We have to know how we truly feel before we can express it. An awareness of our own body language can help to clarify matters.

Be Honest   As we saw with Alex and Candace, it's no use saying that things are all right when they are not. This will simply frustrate your spouse who sees there is a problem yet can't locate it without your help.

Be Tactful   Tactfulness is an approach which involves 'being sincere and open in communication while at the same time showing respect for the other person's feelings and taking care not to hurt them unnecessarily.'[5] In short, it is speaking the truth in love.

For example, when Julie says to her husband, George, 'You are so untidy' she may well be right, but she might improve the effectiveness of her message by saying, 'I feel so cross when you leave three pairs of your shoes in the hall.'

In putting it this way, a vague blanket condemnation is avoided. A clear issue is specified to which George can respond. He can't wriggle out of it by saying to himself, 'I can't think what she means. I'm not untidy.'

In addition, by issuing an 'I feel' message, rather than a 'You are' message, Julie is making the problem a mutual one. This is far more productive than unadulterated blame, which often evokes a response of either self-defence or hostility. Here the door is open to reconciliation.

Don't Nag For some couples, getting the point across means repeating exactly the same thing, except louder and more frequently. Both husbands and wives are equally capable of such behaviour, though men like to refer to it as 'criticism', rather than nagging, when they are doing it.

Paradoxically nagging is more likely to result in deafness rather than improved communication. I know one lady who perplexed several specialists by her selective deafness which couldn't be confirmed by various hearing tests – but then they had never met her husband.

It is often when the nagging stops that the message gets through. When a wife doesn't hear her husband complaining about the cooking any more, the shock may be so great that she becomes aware of the need to improve her culinary skills. Of course if her husband volunteers to do the cooking one weekend, the shock may be even greater!

MESSAGE RECEIVED AND UNDERSTOOD – IMPROVING YOUR LISTENING

Tune In Your Partner's Non-Verbal Communication You will know by now how important this is, so I won't nag you about it!

Concentrate Few people are natural listeners; it requires sustained effort to follow the thread of many conversations. One woman discovered this to her cost when, emerging from a daydream while her friend chatted on, she found herself responding, 'And is your husband still dead...'

Monitor Your Response   Beware of making too many inter-
ruptions. These can indicate that you are more interested in
giving your own opinion than hearing someone else's. Your
partner will know if you are truly listening by such signs as
eye contact, nodding and the noises which you use to punctuate
what they are saying.

On the other hand, eyes on the clock, fidgeting and yawning
all convey the silent message of disinterest. We need to be
aware of such indicators. If you are conscious of wandering
attention, it may be appropriate to acknowledge this openly,
and agree to talk on another occasion.

Clarify   Even if you focus perfectly on what is being said,
there may still be information which you are not sure you have
understood. It is helpful to ask your partner to express it in a
different way, or say, 'Do you mean . . .?'

Empathise   This is the art of 'putting yourself in the other
person's shoes' – to understand so clearly that you feel how they
feel. This skill has to be practised but the formation of such empathy is a good sign that your partner has been clearly heard.

Touch   When deep hurts or other private emotions are shared,
empathy may be beyond expression in words. In these situations
holding a hand, an arm around the shoulders, or a hug may be
the best way of indicating that you have listened and understand what your partner has said.

BREAKING THE BARRIERS

What obstacles do couples run up against in trying to communicate with each other? Let us look at some of the common
ones.

● Physical Defects

The partially-sighted or blind, and the deaf and hard of hearing
will have special difficulties in communicating, as well as those
with speech disorders. Often the extent of these problems is
greatly underestimated, particularly for the deaf, whose impairment may not be immediately obvious.

Roger already had a hearing problem when he and Mary were courting. During the years since their marriage, however, his deafness had slowly but surely worsened. Mary grew increasingly frustrated by the necessity of having to repeat things so often, but Roger had become so used to her doing this, and his hearing loss had worsened so slowly that he denied there was a problem. He became, though, ever more withdrawn into himself.

After some time he could no longer use the telephone, and this finally precipitated his going to see the doctor. The eventual provision of a hearing aid gradually restored his self-confidence, and his ability to communicate with his wife.

Particular patience and skill is needed in dealing with a partner who has such physical limitations.

● The Thief of Time

For most couples, mutual and individual responsibilities increase with time. Promotion at work, community and church activities, greater demands by the children and many other things all compete for our attention. The amount of time that husband and wife spend alone with each other is easily eroded. When a few uninterrupted hours can be scraped together, many couples are too tired to do anything except watch television.

We are all familiar with the scenario of Jim coming home late from work, exhausted and hungry. Susan, equally tired and famished, is in the bathroom with the two children. She wishes he'd come up and help her. He wishes she'd got his meal ready. She puts the children to bed while he sits and reads the paper. They both bolt their meal in silence because the baby-sitter will be coming in a minute. Susan has a school governors' meeting, and Jim has a squash court booked for eight o'clock.

Intimacy cannot possibly grow in such a pressured environment. We need to put a high priority on making time in which to share our hearts with our partner. Sometimes this takes radical measures. 'Often books on marriage and relationships take the busy life as given and make practical suggestions about how one can create time by going away for special weekends or taking an evening off now and then. But these things are like putting a surgical dressing on a gaping wound ... at some point somebody has got to stand up and say "enough is enough".'[6]

A colleague of mine recently realised that this point had been reached. When he had been working in his study all day, his wife opened the door a crack and said, 'Can I have a quick word?' Forgetting he was at home, he spontaneously replied, 'Certainly not. You'll have to make an appointment with my secretary.'

● Decoys

Once time has been set aside for the purpose, and you start communicating with each other, you should never presume that all your troubles will be over. You may, for instance, find yourselves communicating about the wrong thing.

The emotional contraband that we smuggle into our marriages may unconsciously lead us astray at this point.

Sean was always attacking Andrea about the way she dressed, and the state of the house. He also felt that the children's behaviour left a lot to be desired, and that this was largely Andrea's fault. They both had a good relationship in other areas, and talked this issue over a lot. They could not reach a compromise, however, and felt they were getting nowhere. This was because Andrea wasn't Sean's real problem – his mother was.

Sean's mother had been a very domineering woman, who always expected the impossible of him and never helped him in his attempts to achieve it. He had never come to terms with his own inadequacy in his mother's eyes, and was now projecting this rejection on to his wife.

● No-go Areas

If there are areas of your life that you are unwilling to open up to your spouse, considerable problems can arise.

Robert and Diana decided to offer accommodation to students from the local college. Almost from the moment their first allocated lodger, Alan, arrived, Robert became very edgy and irritable with Diana. He lost interest in sex, and began to spend a lot more time than usual at the pub.

Diana wondered if Robert was afraid that she might have an affair with Alan, and she thought that he was deliberately spending time out of the house to see if his fears were confirmed.

Whenever she tried to approach Robert about his moods, he would brush it off and quickly change the subject.

Their relationship became so strained that they came for counselling. In talking with Robert on his own, he confided that he had been in a homosexual relationship in his early twenties, but he had never told Diana. The presence of this young male student in the house had brought back vivid memories of this time, and he was terrified that Diana might find out about it.

Eventually he did share his secret with Diana. She was so relieved to know what was going on that she received his revelation very sympathetically. The shared knowledge, in fact, drew them much closer as a couple, and Alan stayed on without any further problem.

There are several dangers associated with no-go areas. First they tend to expand. If you have a secret fear, you will tend to avoid any situation or subject which might even remotely expose that secret. Thus the person who has never got over the death of a close friend will not only avoid talking about funerals but also about churches, hospitals, and perhaps florists as well.

If you have a no-go area, it can also lead you to expect your spouse to become a mind reader. You half want the secret to come out in order to relieve your stress and heal the rift, but you can't summon up the courage to reveal it yourself. It is then but a short step to misdirected anger if your spouse happens to read your mind incorrectly – 'Can't you see what's the matter? It's staring you in the face.'

Alternatively, if you are determined to keep the secret, a game of 'Let's pretend' occurs where you try to cover up, like Robert, by going out to the pub or using other such ploys.

● **Assumptions**

As we have seen with Diana, assumptions can be totally wrong. Such mistakes do not only stem from sensitive no-go areas, however. They can have much more mundane origins.

Phil takes Amy and their three-year-old son, Luke, out for breakfast at McDonalds. He thinks Amy could do with a break. He assumes that she would like him to look after Luke, so he lets her queue to get their meal while he finds a table. She assumes he is only thinking of sitting his backside down as usual.

Amy comes back with the breakfast and as soon as Luke has got his muffin, he decides to wander off to another table. Plop! He drops the muffin, jam-side down on to the floor. Phil picks it up and gives it back to Luke. There is a large blob of jam on the floor, which Phil intends to mop up after they have finished eating. He assumes Amy too will want to enjoy her breakfast first. Amy assumes that he is being a lazy toad and intends her to clear the mess. She flares up, 'Why do you always leave me to do the work?' He can't understand what she means. After all, he'd only suggested going out for breakfast in order to save her work.

This scenario vividly illustrates what Prof. Deborah Tannen has recently described in her book, *You Just Don't Understand*,[7] namely that men and women view the same situations in very different ways. If you make assumptions about how your partner feels, rather than actually asking, you are likely to misinterpret words and actions. This in turn can lead to feelings of rejection or hurt, even if this was not what you intended. Learning to check rather than assume requires continual vigilance.

DEALING WITH CONFLICT

● Rows and Arguments – Blessings in Disguise?

One of the differences between a shallow and an intimate relationship is that intimacy permits people to say how they truly feel. Within such emotional closeness, it is not surprising that conflict will arise from time to time.

In many ways this is a good thing. 'Frankly expressing what you feel and respecting your partner's right to have different ideas and emotions both contribute to your good feelings about your relationship.'[8] This can show in fact that we really care. Conflict-avoiding couples often pay the price of indifference for their apparently smooth passage through marital waters, whereas strong emotions, such as anger, can be a demonstration of the strength of your commitment.

Moreover, when handled correctly, disagreements can positively enhance a relationship. 'Tension reveals your complementarity, the "otherness" which distinguishes you from your partner. It offers opportunities for adjustment and growth. It forms a gateway to intimacy.'[9]

Barry and Linda had several arguments about Linda's wanting to have an allotment. Barry had no interest whatsoever in gardening, and secretly resented the fact that if Linda worked on the allotment, she wouldn't be paying so much attention to him. Eventually he summoned up the courage to tell Linda of his fears. He came to realise that any attention that was 'forced' out of Linda by imposing restrictions on her was not an expression of her love but only of her captivity. Linda got her allotment and after a few weeks, Barry, seeing how much she enjoyed it, started helping her to maintain it.

Such happy endings do not happen automatically, of course. There are some essential ground rules for ensuring that conflict does not become destructive.

● Seconds Away – Having a Good Clean Fight!

Try to have a clear goal of what you want to achieve from an argument. Do you feel that you must have your way on the issue? Is it that you want your views to be clearly heard before a decision is made? Are you after a compromise?

Always remember that it is possible to win the argument and yet lose your partner in the process.

Choosing the right moment for a controversial discussion is vital. Something which can be calmly considered over a relaxing meal in a restaurant, may turn into a blazing row if you both tackle it late at night after an exhausting day's work.

If your frustration arises, for example, from stress at work or from relationships with others, it is not fair to take this anger out on your partner.

The real source of conflict needs to be isolated. If a wife is unhappy with the way her husband initiates love-making, it is more helpful to specify, 'I don't find it a turn on when you touch my breasts so soon...' rather than to say, 'You're always so clumsy around the house.'

In practice, such displacement of issues much more commonly occurs in the opposite direction. Sexual dissatisfaction is the apparent cause of the row, whereas the real problem lies elsewhere, with sex only being used as a bargaining chip or as an excuse.

Accusations, particularly generalised ones which are impossible to defend, tend to entrench positions rather than resolve problems. 'You're hopeless,' may be an understandable reaction, but it is not a helpful message to communicate.

Clulow and Mattinson in their stimulating and original book, *Marriage Inside Out*, point out that blame may indicate that our familiar enemy of emotional contraband is at work yet again.

> Continued blame is often a communication of despair. This despair frequently relates back to early experiences when adults were literally more powerful than children and were therefore blamed by those children for some of the awful things, real or imaginery, that happened to them. Those who perpetually blame others often find attachment very difficult but are frightened of separating and being alone. They want other people to come close but are petrified when closeness is offered. In their ambivalence their way of asking often ensures that they do not get the closeness they say they want.[10]

No one is right all the time, and yet how difficult it is to admit it when you're wrong. Many an argument would end instantly by 'I'm sorry, I was wrong' if this was both sincerely meant, and followed through with appropriate action.

There is another positive spin-off from admitting it when you are wrong – 'One of the easiest ways to avoid being criticised by others is to make that criticism first ourselves. We find that if we do this others will start defending us!'[11]

Although your partner may well have started the conflict, you are responsible for your own reactions to it. Verbal abuse let out in an angry moment may cause far more damage than the original area of disagreement would ever have done, so keep a careful watch on what you say. There is never any excuse for the use of physical violence. If it breaks out, professional help should be sought urgently (chap. 20).

Whether a resolution of the conflict is reached or you have simply agreed to differ, once the issue has been thoroughly discussed don't bear grudges over it. Forget it.

Keeping a record of old scores to settle in subsequent matches is a recipe for disaster. Forgiveness and tolerance of disagreement are key elements of maintaining intimacy in marriage.

12

POSITION OF THE WEEK: INTIMATE INTERCOURSE

Intercourse is synonymous with communication or communion, consummation may speak of an urge towards completion or perfection, union is to join together as one and to know is to really understand one another.

Jean Shinona Bolen
Goddesses in Everywoman

Sexual intercourse can be a glorious expression of sexual intimacy. At its best, the sex act is sex therapy in itself. When you are feeling good, the unconditional acceptance and self-affirming exhilaration that sex provides can keep your spirits high. When you are feeling down and lacking in self-esteem sex, 'becomes more than a reassurance, it becomes an urgent therapy, perhaps one of the most powerful forms of treatment the spouses can carry out for one another'.[1]

In practice, of course, intimacy can all too easily become absent from our sex-life, and meaningful intercourse degenerates into mere copulation. 'He tells me I just lie there during intercourse. I often asked him just to do some petting and kissing. He says he hates kissing and he is not a teenager to "make-out". I would rather do without sex because I feel like a non-person this way.'[2] This reflects an all too common experience. Sexual penetration is the most intimate form of physical contact we can experience in this life. If, however, we engage in it but are not emotionally attuned to each other or insensitive to each other's needs, then having sex may turn out to be the exact opposite of making love.

There are many books around which deal with the mechanics of intercourse. They can be very helpful and I may well write one myself one day. The general ethos underlying such sex guides, however, is typified by Alex Comfort, in his well-known book *The Joy of Sex*. He writes, 'We put a lot of biology into this book; too much exposition has been devoted to symbolisms in human sex behaviour.'[3] He then goes on to consider how human sexual responses compare with those of baboons. He is not alone in this attitude. One of my patients recently saw a sex therapist who, hearing about his problem, commented quite sincerely, 'Of course that just means you are a normal animal.'

I consider our human sexuality to be more than the sum of our biological sexual responses. In my opinion, far too little exposition has been given to the symbolism and meaning of human sexual behaviour. Without such an understanding of its meaning, sex may indeed be very exciting but it will never be intimate. In this chapter, therefore, I want particularly to focus on some aspects of sexual intercourse which will help you to develop greater intimacy together when you make love. Though we shall inevitably be considering genital activity, the most important organ in intimate love-making is the brain, and our attitudes in bed are always as important as our sexual techniques.

SEXUAL RESPONSES

The human sexual response is usually divided into four phases – excitement, plateau, orgasm and resolution. Let us now consider the most important features of each of these phases in both men and women.

● The Male Response

A man usually becomes sexually aroused in his thoughts. In the excitement phase the key feature is the erection. The spongy tissue of the penis swells with blood, and the penis stiffens. The scrotal skin also tenses and thickens and the testes are drawn up closer to the body. During this phase the pulse rate and breathing also quicken, the pupils dilate, and the blood pressure increases. Nipple erection may also occur in some men.

In the plateau phase, the penis swells even further and the glans deepens in colour. The testes continue to enlarge also. Seminal fluid begins to collect in the area around the prostate gland.

The next phase is orgasm. The state of arousal is now so high that the man has to ejaculate. Contractions in the seminal ducts force the seminal fluid out of the tip of the penis. This is accompanied by an intensely pleasurable sensation deep in the pelvis. Waves of pleasure radiate out to envelop the entire body.

This is followed by the phase of resolution, during which the man relaxes and the penis gradually returns to its flaccid state. After ejaculation, it may take several hours for a man to become arousable again.

PHASES OF SEXUAL RESPONSE

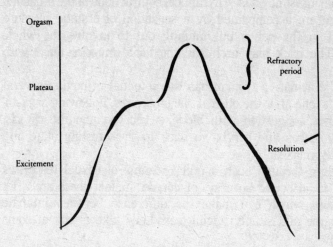

● The Female Response

During the excitement phase, the labia minora and the clitoris swell with blood and darken in colour. The clitoris may increase in size by two or three times, or alternatively may remain the same size even when fully aroused. At the same time the breasts become fuller, and nipple erection occurs. The vaginal walls start to become moist and the labia majora swell and part a little to open up the vulva.

Further breast swelling occurs during the plateau phase, and the areolae englarge considerably. The clitoris retracts under its foreskin, though if stimulation stops it may reappear.

The vagina relaxes and balloons out in its upper two thirds. The uterus and cervix are pulled upwards making the vaginal cavity larger. The lower third of the vagina engorges with blood and contracts down around the penis, forming what is known as the orgasmic platform. Since only this lower third of the vagina is actually in contact with the penis, penile size is of no real consequence in terms of its ability physically to stimulate sexual arousal.

In the orgasmic phase, rhythmical contractions of the orgasmic platform are accompanied by a sensation of ecstatic pleasure focused in the pelvis but fanning out to involve the whole body. The back may arch and the facial muscles tense with delight.

Unlike a man, a woman has the potential of having several orgasms, one after the other if she so desires. Following orgasm, the pelvic congestion with blood is relieved and the clitoris, vagina, uterus and cervix go back to their resting state and the body relaxes.

Reading through such a quick résumé of sexual responses makes it all sound so easy, of course. In fact there are a lot of factors which can make the difference between intimate intercourse and simply having sex. Let's take a look at some of them.

INITIATION – GETTING GOING

The days when it was only considered proper for husbands to initiate intercourse are it is hoped long past, and either spouse should have the freedom to make the first move. If your husband or wife leaps into bed on top of you and starts covering you with passionate kisses, it is usually not too difficult to guess their intentions. Some indicators of interest are more open to misinterpretation however.

'How do you show your wife that you want to make love to her?' asked the counsellor.

'That's easy,' replied Andy. 'I always let her know I'm going to have a shower before going to bed.'

'So that's why you're forever in that bathroom!' exploded Siobhan his suddenly enlightened wife, on hearing this revelation.

Variants of this story are so commonly told at sex therapists' conferences that there must be a lot of Andys and Siobhans around.

Sometimes, indirect signals don't get our intentions across and body language can be misinterpreted. Not every kiss signifies that you automatically want to have intercourse. Talking openly about what you intend and how you feel can be very important in initiating love-making.

After some years, getting started is often the biggest obstacle in most marriages. There are a thousand and one things that busy couples can find to do to fill an evening, and initiating sex has to be a conscious decision much of the time rather than a spontaneous inspiration. It is no shame to plan sexual intimacy together. 'The fact is, we usually are not feeling all that sexy at the moment we make the decision to have sex – we are simply planning on feeling sexy.'[4] And most of the time once we have got started we find we do feel sexy and thoroughly enjoy it.

The process of initiation is not just restricted to the time immediately preceding love-making. Many wives find it difficult to be turned on by a husband with whom they have had little intimate social contact that day. Just spending time together involved in a shared leisure pursuit or even routine housework during the day can be a good way to prepare for sexual intimacy later on.

ENJOYING EACH OTHER – FOREPLAY AND PLEASURING

The term foreplay in many ways is rather unfortunate as it conveys the impression that its only purpose is to lead to orgasm. Such performance-centred sex can be a real barrier to intimate sexual relations. Kissing, cuddling and sexual pleasuring can and should be enjoyed as delights in themselves without either of you feeling committed to intercourse every time. Making love, then, is not just restricted to having intercourse, although I have sometimes used the terms interchangeably here.

Feeling free of demands is a vital key in intimate intercourse. Constant striving to find out what satisfies your partner and having to achieve it, can soon kill off passion altogether. You will best please and stimulate your partner when *you* are obviously enjoying yourself, not when you are preoccupied with having to please them. Taking responsibility for your own pleasure is a crucial aspect of liberating love-making. You need to let your partner know what you enjoy and then get on and enjoy it.

The other key principle is that both of you should agree not to continue with anything that is negative or harmful to the other. Only then can you have the security of knowing that you are not getting your pleasure at the expense of your partner's well-being. Within this boundary the sky's the limit.

● Intimate Touch

The pleasures of intimate touch are infinitely variable. What follows is a brief synopsis of what pleases most couples. What turns a person on the most is seeing that you love them and want them. Once again attitude is every bit as important as technique.

● What Pleases Women

Women are especially aroused sexually by touch, and erogenous zones cover a much larger area of a woman's body than a man's. Virtually all women like to be caressed all over their body, but none the less will have certain areas that they find particularly pleasurable. It is often helpful to gradually build up the sexual excitement by starting caressing away from your wife's breasts or vulva. The soles of the feet, backs of the knees, inner thighs and the ears are areas which are generally arousing, but she will have the pleasure of you discovering for yourself which are the most exciting for her.

Leisurely progression to more erotic areas can then follow. Most women find having their breasts caressed turns them on, but it does need to be done sensitively. Breasts can be tender or even painful if handled too roughly. Stroking, and kissing the breasts are the best initial approach. Your obvious delight in her breasts will be as stimulating as the caresses themselves; the nipples will soon harden and the breasts swell in response to your touch. The buttocks are also another highly arousing area to caress during foreplay.

When your wife is ready she may then guide your hand to her clitoris, or you may gently approach it on your own initiative. Most women prefer to be caressed around the clitoris rather than having it directly stimulated. If she is well aroused the whole area

SEXUAL POSITIONS – MAN ON TOP.

should be moist from vaginal fluids. Gentle movements are best to start with, building up gradually as she either nears a climax or indicates that she is ready for penetration.

● What Pleases Men

Men are much more quickly turned on than women 'like putting a quarter in a vending machine'.[5] They tend to be stimulated much more by what they see, and touch is not so important overall as men have a much smaller number of erogenous areas.

Some men are very turned on by having their back or buttocks caressed. Take time to explore and find out what pleases him best. If you are a gifted teacher, you may be able to heighten his ability to appreciate sexual sensitivity over more parts of his body, as your love-making develops together.

Whether or not this happens, there is no doubt that the most erotic zone for a man is the genital area, and especially his penis. Your husband will probably want you to fondle it as soon as possible when making love. His eagerness is usually all too apparent, but tantalising him and teaching him to wait a little while, will usually enhance his excitement and hunger for you when you finally respond to that burning desire in his groin.

The most sensitive parts of the penis are the rim of the glans and the frenulum. The shaft is comparatively insensitive, but touching the undersurface and the skin of the scrotum can be very exciting. Holding the shaft of the penis and massaging it gently up and down is deliciously stimulating for any man, and you will soon have him captivated.

● Oral Sex

Oral sex consists of cunnilingus – caressing the vulva and clitoris with the lips and tongue, and fellatio – where the penis is kissed, or sucked, or inserted into the mouth.

Though not exactly invented in the swinging sixties, oral sex was certainly enthusiastically promoted during this time. It is still frequently practised, though interestingly fellatio tends to be more popular with men than women, and likewise cunnilingus is more popular with women than with men.

SEXUAL POSITIONS – WOMAN ON TOP.

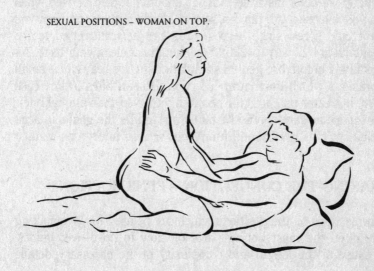

Therein lies a potential problem with intimacy and oral sex. More often than not, one partner is more keen to have it than they are to do it! For some couples, both wife and husband will find even the thought of oral sex off-putting rather than intimate. You should certainly never feel pressurised into trying it if you feel this way. I would share the opinion however that 'oral sex is perfectly acceptable in marriage provided ... neither partner feels forced into something he or she can't cope with'.[6]

This assumes that you will both be able to talk through the issue. It is amazing how many couples who may have been married for years have never even talked about oral sex. Perhaps if there was more 'oral sex' of the kind involving talking through issues together, the other type of oral sex would not be such a sensitive subject.

Most objections to oral sex derive from the fact that it can spread infection. It can indeed be the route of transmission for a wide variety of sexually transmissible diseases including

AIDS,[7,8] but it must be remembered that genital sex can do this equally well. For instance, oral sex should not be practised when you have loose tooth fillings, sore or bleeding gums, or when you have cold sores, since herpes virus can be transmitted to the genitalia in this way (p. 280). You should not clean your teeth immediately before oro-genital stimulation, as this may cause small abrasions which may carry infection. Human bites in any case have a greater potential for becoming infected than animal bites, so particular care should be taken not to bite the genitalia accidentally. This may sound funny but serious injury can result.

MAKING THE CONNECTION – PENETRATION

The sections on the positions which can be used for love-making are often the most boring parts of 'how to do it' sex guides, because of the length and complexity of the necessary details

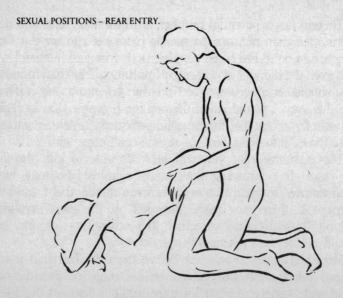

SEXUAL POSITIONS – REAR ENTRY.

SEXUAL POSITIONS – SIDE BY SIDE.

to get the description of the position right. One manual in my library has a chart of twenty positions and another mentions over seventy! The *Kama Sutra* manages only sixty-four.

Most of the positions are a variation of the basic four of husband on top, wife on top, side by side, and rear entry. In fact, almost any position which will bring the penis and vagina into alignment will suffice for copulation, but intimate intercourse requires some understanding of the significance of position.

Position affects the angle of entry of the penis, the degree of penetration, the range of movement for both husband and wife, the amount of possible body contact, and to some degree the likelihood of pregnancy resulting if no contraception is used or desired (p. 195). The position may also reflect sexually your emotional mood at the time. For example the wife who is feeling particularly assertive may prefer to be on top, as this enables her to feel that she is closing down on her husband, rather than passively receiving his penetration.

The method as well as the position of penetration will also vary, as intimacy in love-making develops. For example, when a couple communicate well together sexually, the husband will know when his wife wants the full length of his penis to be inserted all in one go, or when she prefers the tip to hover tantalisingly at the entrance for a while. Penetration does not of course have to signal the end of foreplay. Withdrawal and re-entry can help to heighten the sexual tension and desire of both partners.

A principle of great psychological importance here is that intimacy never invades. Sexual penetration is the most intimate human physical contact that any couple can experience – 'separate persons but one flesh'[9] as Robin Skynner describes it, taking his cue from the book of Genesis. If such union is to be intimate rather than an imposition, it should only be when your wife is ready to receive it.

● Anal Sex

Anal penetration is still advocated in some current sex manuals as perfectly acceptable. I consider that it should be totally avoided. Quite apart from the fact that it is an indictable sexual offence between men and women in the UK, it is a most unwise practice.

It has a high risk of spread of infection, including AIDS (chap. 24) and is generally uncomfortable or painful for the woman. The lining of the anus is very thin and bleeding frequently occurs from the friction of intercourse. If anal intercourse is repeated frequently, the anal sphincter may be damaged, causing incontinence.

It is fascinating to me how, in writing about anal sex, almost all writers – believing and pagan alike, use expressions such as 'a canal primarily *engineered* for other purposes [than sex]'[10] in referring to the anus, and 'Nature *designed* it for the penis'[11] (my italics) in referring to the vagina. Such statements not only bear witness to the folly of anal sex, but also to the existence of a wise Designer!

COMING TO A CLIMAX – ORGASM

Most men have little difficulty in reaching orgasm, the intense pleasure of the climax being accompanied by the ejaculation of seminal fluid. In women, orgasm is often a more elusive affair, though no less exciting. It may be quickly reached on some occasions but only attained at a more leisurely pace at other times. Clitoral stimulation is usually essential either from the penis, manually or both simultaneously.

The quest for the ultimate orgasm is a bit like that for the holy grail – neither has much to do with intimacy, and you could waste a whole lifetime looking.

The quality of the orgasm has to be put in the context of the entire sexual experience. A love-making encounter that is truly satisfying is one that includes the element of loving closeness, whether the orgasm was intense or less so – and even when there was no orgasm at all.[12]

Sex under the tyranny of orgasmic *timing* can also be an abysmal affair. Intimacy can be blighted rather than enhanced under such a taskmaster. This is particularly so if you always try to aim at reaching a climax together. 'Even though it is a delightful experience if your sexual activity can flow that way, simultaneous orgasms are far from necessary for a fully satisfying sexual relationship. They must remain an exciting option and not become a demanding goal.'[13]

Excessive anxiety over who climaxes first can also be very restricting. Dagmar O'Connor refers to this as a particularly common example of 'Excuse Me Sex'. 'For some couples it becomes almost a comedy of manners, like two overly polite people trying to get through a door: "You come first"; "No, please you come first"; and finally, "Excuse me, I came first." It is enough to make anyone scream.'[14]

Intimacy involves the opening up of your innermost being to one another. It is a relationship with vulnerability, rather than control, at its heart. Orgasm at its very best involves a loss of control. It is the essence of abandonment – an overwhelming pleasure. The intimacy of the orgasm is that it reveals us to our beloved in a way that no one else sees us. It may not be beautiful in the sense we normally consider beauty – there isn't much glamour in a grimace of orgasmic ecstasy, but it is intensely bonding. It draws us close in a way that nothing else can even remotely match.

AFTERGLOW – WHEN THE ACTION SLOWS

The phase of resolution following orgasm is an immensely important and often neglected part of intimate intercourse. The caricature of the quickly satisfied husband falling off to sleep within minutes is all too often reflected in real life.

Though men's passion may quickly be over, most women find that their arousal subsides much more slowly. Consequently the time immediately following intercourse may be particularly meaningful for them. Husbands should be sensitive to this situation. There may, of course, be good reason for either partner making an abrupt end to intercourse. Use of a condom necessitates it. Some women get urinary infections easily if they do not pass water immediately following intercourse, and some men get penile discomfort if they do not withdraw promptly after ejaculation. However, no matter what the cause, prompt disappearances to the bathroom may be misinterpreted as dismissal or rejection unless the reason for them is talked about.

Even if such concerns do mean a quick exit is needed, there is no reason why a further time of closeness should not follow on afterwards. When sincerely meant, every moment taken to affirm each other is always rewarded by a deepening of intimacy, and there can be no better time for this than after making love. 'Generous praise is rare in our cynical society, but it's one of the best investments any of us can make in our partner in love.'[15]

FURTHER READING

Paul Brown and Caroline Faulder, *Treat Yourself To Sex – A Guide For Good Loving* (Penguin, 1989).

13

WHEN THE EARTH DOESN'T MOVE: SEXUAL PROBLEMS

> Tossed up like flotsam from a former passion,
> How cool they lie. They hardly ever touch,
> Or if they do it is like a confession
> Of having too little feeling – or too much.
>
> Elizabeth Jennings
> *One Flesh*

THERE'S A LOT OF IT ABOUT

The positive, life-enhancing and bonding effects of sexual inter-course depend upon the degree of intimacy that exists between a couple. True intimacy, as we have seen, involves emotional exposure as well as physical nakedness (pp. 129–30). The heights of orgasmic abandon can never be reached without making our-selves vulnerable to some degree. We can only do that within a relationship in which we feel secure.

A security strong enough to allow us truly to 'let go' and drop our defences requires considerable effort to build and sustain even within marriage. It is usually much harder out-side it. It is not surprising, then, that sexual problems are commonplace in Western society.

The frequency of sexual problems in marriage is not easy to determine. William Masters and Virginia Johnson, the pioneers of modern sex therapy, suggest that as many as 50 per cent of all married couples develop sexual problems of one kind or another.[1] In one American study of a hundred couples,[2] 80 per cent rated their marriages as happy or very happy. Yet 40 per cent of the men reported some degree of sexual dysfunction (36 per cent having premature ejaculation) and 63 per cent of the women reported problems such as difficulty in getting sexually excited (48 per cent) and in reaching orgasm (46 per cent). What is interesting, though, is that only 20 per cent of the women (and 33 per cent of the men) reported that they were sexually dissatisfied. Clearly a sexual dysfunction does not necessarily equate with a perceived sexual problem, particularly for women.

This does raise an important issue which I believe needs to be stressed in our sex-dominated society. Marriages in which couples do not have regular mutually satisfying sexual intercourse are not inevitably doomed to failure. David Mace, the first General Secretary of the National Marriage Guidance Council (now called Relate), states,

> I have personally, as a marriage guidance counsellor, encountered sexless marriages that were very happy marriages. And I have encountered marriages that were so miserable that they broke up in spite of the fact that the couples concerned had a sexual relationship which the marriage manuals would have viewed as almost a model of perfection.[3]

Sex is not usually the central factor that determines the success or failure of a marriage. As the title of Liz Hodgkinson's book puts it, *Sex is Not Compulsory*.[4]

Sex is, however, a tremendous asset in developing and maintaining mutual intimacy in the vast majority of marriages. Bad sex may not wreck an otherwise good marriage, and good sex may not save a bad one. Nevertheless if things are persistently going wrong sexually, it is likely to cause considerable distress and put a strain on the rest of the relationship.

The root causes of sexual problems are highly varied. All of the enemies of intimacy discussed in Part V of this book can contribute towards sexual difficulties. So too can life events at various stages in the ages of intimacy. Such events can be normal, such as childbirth (pp. 200–7), or pathological, such as negative 'sex is dirty' attitudes picked up from parents or peers in sex education (or lack of it).

Whatever their origin, sexual difficulties are classified into two main groups – those relating to actual sexual functioning, and those relating to sexual desire. Before dealing with specific sexual problems and their treatment, it is necessary briefly to consider the concept of sensate focus exercises or pleasuring – a universal technique of current sex therapy.

PLEASURING – SENSATE FOCUS EXERCISES

If as a couple you are experiencing sexual difficulties, one of the mainstays of current treatment is for you to agree together to a complete ban on penetrative intercourse for a time. Although this may seem somewhat surprising, it makes sense when you are having an unsatisfactory and frustrating sex life anyway. It takes the pressure off both having to perform.

Instead, you arrange to put aside at least one hour, three or more times each week to engage in a graded sequence of sensate focus tasks aimed at increasing your sexual intimacy with each other gradually. At least three sessions should be spent getting used to each level of task, and a further three spent thoroughly enjoying that level, before moving on to the next.

The number of stages involved in the pleasuring exercises varies, and full details can be found in the books recommended at the end of this chapter. The four key elements in any sensate focus programme are:

● Non-Genital Touching

You take it in turns to explore any part of your partner's body except the genitals and breasts. The aim here is not necessarily to arouse at all, but just to enjoy any pleasurable sensations that may arise.

● Genital Touching

Now touching and exploration should begin as in the previous task, but after a while progression to the genitals and breasts is permitted. The ban on penetrative intercourse is still maintained during and after the sessions, but you may stimulate each other to orgasm at the end of the exercise if you wish to do so.

● Vaginal Containment

The exercise begins in the same way as the previous stage. When both of you are fully aroused, however, the wife should guide her husband's penis into her vagina. The side-by-side or wife-on-top positions are the best for this exercise. The husband should not thrust, but the wife should contract her vaginal muscles down on his penis for a few seconds or minutes. Withdrawal should occur before either of you has an orgasm. Penetration can then be repeated like this two or three times, but neither of you should have an orgasm during actual penetration or while the penis remains in the vagina.

● Vaginal Containment with Movement

This stage repeats the previous steps, but now movement is allowed following penetration. The wife should move first, and concentrate on finding the type of motion that brings her the most pleasure. The husband should then have his turn. The aim initially is again not to have an orgasm, and either partner has the right to stop the session at any stage.

Following completion of these exercises, progression to full intercourse is usually easy.

PROBLEMS OF PERFORMANCE

● Premature Ejaculation

Premature ejaculation is when the husband is unable to control his timing and comes too soon – either immediately after penetration or even before this, and certainly long before his wife has had sufficient arousal to bring her near to orgasm. It is probably the commonest sexual dysfunction in men – particularly young men just starting sexual intercourse for the first time. Fortunately it is also one of the easiest of sexual problems to treat successfully.

The aim is for you as a couple to learn more about the husband's sexual reactions, and for him to recognise the sensations occuring in his penis just prior to ejaculation.

You work through the sensate focus programme outlined above. During the genital touching phase, several methods can then be used to instruct the husband in gaining ejaculatory control.

One way is to use the *stop-start* technique. You stimulate your husband's penis until he is highly aroused. Just as he is reaching the point before ejaculation he lets you know. You then stop stimulation, and let his excitement subside. The whole process can then be repeated.

If this method fails, the *squeeze* technique should be applied. When your husband indicates that he is about to come, squeeze his penis firmly for twenty seconds or so by firmly pressing on the glans. Your thumb should be on the frenulum underneath the glans, with your first and second fingers on top as shown on p. 164.

Neither of these techniques will necessarily result in instant success, but with patience and continued practice, most husbands will develop good ejaculatory control within a few months.

● Erectile Problems

Difficulty in either getting or maintaining an erection is another common problem. Most men at some time in their lives will have a temporary problem with keeping an erection and this can be considered quite normal. Persistent or recurrent difficulty, however, can have several causes and is likely to require expert help in assessment and treatment.

Physical illness such as diabetes or blood pressure can result in erectile impotence (pp. 214, 271). So too can the drugs given to treat such diseases. Doctors do not always warn you that impotence may be a side-effect of drug treatment, particularly with antihypertensives and antidepressants, so if you have erectile difficulty after taking prescribed medication, it is always worth enquiring directly about a possible link.

The normal processes of ageing can also adversely affect your ability to get a strong erection (p. 214). A physical cause for impotence is particularly likely if you have no spontaneous morning erections or nocturnal emissions. You should have a full medical examination by your doctor if you think a physical problem may be the cause.

Most cases of erectile difficulty, however, have psychological origins. Depression (pp. 274–5) and alcohol abuse (pp. 277–8) are two psychiatric conditions which may have this effect. Much more commonly, however, problems with poor erections result from performance anxiety.

Sex is a gift to be enjoyed, not a test to be passed, and any unconscious desire to avoid intercourse from fear of having to meet up to your partner's expectations can easily lead to loss of erection. Fear then 'entwines itself around the sexual urge like ivy choking a young sapling'[5] and as the vicious circle of fear and failure follows, it kills off erectile ability altogether.

If there is no physical cause for erectile problems, the treatment

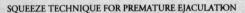

SQUEEZE TECHNIQUE FOR PREMATURE EJACULATION

is again based in sensate focus tasks. During the non-genital touching stage, you should just enjoy the sensations resulting from being caressed by your wife. You should in fact aim at *not* getting an erection during these sessions.

In the stage of genital touching, your wife should focus on stimulating your penis for her own delight and pleasure, not for your response. You should again try not to get an erection. When you do get a strong erection, your wife should stop stimulation for a brief while until the erection subsides and then restart until you become hard once more. This will increase your confidence that a lost erection can be regained.

When you are regularly getting strong erections during the genital-touching stage, you can then progress to penetration. This should be done with your wife on top. She lowers herself on to your erect penis. She will control the length of time she wants it there, and you must just relax and enjoy the sensations this provides for you. If the erection is lost at this stage, your wife will know by now how to re-stimulate it, so it is simply removed from the vagina and you both move back one stage together before trying again.

When there is a physical cause for erectile failure, various treatments are used. Injection of a drug called papaverine into the penis can induce an erection. The injection technique can be easily learned. The aesthetics of injecting drugs into the penis before making love are obviously not wonderfully erotic, and currently trials are being carried out on a similar drug which can be taken by mouth instead.

Other possibilities currently available include the insertion of a penile prosthesis, which permanently gives the penis partial stiffness sufficient to enable penetration to occur. There is also a device which creates a partial vacuum when fitted around the penis. This draws sufficient blood into the penis to cause an erection. No less than with sensate focus exercises, injections, prostheses and vacuum pumps require a sensitive and loving partner to adapt and co-operate with their use. With such co-operation, however, they can be useful aids to restore sexual intimacy.

● Vaginismus

If erectile problems make it difficult to knock at the door, vaginismus makes it impossible to open the door. It consists of an involuntary, reflex spasm of the muscles at the entrance of the vagina, thus preventing penetration. Together with erectile failure, it is a common cause of an unconsummated marriage.

The root causes include fear of intercourse resulting from a repressive or negative family attitude towards sex, or a traumatic previous sexual experience, such as child sexual abuse (pp. 306–7), or rape.

Vaginismus is one cause of dyspareunia, or pain on intercourse. Other causes of dyspareunia, such as endometriosis (p. 220) and pelvic inflammatory disease (p. 283) can lead to vaginismus. Such conditions should be excluded by your doctor.

The principles of treatment of vaginismus involve talking through damaging attitudes and experiences and encouraging a more positive approach towards your body. You will be given tasks such as examining your genitalia with a mirror. You might then be asked to explore your vagina gently with one finger at first, then gradually progressing to using two or three fingers at a time. Alternatively you may be supplied with increasing sizes of graded vaginal 'trainers' to use. In the past these devices were made of glass and called dilators. They are now made of plastic, and help to introduce you to the feel of both the girth and length of the penis in a non-threatening way. Their new name of 'trainer' is more appropriate, as it emphasises the fact that your vaginal muscles need training rather than stretching.

When you are ready for the stage of penetration, you should be on top as this provides you with a greater sense of control. You should lower yourself gently on to your husband's erect penis, and you entirely control the speed and depth to which he enters.

● Orgasmic Problems

As we noted in the previous chapter, orgasm is a more elusive end-point for a wife than for her husband. Anorgasmia – a persistent inability for her to achieve orgasm may result from ignorance about or inexperience with her own body, fear of letting go, too much self-consciousness during intercourse – the so-called 'spectatoring role', or insufficient clitoral stimulation.

Overcoming this problem involves you in feeling comfortable with your own body first of all. Exploring it and discovering what brings you pleasure on your own is an important first step before embarking in the sensate focus exercises with your husband.

The emphasis during these sessions is again on the experience of pleasure without demand. In the genital touching stage, your husband should manually stimulate your clitoris, but only after you have been aroused by non-genital touching. You may well reach orgasm in this way.

When moving on to the stage of vaginal containment, positions giving maximal potential for clitoral stimulation by his erect penis should be used. Wife-on-top positions are ideal for this. You should control the timing of entry since you will know best when you are ready to receive his penis. Following penetration the 'woman who is aware of her vaginal sensations will know the pleasure of holding a slow-moving, deep thrusting penis within her is quite different from the sensations she gets when her clitoris is stimulated'.[6] You need to let your husband know when clitoral stimulation is taking place. Further manual stimulation even after penetration may also help you to climax.

DISORDERS OF DESIRE

There is really no distinct boundary between the problems with performance we have already considered above, and the more general sexual difficulties to be discussed in this section. The two types intertwine. Lack of desire, for example, can contribute to anorgasmia which will further fuel the lack of desire.

● I'm Just Not Interested

Loss of sexual desire is very common. One psychiatrist[7] records that of those attending his sex therapy clinic, 52 per cent of the women complained of 'impaired sexual interest' and 60 per cent of the men had erectile problems which often resulted from declining interest in their partner.

There are many reasons why sexual desire in marriage may decline.

Physical Change   Illness (chap. 21), surgery (pp. 219–24), hormonal changes, especially the menopause (pp. 213–16), ageing (pp. 212–15) and drug therapy can all adversely affect libido.

Mental Illness   Loss of sexual interest is a cardinal symptom of such common disorders as depression and anxiety (pp. 274–7).

Problems From the Past   Negative attitudes towards sex, or painful past experiences can be resurrected even after many years. 'We can say that sexual delight, or the lack of it, is the direct heir of infancy.'[8] Memories of an anti-sex stance from a mother, for example, may be rekindled if she comes to stay for a visit. Similarly, sexual abuse from a father may spark off repressed fears following the birth of your first baby.

Changes in Your Relationship   We have already seen that most marriages go through an emotional trough, once the initial excitement and novelty have died down (p. 123). This can often be reflected in decreased sexual interest. This is quite normal and often resolves itself in time.

If, however, the general quality of communication in the marriage is poor, and anger, jealousy, and provocation characterise the overall atmosphere of the relationship, then interest in sex is quite likely to plummet uncontrollably.

Stressful life events can also decrease sexual interest. Bereavement and redundancy are just two pressure which may diminish libido. Childbirth is another common time for this particular problem to escalate (pp. 200–6). Looking after babies and young children is a full-time job that is frequently exhausting. In such a situation, loss of libido may be caused by simply being worn out.

Positive life changes can also cause problems. Promotion at work for either partner may channel their sexual drive so much into creativity in their work that there is little energy left for making love.

Sexual Boredom The fiery erotic passion of newly-begun sexual relations cannot last for ever. As familiarity increases, so variety in sexual technique becomes increasingly important. If the marital bed holds about as much excitement as a cemetery, and love-making becomes as predictably routine as the pre-flight checks of a pilot prior to take-off, it is no wonder that indifference sets in.

Other Sexual Problems Fear of an unplanned pregnancy, and involvement in adulterous relationships (chap. 18) are common examples of other factors leading to loss of sexual desire in marriage.

Many of these problems, as indicated, are discussed in other sections of this book, but the antidote to sexual boredom deserves further comment here.

Adding variety to your love-making can make such a difference to the depth of intimacy you can achieve together. If you always make love in the bedroom, why not try the sofa in the lounge, or the hearth rug? Another variation is provided by what Dagmar O'Connor calls 'sexing out' in her helpful book, *How to Make Love To the Same Person For The Rest of Your Life and Still Love it*.[9] Instead of going out for a meal or a show together, you book an evening in a hotel to make love.

If you cannot easily change the location of your love-making, try changing the ambience of the room. Different lighting or 'orgasmic' music (Samuel Barber's 'Adagio' is a good classical example, but pop fans will soon find your own) can help to put you in the mood.

As well as location and ambience, changes of position can do much to enhance sexual interest and involvement. The sensations from making love sitting up rather than lying down for example are totally different, and offer a whole new range of possibilities for you to explore together.

● The Jack Sprat Syndrome

Differing sexual appetites are another common problem with sexual desire. Usually it is the husband who wants more frequent sex than the wife, but it is by no means always this way round.

In middle life particularly, many wives find their sexual desire increasing at a time when their husbands find sexual arousal becoming less easy.

There is no golden rule about how frequently you should make love. The usually quoted statistic of twice a week for a British couple makes this the average, not the normative rate.

In dealing with differences in sexual appetite, good communication is again vital. If you feel your sexual needs are being neglected, then talk about it with your partner. Where love and generosity form the foundation for intimacy in a marriage, a compromise on differing sexual appetites is always possible. For example, if your husband has the greater sexual appetite, you may agree to put all the enthusiasm you can muster into intercourse with him once a week, on condition that you only have sex at other times when you initiate it. Similarly if your wife is more keen on sex than you are, you may agree to stimulate her manually without necessarily having penetrative sex each time she desires sexual release.

In conclusion, I would mention that, although an uncommon problem, sudden dramatic increases in sexual demands may herald the onset of psychological illness. I well remember a husband ringing me up in desperation for advice one weekend, because shortly after the birth of their first child, his wife was insisting on intercourse three or four times every day. It turned out that she had a puerperal psychosis (p. 201), and the insatiable sexual hunger was all part of her symptoms. Following treatment, her sexual appetite returned to its usual level, and she and her husband are still happily married.

FURTHER READING

Sarah Litvinoff, *The Relate Guide To Sex in Loving Relationships* (Vermilion, 1992).

Clifford and Joyce Penner, *The Gift of Sex* (Word, 1989).

CONTACT AGENCIES

British Association For Sexual and Marital Therapy, PO Box 62, Sheffield, S10 3IS

Institute of Psychosexual Medicine, 11 Chandos Street, London, W1M 9DE. Tel 071-580 0631.

Relate, Herbert Gray College, Little Church Street, Rugby, CV21 3AP. Tel 0788-573241.

14

FRUITLESS SEX: CONTRACEPTION, ABORTION AND INFERTILITY

> If I could choose
> Freely in that great treasure house
> Anything from any shelf,
> I would give you back yourself,
> And power to discriminate
> What you want and want it not too late ...
>
> Edward Thomas
Helen

CONTRACEPTION – DRAWBACK OR APHRODISIAC?

The ideal contraceptive would never fail, be 100 per cent safe, be easy to use and to obtain, be universally acceptable and preferably cheap as well. In practice, despite the wide variety of contraceptive methods currently available, there are snags as well as advantages with all of them.

My aim in this section is not to give a full account of every known contraceptive technique, but to consider how most of the main methods affect sexual intimacy.

● Withdrawal Or Deposit? – Coitus Interruptus

Coitus interruptus, often referred to as 'being careful', involves the husband's withdrawing his penis from his wife's vagina before he reaches orgasm.

The withdrawal method is not widely discussed since it has the reputation of being unreliable (as sperm are present in the pre-ejaculatory fluid). Coitus interruptus also makes no profits to motivate those who might otherwise promote it. Accurate data on its reliability are in fact remarkably hard to find. John Guillebaud, however, quotes a study from Indianapolis[1] which showed a failure rate for coitus interruptus of only ten per hundred woman-years. This means that for every hundred women using the method for a year, ten of them will become pregnant. This rate compares well with many other methods.

The main disadvantage of withdrawal is that in order to be used successfully it requires the man to be very in tune with his own sexual functioning, and closely aware of his build-up to orgasm. This takes time and practice. The advantages, however, are that withdrawal is 'free of charge, requires no prescription, and cannot be left at home when the couple go on holiday'.[2]

The most well-known contemporary advocate of coitus interruptus is Germaine Greer, who points out that withdrawal only causes frustration and anxiety when it is regarded as an unsatisfactory substitute for 'normal sex' until the last minute. If approached in a more considerate and positive way, it need not be sexually disappointing for either partner. As Greer rightly observes, 'Most intelligent sex contains an element of coitus reservatus in that the male attempts to prolong his erection by avoiding orgasm, thereby enhancing his own and his partner's pleasure.'[3]

● Doing What Comes Naturally? – Natural Family Planning

Natural Family Planning (NFP) depends upon having intercourse only during the infertile parts of the menstrual cycle. The first day of menstruation is counted as day 1 of the cycle. A woman with a 28-day cycle can possibly become pregnant during days 7–16 of her cycle and it is really only days 17–28 that constitute a truly safe period.

Fertility awareness is an essential part of the method. Women using NFP are taught to pinpoint their time of ovulation by recording changes in basal body temperature and noting changes in cervical mucus (the Billings method). Thus NFP works with the normal cycle of reproduction rather than interrupting it; it is in this sense that the method is natural.

Therein lies the attraction for those couples who use it. Many women enjoy the sense of awareness of their own bodies that they have to develop in order to use NFP. 'We need to understand the natural laws of our bodies in order to achieve optimal enjoyment as well as new depths of communication.'[4]

Mary Shivanandas in her book *Natural Sex*,[5] describes how many couples find their intimacy blossoms as a result of such heightened fertility awareness. You can't afford to be casual with each other when using NFP. Husbands have to take an interest in their wives, and can't dominate the sexual relationship by having sex just as and when they please. NFP can and does enhance mutual tolerance and respect between partners. There has to be a high degree of mutual communication and commitment for NFP to work.

The very strength of the method is at the same time its great weakness, however. Sexual spontaneity is intrinsically lost in NFP, and for some couples the resulting frustration will impair their intimacy rather than enhance it.

The reliability of the method is obviously an important consideration for most couples. The fear of an unplanned pregnancy can greatly inhibit sexual intimacy even in the most dedicated of marriages. The method failure rate (which assumes 100 per cent accuracy in use) for NFP can actually be very low – about one per hundred woman-years.[6] In the real world, however, imperfect use is common, hence the actual user-failure rate (which allows for such user error) is found to be much higher, at around fifteen per hundred woman-years. This is no worse than the failure rate of condoms (p. 315).

● The Great Barrier Grief? Barrier Contraception

Diaphragms   The diaphragm or Dutch cap, like NFP, involves a woman being in intimate contact with her own body. This can be a liberating experience, rather than the intimidating one portrayed in the generally bad press which the cap has often tended to receive.

It is quite true that 'the loaded diaphragm is quite likely to shoot out of the inserter's tentative grasp and to fly through the air, splattering glob in all directions'.[7] But such criticisms are made in loaded language. Shared comedy can often deepen intimacy, and a flying diaphragm can lead to a good laugh together before trying again. A night of passion doesn't have to turn into a spermicidal bath every time you use a cap. Good sex isn't usually solemn sex in any case.

Many writers comment on the cap's potential for interference with sexual spontaneity, but this need not impair intimacy and it may even increase sexual desire; having to wait for a minute before intercourse can heighten sexual tension. With regular use, cap insertion actually becomes very automatic, just like using tampons. Alternatively, the cap can be inserted at leisure before foreplay begins.

Occasionally both husband and wife may complain about discomfort from the presence of a diaphragm during intercourse. This is very unusual though, and often indicates that the wrong size of cap has been fitted.

The failure rate of the diaphragm ranges from two to fifteen per hundred woman-years. It also offers some protection against sexually transmitted diseases. A further advantage is that it can facilitate intercourse during a period by acting as a reverse barrier to contain the menstrual flow.

Female Condoms   The female condom only became generally available on sale from chemists in the UK in 1992, so its effects on sexual initimacy are not well documented. Its appearance and size certainly require some time to be spent getting used to it. It is a polyurethane vaginal sheath measuring 170mm by 80mm. In an article amusingly entitled 'Is that an Amoeba Between Your Legs?' one of the earliest users commented, 'If it were to burst, it would probably be the biggest balloon disaster since the Hindenburg!'[8] But actually bursting is something the female condom is less likely to do than its male latex equivalent.

The female condom does however offer an effective alternative female barrier method which provides a higher degree of protection against infection (including HIV) than the standard diaphragm. Once familiarity has conquered the shock of novelty, this method should not greatly impair intimacy, and the female condom is likely to increase in popularity given sufficient time.

Male Condoms The male condom, or sheath, has already become much more popular in recent years. This is principally because of its association with AIDS prevention, an issue discussed in more detail in Chapter 24.

The sheath has several potential disadvantages. It if is to provide effective contraception, is has to be put on properly. The need to ensure this is done can tend to dominate your entire sexual play from beginning to end. First, the condom must be unrolled the correct way round. The teat at the end needs to be squeezed empty of air before the condom is gently unrolled over the fully erect penis. This needs to be done immediately erection occurs because, as already mentioned, the fluid which emerges before ejaculation may contain enough sperm to lead to pregnancy.

Then, as we have seen (pp. 148-52), a wife usually takes longer to reach full arousal than her husband does, and while she is enjoying his stimulating foreplay, he may lose his erection and the condom can fall off.

Finally, prompt withdrawal while holding the condom on the penis, is essential. This is because the penis soon begins to become soft again following a climax, and sperm may then leak out of the sheath or it may slip off altogether. Thus the afterglow phase of intercourse (p. 158) is jeopardised if not necessarily completely lost.

Of course, you can buy sheaths in a whole rainbow of colours and an equal variety of textures to enhance their aphrodisiac potential, and the unrolling of a condom can, with practice, be effectively incorporated into imaginative and exciting foreplay. One writer expresses his enthusiasm about condoms thus: 'The used sheath floating in the river conjures up images of illicit sex which may be quite erotic.'[9] For others, however, the imagery is not so arousing '... when he pulls out, it feels like being a chicken and having the plastic bag of giblets pulled out'.[10]

If you both find the sheath a stimulating symbol of rampant sexuality, then it's a highly suitable contraceptive for you. If however you are turned off by the thought of a limp sack of semen as a by-product of an evening of intimacy, then use another method.

● Bitter Pill or Sweet Success? Hormonal Contraception

Oral hormonal contraception ('The Pill') is by far the most widely used method in the UK, and the most reliable. The failure rate is only 0.2–3 per 100 woman-years.

Freedom from anxiety over unplanned pregnancy, and a usage which is independent of intercourse are the main sexual advantages of this method.

Interference with intimacy is most likely to stem from concerns about harmful side-effects, especially of the combined pill (containing both an oestrogen and a progestogen). Pill scares are a frequent cause of media-induced panic.

It is important to evaluate such scares in the light of the fact that overall, pill users are likely to live longer than non-users. Pill usage, for example, reduces the incidence of ovarian cancer by around 40 per cent. True, there is a greater risk of raised blood pressure and circulatory problems such as heart attacks, but most of these episodes occur in smokers, and very few happen in women under the age of thirty-five. For non-smoking women under that age, the combined pill is remarkably safe.

The progestogen-only pill (POP), or mini-pill, does not carry any increased risk of circulatory disease, but there are a few drawbacks with it. One is an increased failure rate over the combined pill of 0.3–4 per 100 woman-years. Another is a high initial incidence of menstrual irregularity. Heavy periods can as obviously dampen sexual enthusiasm at one end of the spectrum as anxiety over absent periods can at the other end. Most women do settle down, however, into an acceptable pattern after 3–6 months. A final problem is that POPs have to be taken within an hour of the same time each day.

There is no clear evidence that either combined or mini-pills have any direct adverse effect on either libido or mood generally. Some women do complain of depression and low sexual interest after taking hormonal contraception; others find their sex drive is enhanced.

● Devices and Desires – IUDs

There is very little evidence about the direct sexual effects of intra-uterine devices (IUDs). They often lead to increased bleeding when first inserted. They are also associated with an increased risk of pelvic infection, particularly in women who have never had a child. For this reason, many doctors do not recommend using this method until after a pregnancy. These complications have obvious implications for sexual intimacy. In addition, if the thread attached to the device (to enable its removal) is cut too short, it may cause considerable discomfort to the penis during coital thrusting.

The failure rate of modern copper IUDs is around one per hundred woman-years, and as with the POP, there is an increased risk of an ectopic pregnancy (where the pregnancy develops outside the uterine cavity) should conception occur.

One further area of possible difficulty concerns the acceptability of the method. Germaine Greer unequivocally refers to the IUD as the 'abortionist's tool'.[11] This comment is a gross over-simplification as far as the mechanism of action of IUDs is concerned. They work by a complex series of biochemical changes which interfere with sperm transport and impede fertilisation, but also make the lining of the womb hostile to implantation should fertilisation occur. Reservations about the use of IUDs may arise on these grounds, but it is clear that in sustained use, modern copper IUDs operate almost invariably by preventing sperm meeting the egg, and the levonorgestrel-IUD (a progesterone-containing device) operates so strongly by preventing fertilisation that most authorities consider it can be offered to those who would object to using a method that might work by preventing implantation.

Certainly for those women for whom it is ethically acceptable and causes no side-effects, it is a brilliant method. It's always at the ready, only needs an annual check, lasts five to ten years before it needs changing, and takes less than thirty seconds to remove.

● It's A Snip – Sterilisation

Sterilisation should be considered as irreversible. This means that after sterilisation, if you should remarry following the death of your spouse or a divorce, intimacy with your subsequent partner could be severely affected if you then both want children.

Male sterilisation, or vasectomy, is a relatively simple procedure, usually done under a local anaesthetic and taking only around half an hour to perform. Once the initial post-operative pain and swelling settles, there are no adverse effects on sexual function. Strength of erections, orgasmic sensation and volume of the ejaculate remain exactly as before, and the majority of men report an increase in sexual satisfaction following the operation. Indeed research has shown that generally the quality of marriage for both partners increases following vasectomy. This is thought to result not only from removal of both the need for contraception and the fear of pregnancy, but also to relate to a caring attitude on the part of the husband, and his assumption of responsibility for the contraceptive needs of the couple.[12]

Though there are intermittent scares about vasectomy leading to an increase in both cancer of the testes and the prostate gland, at the time of writing these remain unproven. The failure rate is around one per thousand operations when the procedure has been correctly performed. Failure in such circumstances arises from the unpredictable eventuality of the cut ends of the vas spontaneously rejoining.

Female sterilisation is usually carried out under a general anaesthetic. The tubes can either be cut and tied, or clips or rings applied to block them off. The procedure can often be done via a special instrument called a laparoscope (a kind of telescope for looking into the abdomen through a small cut made near the navel). This method avoids leaving a large abdominal scar.

Female sterilisation is not 100 per cent effective. The failure rate is 0.37 per 100 woman-years in the first year after the operation. This means that for every 1,000 women sterilised, four will become pregnant within a year. An ectopic pregnancy is an additional risk with a failed sterilisation.

If there are relationship problems preceding the sterilisation of either partner, then the operation offers a convenient excuse on which to blame subsequent sexual difficulties. Both spouses should therefore be quite happy about the operation before proceeding. Even then, the decision for one partner to be sterilised can occasionally produce an unusual sequel.

Marilyn and Anthony had been married for fifteen years and

had three children before Marilyn was sterilised. Both she and her husband had been very sure about the decision, so I was very surprised when they both came to see me because things weren't working out as well as they had hoped.

They had always been a very intense couple, living 'in each other's pockets'. Now Anthony was unable to cope with the fact that there was something between them since Marilyn had been 'robbed of her fertility', while he still had his. He wanted so desperately to be united with her in her loss that they both decided that he should have a vasectomy as well – which he duly did! So far as I know, their marriage has continued to flourish just as intensely ever since.

● A Final Word

Whatever form of contraception you choose, it can only enhance your intimacy if both of you are happy with it. If either of you has doubts about its acceptability, safety, or effectiveness then don't use it. It is worth remembering, though, that what John Guillebaud says about the pill is equally true of all contraceptive methods: 'the pill cannot be expected to be a cure-all of society's ills. Nor should it be blamed for too many of them – they are caused by people, not by the pill'.[13]

ABORTION – LIBERATION OR SLAVERY?

Abortion is one of the commonest operations performed. Over 50 million abortions are carried out worldwide each year. In England and Wales the number of abortions each year continued to rise steadily until 1991 when there was a small decline. In 1969, soon after the Abortion Act came into effect, there were less than 50,000 abortions carried out; in 1990 the number totalled 173,900. Recently the Leeds obstetrician, Prof. James Owen Drife,[14] indicated that one in three women currently of reproductive age in the UK will have an abortion.

It is not my purpose here to give an account of all the various methods of abortion. It is the effect of abortion on human intimacy that is my primacy concern, and I will largely restrict my comments to this topic. There is one broader area, however, that must be considered first – the social environment of the abortion debate.

● Private Agony In A Public Arena

In the issue of abortion, personal intimacy meets face to face with unparalleled public exposure. 'Abortion is both an intimate and intensely private act and a national issue.'[15] Feelings about abortion run so high, because abortion frequently stands for an individual's entire world view. It is inevitable that what is a personal matter should also become a political flashpoint.

This makes the personal dilemma all the more difficult. Objective information becomes difficult to find in the midst of a tangle of suspicion and prejudice. To take just one example, a doctor tells us in a recent paperback that 'many Roman Catholic women request abortions – an estimated 34 million a year in Latin America alone'.[16] Clearly this figure is absolute nonsense since as we have seen, the world total of abortions is currently 50 million and there are tens of millions performed in the former Soviet Union and Warsaw Pact countries, let alone Asia and Africa. Why then does this particular doctor make such an assertion? Is it through ignorance, genuine error or a deliberate intent to portray Catholics as hypocrites? There are similar exaggerations from the other side of the debate, particularly about the physical risks of legal abortion.

A further problem is that language is easily adjusted to suit our particular world-view. Most pro-abortion literature speaks of 'the contents of the uterus being sucked or shelled out', while those who oppose abortion often refer to the 'unborn child being dismembered'. With such a conflict implicit in even the terminology of terminations, the truth is hard to disentangle.

● Abortion and Intimacy

There is general agreement that the physical risks of termination of pregnancy are low. With regard to psychological risks the evidence is less clear. As one doctor puts it, 'Observers often seem to lose their critical faculties when they enter this field of study.'[17]

What is clear is that very few women regard abortion in the same way as they do an appendicectomy, for example. Julia Mosse and Josephine Heaton, writing very sensitively from a feminist perspective, make this salient point: 'The dilemma facing many women who choose abortions, whether they call themselves feminists or not, lies in the recognition of the fact that they *do* feel for the fetus and believe it to have moral status...'[18]

Therein surely lies the sting of abortion in its effects on intimacy. Abortion can never enhance human bonding; it tends only to diminish it. 'Because there is a symbiotic bond between an unborn baby and its mother, the baby being an essential part of her, its death can feel like the death of part of herself. Arms and breasts can ache to hold and nurture.'[19] I think this explains why, as many psychotherapists acknowledge, nine months after the conception of a terminated pregnancy can be such a vulnerable time for the women involved.

Angela came to see me complaining of insomnia and increasing lack of concentration at her work as an accountant. I thought she was clinically depressed, and started her on antidepressant drugs. It was on her second visit that her mother came with her and drew my attention to the fact that 'Angela's baby would have been due this month'. I had completely forgotten about Angela's termination the previous year. Clearly Angela had not. It turned out that she still had a tremendous burden of unresolved guilt and grief related to the termination, even though she was not at all religious.

Though such disrupted bonding is most often discussed in the context of the mother-child relationship, in my view it can have profound implications for the father too. In the first place, the decision to have an abortion often means that bonding between the couple has already been completely severed, and the father has disappeared altogether.

In all the many years I have been involved in counselling women requesting an abortion I can only twice recollect the father accompanying his partner to the consultation. 'Men seemed to be absolved from any responsibility to women whom they have impregnated...' contends one gynaecologist, and she continues, 'I believe the hazards to women's health occasioned by unplanned pregnancy are compounded by the perception of unplanned pregnancy as the woman's problem. Until men honour their responsibilities to women these hazards will remain.'[20]

Second, if there is disagreement between the couple over the fate of the pregnancy, then intimacy is obviously jeopardised. Whether it be husbands or boyfriends coercing their partners into having abortions, or wives or girlfriends having abortions against the father's wishes, the results can be equally catastrophic in destroying the couple's relationship.

There is yet one further intimate bond which abortion may threaten – that between parents and their existing or future children. One of the most hideous twists of history is that the 1967 pro-abortionists' battle-cry of 'every child will be a wanted child', rings so hollow now in a world where soaring child abuse statistics have exposed it as an utterly false hope. This does not come as a surprise to many observers: 'It is no wonder, perhaps that if we treat human life before birth as disposable and of little value, then the same mentality may gradually pervade our society in its dealings with children.'[21]

The Canadian professor of psychiatry, Dr Philip Ney, comments, 'Although permissive abortion has been advocated on the grounds that it will reduce the prevalence of child abuse and infanticide, there is no evidence to prove it has. There is a growing concern it may have contributed to the problem.'[22] Ney suggests that abortion, by disrupting the developing psychological bonding mechanism between mother and child in one pregnancy, may interfere with the ability to bond to subsequent or existing children.

This hypothesis, though far from proven, does interestingly bring us back full circle to the effects of abortion on the fabric of our society as a whole. Though the desire to have an abortion is fully understandable in many of the individual cases that I encounter, seeing that desire in the context of what abortion has done to relationships in society as a whole, gives me pause for thought. After twenty-five years of legal abortion are we a more loving and caring nation? Loosed from the shackles of unwanted pregnancy has intimacy been free to grow more luxuriantly in our lives? Or can it be that as the late Dr Francis Schaeffer claimed, 'Abortion does not end all the problems; often it just exchanges one set for another.'?[23]

INFERTILITY – DIAGNOSIS OR LIFE-SENTENCE?

Perhaps the greatest sexual paradox of our time is that every year while thousands of couples have pregnancies they do not want, thousands of others want pregnancies they cannot have. Infertility is a common problem affecting between 10–15 per cent of all couples of childbearing age.

If a couple aged twenty to thirty have intercourse without contraception at the time of ovulation, there is a one in three to one in four chance of having a baby from that single occasion. The chance of becoming pregnant is even higher, since not all pregnancies go to term.

After a month of unprotected intercourse 25 per cent of couples will conceive, after six months the figure rises to 63 per cent and again to 80 per cent after a year. The average time for pregnancy to occur in couples having regular sex without any contraception is just over five months.

If conception has not occurred within a year of trying for a baby, this suggests that the situation should be investigated. Most couples concerned that they may have a problem with fertility seek medical advice between nine months to a year of trying for a child unsuccessfully.

● Origins of Infertility

There is general agreement that infertility is an increasing problem. Various reasons have been put forward to explain this.

A woman's fertility is at a maximum when she is twenty-four and thereafter declines steadily with age. A growing tendency to delay pregnancy for financial or personal reasons will therefore tend to move women into a less fertile decade of their lives. The increasing incidence of sexually transmitted diseases such as salpingitis and pelvic inflammatory disease (PID) has also had an adverse effect on fertility rates. After one attack of salpingitis 10 per cent of women are infertile, after two attacks this figures rises to 30 per cent and leaps to 50 per cent after three episodes.

Men are generally becoming less fertile too, though the reasons for this are not clear, and a variety of occupational and environmental toxins have been suggested as the culprits.

Sexual problems also may give rise to difficulty in conceiving, and some advice on sexual technique to maximise your chances of getting pregnant is given in the next chapter.

Infertility affects both sexes equally. In men, it is most often due to diminished sperm production, abnormal sperms, or both. In women, the problems include absent ovulation (often indicated by irregular periods), and faulty transportation of the egg along the Fallopian tube.

There are also problems involving both partners, such as an immune incompatibility between sperm and eggs. Therefore, even when a possible problem with fertility is found in one partner, the other partner may also need investigation.

● The Long and Winding Road

The investigation of infertility sounds innocent enough, but it can rapidly turn into a nightmare for many couples. Intimacy is invaded by probing physicians who want temperature charts kept daily, or sperm specimens taken weekly. As one of my patients expressed it, 'Investigation for infertility was the worst thing ever to happen in my life.'

'The knowledgeable couple may experience a reduction in libido as biological processes are demystified and the body treated as a machine in need of repairs.'[24] Further frustration develops as time progresses and you may see a different doctor each time you visit the clinic. Your notes may be missing on some visits, and the whole painful story has to be rehearsed from scratch again.

The medical language of infertility can do further damage by its pejorative emotional undertones. 'Failure to ovulate', 'hostile secretions', 'poor quality sperm', are all frequently used terms which, albeit unintentionally, can cause intense emotional hurt.

On the other hand, attempts to be more light-hearted can also badly misfire. To be informed that 'You've got enough sperm to populate the whole of North America,' is no more comforting than being told 'You're shooting blanks,' when your heart is breaking over continuing childlessness.

The heartbreak isn't helped either by insensitivity so often displayed by friends as well as doctors. Usually when people are undergoing a protracted course of medical investigation for a long-term condition, it arouses at least some empathy and understanding. Not so with infertility. Another of my patients expresses it graphically: 'Infertility is a really taboo subject. When we mention it to our friends, their immediate response is "Oh, why don't you adopt?" There is never any expression of concern like "That must be really hard for you."

'Even in hospital there's no sensitivity to your feelings. When I was in for investigations, I was on the same ward as two young girls who were having abortions. One of them was in the bed next to me. The ward was also used by antenatal patients and there were pictures of pregnant women and adverts for baby milk on all the walls. It was like a form of mental torture.'

Time is a further source of potential torment. Investigations may take years to complete. At their most intense they are so exhausting. 'Three mornings a week I had to be at the hospital for nine o'clock.' On top of this strain, the necessity to arrange intercourse at particular times to increase your chances of conception, if taken to extremes, can totally destroy your intimacy as a couple.

Coitus on command so easily becomes a joyless ritual rather than a source of mutual delight. The 'sex on schedule' syndrome may be just one of many sexual difficulties which ensue from infertility. When the focus of sex is entirely centred on conception it can eventually lose all pleasure. I have lost track of the number of couples who in one way or another get into the frame of mind which asks, 'If we can't have children by having sex what's the point of having sex at all?'

● **Sexual Reactions To Infertility**

In our society, potency is still often linked with virility. You are often considered only 'half a man' if you can't father a child.

Similarly, in spite of many changes and wider opportunities for women, motherhood is still popularly considered to be an intrinsic part of femininity. These attitudes inevitably lead to a lowered self-esteem if you happen to be infertile.

This lowered self-image can be reflected in your feeling about your body. Infertility can make you feel less sexy or desirable, and this can lead to decreased interest in or enjoyment from sex.

The balance of your relationship may also be deeply disrupted if the 'cause' of the infertility is found in one partner only, or if one partner seems less interested in having a child or complying with treatment than the other. If a planned delay in parenthood to further one or both of your careers preceded the discovery of your infertility it is all too easy to fall into self-reproach or recrimination of your spouse. Apportioning blame and harbouring resentment can soon tear the delicate fabric of marital intimacy to shreds. Infertility is a most fertile breeding ground for such problems as erectile impotence, dyspareunia and anorgasmia to develop (chap. 13).

The desire to prove sexual prowess, combined with the sexual frustrations that infertility imposes, drives some husbands and wives into affairs or other forms of promiscuity which in other circumstances they would never have contemplated. You need to take particular care, therefore, in nurturing your intimacy during this difficult time.

● Intimacy In Infertility

What steps can you take to maintain intimacy while coping with the realities of infertility.

Be Informed   I am more concerned in this book with the emotional impact of infertility, rather than discussing every aspect of causes and treatment. Some useful books and organisations are mentioned at the end of this chapter. Find out all you can. Not only will you be more aware of new advances in treatment, you will also be able to share the insights of others who are facing the same problems as you.

Enjoy Sex for Pleasure   Make sure that not every act of intercourse is planned for conception. Take time to enjoy each other's bodies other than around the time of ovulation. Even when 'tonight is the night', the atmosphere can be made special by preparing for sex in a way you find particularly romantic – making love by candlelight or in front of a log fire, or just with some of your favourite music in the background.

As I have emphasised throughout this book, the pleasure of sex depends on the quality of the rest of your relationship, so keep affirming each other in non-sexual ways by doing things together that you enjoy.

● Explore The Possible Options

Medical Treatment Some causes of infertility are treated relatively simply. Clomiphene, for example, is a drug which is widely used, and successfully, to stimulate ovulation.

Other treatments are much more complex and require careful consideration. Clulow and Mattinson comment from their vast mutual experience that many couples 'too quickly resort to artificial insemination by donor, IVF or embryo transfer without first considering the full implications for themselves and the child so conceived'.[25]

Adoption Adoption of a newborn or young baby is an option for only a very limited number of childless couples. The principal reason for this is that since the implementation of the 1967 Abortion Act there have been far fewer babies for adoption.

There is still considerable opportunity for couples to adopt older children or a sibling group of three or four together. It is important to realise that the adoption agencies' priority is to provide the best parents they can find for the children on their books – not primarily to fulfil the needs of childless couples. Most agencies require a couple to have completed all fertility treatment before embarking on the approval process. This is to try and ensure that both are 100 per cent committed to adoption.

Acceptance Acceptance of childlessness is a hard path. The most intense personal difficulty often relates to channelling appropriately the thwarted love that would have been given to a natural child. 'Childless couples may have to absorb a greater part of their partner's love. Such couples can become very absorbed by one another.'[26] Counselling may be required in order to work through such issues thoroughly.

● Never Lose Hope

The figure of 10–15 per cent of couples who do not conceive within a year of trying, falls to 5–7 per cent after a further year. This offers good reason for continuing hope. One of my own patients rang me today to say that she was pregnant even before her fertility treatment had commenced.

It is a frequent experience in every fertility clinic for couples to conceive even after they have finished all treatment without success. I can immediately think of two couples who had been categorically told by their specialist that there was no way that they could have children, and nothing more could be done. Both couples are now proud parents having conceived with no further treatment!

FURTHER READING

Mary Anderson, *Infertility. A Guide for the Anxious Couple* (Faber & Faber, 1987).

Peter Bromwich and Tony Parsons, *Contraception: The Facts* (OUP, 1990).

Nigel Cameron and Pamela Sims, *Abortion* (IVP, 1987).

John Guilleband, *Contraception: Your Questions Answered* (Churchill Livingstone, 1993).

CONTACT ORGANISATIONS

Family Planning Association, 27–35 Mortimer Street, London W1N 7RJ. Tel 081-636 7866

Margaret Pyke Centre for Family Planning, 15 Bateman's Buildings, Soho Square, London W1V 5TW. Tel 071-734 9351

National Association For The Childless (ISSUE), 318 Summer Lane, Birmingham B19 3RL. Tel 021-359 4887. Fertility Helpline 021-359 7539

British Agencies For Adoption and Fostering, 11 Southwark Street, London SE1 1RQ.

15

THE PATTER OF TINY FEET: PREGNANCY AND PARENTHOOD

When I was a boy ... my father was so ignorant I could hardly stand the old man around. But when I got to be twenty-one, I was astonished at how much he had learned.

Mark Twain

To try for a baby is probably the most momentous decision you as a couple can make. The arrival of a newborn child will change your relationship for ever. Some books on preparing for parenthood make having a baby sound like the best thing you could ever do – 'Babies are wonderful – no home should be without one.' Other writers give the impression that children are just an inconvenience to be endured rather than enjoyed. 'Babies are tyrannical; they cry endlessly, they make a mess everywhere, they wake you up at night and when they grow up they break your heart.'

In practice, parenthood is a mixture of pleasure and pain. Children are both a source of great satisfaction and considerable stress. Knowing this fact in advance will in no way rob you of the many joys of being a parent, but ignorance of it could lead to unrealistic expectations which end in disaster.

Motives for wanting a child vary considerably. Parental or peer pressure should be firmly resisted – only you can decide together if you are ready for taking on this responsibility.

All too frequently I see couples who have a baby in the forlorn hope that it can miraculously mend an ailing marriage, but this is one of the worst moves you can make. The demands of a new arrival will tend to accentuate rather than heal marital tensions.

'In contrast solid relationships composed of two individuals deeply desiring a child can regularly be seen to grow and prosper through reproduction.'[1]

ENCOURAGING THE STORK

So you've decided to go for it. What practical steps can you then take to maximise your chances of getting pregnant?

Stopping Contraception   If you have been using either the pill or an IUD for contraception until now, I would recommend changing over to an alternative method such as the condom or cap for a couple of months. This will enable your hormones and the lining of your womb to settle down to normal, as well as helping you to date any pregnancy more easily.

General Health Measures   Keep as fit as you can. Smoking, excess alcohol, drug abuse and obesity all tend to impair fertility in both sexes. For women it is now clear that, before conception, supplementing your diet with 0.4mg of folic acid a day will help substantially to reduce the risk of your baby's developing conditions such as spina bifida. Continuation of such supplementation seems sensible throughout pregnancy. A blood test from your doctor to check your immunity to rubella (german measles) is also a good idea before trying for your first child.

Timing And Frequency of Intercourse   On average, couples having intercourse two or three times a week will take just over five months to conceive. There is no evidence that having intercourse at any particular time of day, or season of the year, will improve your chances of conception. The timing of intercourse in relation to ovulating is, however, crucial.

The egg-cell only remains capable of being fertilised for up to twenty-four hours after its release. Though in extreme cases sperm may survive up to six or seven days in the womb most begin to die after forty-eight hours. For the maximum chance of conception, therefore, intercourse should take place close to the day of ovulation. Ovulation takes place roughly fourteen days before the first day of the next period. If your cycles are regular, calculation of the fertile period presents no problem.

If your periods are irregular, for example between twenty-six and thirty-four days, conception is most likely if you have sex regularly between days twelve and twenty of your cycle.

Positions for Sex   Positions for intercourse which allow maximal deep penetration are those most likely to favour pregnancy, since sperm will then be deposited where they need to be – at the neck of the womb.

If you have never had a pelvic examination by your doctor as part of a well-woman or family-planning check, you should ask for one to determine the direction of tilt of your womb. For women with a womb which tilts forwards – anteverted – (p. 34), the best position is for you to lie on your back with your knees drawn up. A pillow may be used under the small of the back if desired. For women with a womb which tilts backwards – retroverted – it is best if you lie on your hands and knees and your husband enters his penis from the male-behind position.

Ejaculation and Afterwards   The *husband* should aim for the deepest possible penetration before ejaculating. Over three-quarters of the sperm in the ejaculate are present in the first few drops. In order to give minimal disturbance to the semen deposited around the neck of the womb, you should stop thrusting as soon as ejaculation begins and withdraw your penis immediately after the ejaculation is over.

The *wife* needs to keep the sperm in contact with the neck of the womb, so you should lie in the best position for intercourse (as described above) for an hour or so after making love. Standing up, going to the toilet, or having a bath will all tend to displace the semen from where it needs to be.

PREPARING THE NEST

THE PSYCHOLOGY OF PREGNANCY

Pregnancy leads to profound physical, emotional, social and sexual changes. Women's reactions to these changes vary considerably. Initially, some may feel an increased sensuality, an opening out to the world, like being in love. Women report feeling fertile, creative and excited. For some, it is the ultimate affirmation of being a woman.'[2] If you feel this way, enjoy every minute of it.

If, however, you feel quite the opposite, don't despair. This is also quite normal. Pregnancy can be a big shock to the system: fatigue, discomfort, distraction and distaste – 'the four evil horsemen of sexuality'[3] can all gang up to form a posse of potential problems.

Feeling tired and sick, with little visible benefit to show for it, can sometimes be the predominant mood in early pregnancy. Almost all mothers have some moments of anxiety during pregnancy. Feelings of inadequacy, the loss of your figure, financial worries, fears that your baby may be abnormal or die, anxieties about loss of intimacy with your husband, all are possible sources of concern.

Husbands are not immune to stress resulting from pregnancy either. You tend to worry less at the beginning of your wife's pregnancy, but as it progresses your anxiety levels may increase also. About one in ten expectant fathers will develop symptoms themselves during their wife's pregnancy. These include nausea, vomiting and abdominal pain. Such symptoms are usually psychological in origin and are known as couvade.

In our contemporary society which majors on equality between the sexes, pregnancy still accentuates their differences. Many modern couples will experience 'the fantasy of fusion',[4] believing that they will go through the parenting experience equally together. They choose the possible names, prepare the house, attend antenatal classes together, and then following the birth are rapidly propelled into separate orbits. Fathers-to-be are often prepared for what to expect during the delivery but have little idea of their postnatal role.

This sense of lostness is compounded by the fact that the majority of men will have received most of their childhood nurturing from their mother, not their father. 'Unconsciously the role of nurturer is not something his maleness prepares him for.'[5]

Another aspect of pregnancy, which may be a further source of stress in Western society, is the medicalisation of motherhood. The mass technology of ultrasound scans and other screening tests can be overwhelming. 'The obstetrician assumes many of the directive and nurturant roles, often usurping those of the husband.'[6] Appropriate antenatal education and preparation for both partners can do much to counter this tendency and 'help to focus on childbirth not as a clinical crisis, but as one aspect of a woman's and a couple's psychosexual life, and part of the developing relationship between them'.[7]

Your sexual relationship will inevitably be affected for better or worse by pregnancy. It can be a wonderful time. There is no need to worry about contraception, and particularly in the second trimester, many women say they feel more sexually aware. Likewise, many men get a great sense of satisfaction in being fathers, and enjoy their wives' new shape, although paradoxically women often fear that their husbands will find their pregnant shape unattractive.

In general, however, most research has shown a steady decline in sexual interest and frequency of intercourse throughout pregnancy.[8,9] This probably results from a combination of factors including the physical symptoms and changes of pregnancy, fear of injuring the baby, cultural taboos, and misguided or misunderstood 'doctor's orders'.

Even if the desire for intercourse does diminish, the need for affection and intimacy does not. Husbands must take care not to misinterpret diminished frequency of sex as the beginning of their rejection by their wives in favour of the child. 'To have the tap turned off, without warning, after ten years together is the most devastating painful thing. It's caused a massive tension between us. I feel like I've been dispensed with – as if my function is finished.'[10]

Similarly wives must not become resentful at the slowness of some husbands to see their continuing need for closeness and being held, even if penetrative sex is not desired so often.

Pregnancy once again provides an opportunity to enhance interpersonal communication which can enrich your marriage relationship for ever. On the other hand it can impose strains which may break the relationship apart. More marriages break up in the first eighteen months after childbirth than at any other time.

SEX IN PREGNANCY

In the dark, it is difficult to distinguish friend from foe. Most of the widespread fears concerning sex in pregnancy are totally unfounded, and arise from the double darkness of ignorance and prejudice.

Many couples say their main worry is that enthusiastic thrusting of the penis during intercourse may cause damage such as rupture of the membranes, vaginal bleeding or precipitating a miscarriage. Extensive research has not found any support for such fears.[11]

Another common fear is that contractions of the uterus during orgasm will start off labour prematurely. Again the evidence shows this is not so.[12] On the contrary, one obstetrician has even suggested that a satisfying sex life during pregnancy 'may predispose to contentment and a lessening of tensions which might equally be incriminated in the genesis of premature labour.'[13]

The third main area of anxiety is about introducing infection. In fact a normal closed neck of the womb and intact membranes offer more than enough protection from infection for a healthy pregnant woman. If there are problems or complications of pregnancy such as incompetence of the cervix or premature rupture of the membranes, then intercourse is best avoided. It is also not recommended to have sex very late in pregnancy if the cervix is known to be very soft (effaced) and starting to dilate.

One further situation in which intercourse is not advised is when there is undiagnosed vaginal bleeding, especially in the later months of gestation. When this occurs, the potentially dangerous situation where the placenta is sitting right over the neck of the womb (placenta praevia) needs to be ruled out first, before resuming an active sex life.

There is no medical reason for any restriction on the form of sexual activity you engage in during pregnancy with one important exception. The forceful inflation of air into the vagina during oral-genital sex is well documented as a rare cause of maternal death.[14] This practice may dangerously cause entry of air into the maternal circulation. You should therefore avoid it.

In early pregnancy the positions used for intercourse will

probably not be affected by the enlarging uterus. If, however, the wife feels discomfort, then using the female-above position may be easiest.

As the pregnant abdomen swells, it will obviously have greater influence on the positions you use for making love. Some of the most helpful are:

The 'Spoons' Position   Husband and wife lie side by side, knees flexed, facing in the same direction with the wife in front. The husband inserts his penis from behind.

This position allows maximum flexibility for caressing the front of the wife's body, and for manual stimulation of the clitoris if she desires it. This angle of approach also permits shallower penetration and the penis will stimulate the anterior wall of the vagina, where the G-spot may be located in some women (p. 32).

T Position   The husband lies on his side with his wife lying at right angles to him on her back, forming a T shape with

SEXUAL POSITIONS – SPOONS POSITION.

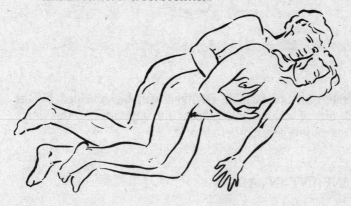

her knees flexed over his body. The vagina is brought up into close contact with the penis which can then be inserted. This position is not so good for penile stimulation of the clitoris and manual stimulation may be required for the wife to reach orgasm.

SEXUAL POSITIONS – T POSITION.

The range of comfortable positions can be extended by the careful use of chairs and pillows for support but this obviously needs preparation beforehand.

THE INFANT INVADER

It is outside the scope of this book to consider all the aspects of childbirth itself except to emphasise that it is a natural sexual event – not a disease – and you should aim to be together during the delivery, with the minimum amount of medical intervention necessary for the safety of both mother and baby.

The arrival of a newborn child is usually a time of unspeakable happiness. 'I never knew a baby could bring so much joy. It's as if someone squeezes love juice in your eyes.'[15] Congratulations! Enjoy it to the full.

For many new parents, though, there is often a sobering element present as well. It is quite possible for many of the more impulsive aspects of your adolescent behaviour to persist well into the first phase of your married life, but 'the arrival of the first child forces young married couples to take the last painful step into the adult world.'[16] There is no divorce from an infant; no turning back. The survival of your intimacy as a couple now depends on your ability to come to terms with the changes in role and function that parenthood brings.

BABY BLUES

For the vast majority of couples, early parenthood will involve some measure of depression. This fact may come as a big surprise for you, if your only images of the newborn are conditioned by advertisements for baby-powder.

For new mothers the experience of depression may vary from 'baby blues' at one end of the spectrum to post-puerperal psychosis at the other. Post-puerperal psychosis is a serious form of mental illness which is fortunately extremely rare (only around three in every thousand mothers is affected). Baby blues, by contrast, are very common and in one study, 84 per cent of mothers experienced such feelings as undue tearfulness and a tendency to be upset easily in the first few weeks after delivery.[17]

This vulnerability to depression in new mothers has been explained in a variety of ways. Katherine Dalton, for example, has emphasised the importance of hormonal changes taking place in pregnancy and after birth.[18] Hormonal changes are unlikely to be the full story, however.

The social environment of the birth is also highly relevant. The 'colonisation of birth by medicine'[19] may well have a significant effect, and there is certainly evidence of an association between 'baby blues' and medical intervention (epidurals, forceps delivery, etc.) during the birth.[20] Feelings of helplessness and lack of power often precede depression and may be particularly crippling coming immediately before the increased responsibilities which new mothers have to face on discharge from hospital.

The extent of support at home is also crucial. The importance of a secure marriage in alleviating postnatal stress is well recognised. Poor housing, financial pressures and unemployment will also tend to add to the baby blues.

The way that a new mother feels about herself will also be determined to some extent by her relationship with her own mother. It this was warm and loving during her own childhood, it later provides the emotional resources for the new mother to draw on to equip herself for parenting.

Recently attention has focused on the presence of postnatal depression in men too.[21] This is perhaps not surprising in view of the changes in family dynamics which result from becoming a father. Social (p. 196) and sexual pressures (pp. 203, 206) can compound the problem.

THREE'S A CROWD

The arrival of a new baby takes considerable adjustment in a marriage. Husbands can feel woefully left out and become resentful of the time and attention being given to the baby. Wives can feel terribly trapped, and resent their husbands' freedom to go off to work and do what they like. The nature of envy is such that it always makes you think your partner has the better deal!

One of the great paradoxes of parenthood then is that the very child which symbolises your unity can actually bring division. This tendency to divide occurs in two principal areas:

Social Roles   The arrival of children tends to define couples' roles along traditional gender lines. Though paternity leave is becoming more common, it is nevertheless still the mother who usually has a period of at least several months off work following the birth. Men tend to become much more absorbed in their work when they become fathers partly because they are displaced by the baby at home.

Sexual Relations   The arrival of a baby not only stresses sexual relationships by his or her demands on a couple's time and energy, but also in more subtle ways. For example, at the very time that the wife's breasts are at their fullest and most sexually attractive, they are principally used for feeding baby rather than making love.

With all the latent envies which the arrival of a baby can arouse, it is no surprise that both marital violence and extra-marital affairs are much more common during pregnancy and the postnatal period. You should therefore take special care to keep intimacy alive during this very vulnerable phase.

IS THERE SEX AFTER BIRTH?

There is generally no medical reason why sexual intercourse should not occur within two to three weeks of delivery, but most couples generally take longer than this. One British study found that nearly 40 per cent of women had not resumed by between ten and thirteen weeks postnatally.[22] The majority of couples, though, start having sex again between the fifth and eighth week post-partum.

Before returning to an active sex life it is important to think about appropriate contraception if you do not wish to extend your family straight away. While most women who breast-feed exclusively and on demand will not ovulate for around fourteen months, those who partially breast-feed or exclusively bottle-feed are capable of conceiving again within a few weeks, and certainly before they have their first post-partum period.

Once contraception has been considered, what are the major hurdles to overcome in postnatal sex?

PAIN
Pain on intercourse (dyspareunia) is a frequent problem after childbirth. During delivery the perineum (the area between the vagina and the anus) is usually cut by the midwife to facilitate delivery and prevent tearing. This cut is called an episiotomy, and since it increases substantially the chances of postnatal

dyspareunia it has also been referred to as 'the unkindest cut of all'.[23]

It is well recognised that a midline episiotomy (a cut directly backwards from the vagina towards the anus) is much less likely to give persistent pain than a cut to the side (mediolateral), yet most obstetricians in the UK (though not in the USA) routinely perform a mediolateral cut. This policy urgently needs review. Post-episiotomy pain on intercourse can take a long time to go. In one study 8 per cent of women surveyed were still affected one year after delivery.[24]

With births by Caesarean section (where the uterus is opened surgically through an abdominal incision), a vertical scar is usually much more painful than the more common horizontal (or Pfannenstiel) incision. Some women complain of persisting painful spasm of the vertical scar during orgasm, but this does not seem to result from the Pfannenstiel incision. A further advantage of the horizontal cut is that it is cosmetically much more appealing. It is hidden by the pubic hair when it regrows, and such factors may be important at a time when body image tends to be poor.

Dyspareunia may occur even when delivery is not complicated by surgical cuts or spontaneous tears. The postnatal hormonal deprivation of the vulva and lining of the vagina has some similarities to the post-menopausal state (pp. 215–16). It may result in a sense of tightness, dryness and discomfort, especially in mothers who are breast-feeding.

The problem of dyspareunia may be helped as follows:

Use a lubricant   Water soluble lubricants such as K-Y jelly can be used, not just prior to intercourse, but applied to the vulva and vagina on a daily basis to prevent soreness.

Choose the optimal positions   The wife-on-top, and the side-to-side positions minimise trauma to the episiotomy site. Pressure on this site can also be reduced by placing pillows under the wife's buttocks to direct the penis on a more forward direction.

Adapt your sex technique   Shallow or even partial penetration is advisable at first. Letting the erect penis rest gently in the vagina for a while prior to commencing thrusts can also reduce vaginal discomfort.

BREAST SYMPTOMS

Breast-feeding sometimes leads to sexual arousal which may even result in orgasm. Around 10 per cent of nursing mothers report enhanced sexual desire postnatally.

For the majority of couples, however, breast symptoms can be problematic rather than aphrodisiac. Infant envy has already been mentioned above. In addition, the breasts can spontaneously leak milk, which both husband and wife may find sexually inhibiting.

Breast pain may also be a problem. Cracked nipples can cause intense pain in breast-feeding mothers, and engorgement of the breasts in those mothers who give up breast-feeding may equally render the breasts untouchable. If over-the-counter pain killers, such as paracetamol, do not relieve the pain, stronger analgesic and also hormonal treatments are available on prescription from your doctor.

Coping with these difficulties requires a good deal of mutual patience, and a strong sense of humour. If breast stimulation forms an important part of your foreplay, allowing your baby to feed prior to your love-making may help.

Alternatively, you may express the milk manually first or your husband can include sucking of your nipples as part of your foreplay. Wives need often to encourage husbands to touch their lactating breasts, as many men do have a sense of reluctance about this during the postnatal period. Encouragement to share will help to defuse the possible envy discussed above.

BODY SHAPE

A positive body image is very important in the postnatal period. Exercise is a key way of improving the way you feel about your body. Exercises to tone up the pelvic muscles (Kegel exercises) should ideally be started prior to postnatal discharge from hospital.

The most important of these exercises consists of tightening your pubococcygeus muscle in the pelvis and holding it tight for a count of ten before relaxing it again. This muscle is used to stop urination, and is consciously contracted by trying to draw up your anus, bladder and perineum into your pelvis. The contractions should be repeated thirty or so times a day.

Postnatal obesity is another worry for many new mothers. Severe dieting is however not a good idea postnatally, and a goal of regaining pre-pregnancy weight in three to six months after delivery is reasonable.

Husbands need to be particularly understanding with their wives' sensitivities about body shape at this time.

PARENTS AND LOVERS

'Children are passion killers...'[25] and you must take care that their albeit innocent homicidal tendencies don't succeed.

Whether it is the baby's cry of hunger, or the young child's cry of 'What are you two doing in there?' raising children poses unavoidable obstacles to having a relaxed time of love-making. More advance planning will be required than before, and a lock on the bedroom (or whatever room!) door may be an essential extra.

If you are interrupted by your young child during your love-making, then a few words of explanation will need to be given to them. Intercourse can seem a very curious business to a youngster. Never be ashamed or unduly embarrassed, however. One of the best gifts any parent can give their child is to love (in every aspect of the word) the other parent. Our children need to know that we are enthusiastic about sex and regard it as an important and exciting part of our married life. We will never convince them that it is worth waiting for marriage to have sex, if our own marital sex-lives are impoverished and burnt out.

FURTHER READING

Gordon Bourne, *Pregnancy* (Pan, 1989).
Christopher Clulow, *To Have and To Hold. Marriage, The First Baby and Preparing Couples For Parenthood* (Aberdeen University Press, 1989).

CONTACT AGENCIES

National Childbirth Trust. Alexandra House, Oldham Terrace, Acton, London WC1 6NH. Tel 081-992 8637.

Meet-A-Mum Association, 14 Willis Road, Croydon, Surrey CR0 2XX. Tel 081-665 0357.

Homestart, 2 Salisbury Road, Leicester LE1 7QR. Tel 0533-554988.

Association For Postnatal Illness, 25 Jerden Place, Fulham, London SW6 1BE. Tel 071-386 0868.

IV

GROWING OLDER –
THE CROWNING AGE

16

ALL PASSION SPENT?
AGEING AND INTIMACY

> But when we seek our bed each night,
> The wrinkles melt away:
> Our flesh is firm, our kisses warm
> Our ardent hearts are gay!
> The Fountain of Eternal Youth
> Is not so far to find:
> Two things you need – a double bed
> A spouse who's true and kind
>
> Anonymous

SOCIETY, SEXUALITY AND AGEING

Western society does not generally give a high priority to the elderly. Ageism – the adoption of negative attitudes and behaviour towards the elderly simply because of their advanced age, is widespread today. This general philosophy inevitably affects sexual attitudes also.

'The trouble is that despite the so-called permissive society ... there are still cultural taboos against sex for older people. Many people take the view that it does not happen, or that if it does, it is something rather perverse and disgusting. How could they!'[1]

I believe the 'so-called permissive society' has actually contributed towards the sexual stigmatising of the elderly. When so much attention is fixed on the athletics of intercourse, and its imagery is totally centred on youthfulness (have you ever seen a naked couple over forty let alone seventy, on the cover of a sex manual?), the elderly will inevitably be neglected.

Another factor which is rarely mentioned, is that the elderly have no exploitable value for both the contraceptive and pornography industries – both of them powerful manipulators of sexual mores. As I have written elsewhere, '"Page three grandmothers" are not likely to prove popular, and these days anything without a glamorous media image has to fight for survival.'[2]

We are a society with double standards. I well remember the scandal caused in a geriatric ward I once worked on, when two patients in their eighties (as well as their nighties!) were discovered having a kiss and a cuddle behind the curtains. Yet the extra-marital affairs of ward staff were just accepted as the norm. No wonder that the older generation often feel hurt and confused about their sex-lives. We all know what the it in "past it" refers to.

YOU'RE NEVER TOO OLD!

'What can you expect at your age?' is a common response met by many an older person seeking advice from their GPs about sexual difficulties. Though such an unfortunate rebuke often betrays ignorance or lack of interest on the part of the doctor, it is actually a question well worth answering – what exactly can you expect?

In essence, you can enjoy a full and satisfying sexual life well into old age. The physical changes of ageing will mean learning different expressions of sexual affection, but these need not be any less enjoyable. Difficulties such as slower responses and reduced sensitivity of vagina and penis, may be compensated by greater availability of time to give to each other and the discovery of new ways of giving and receiving sexual pleasure.

As far back as 1915, (in a book then reserved exclusively for the medical profession), Dr H.W. Long wrote '...the functioning power of the sex organs will remain, even to old age, with all their pleasure-giving powers and sensations intact. This is a wonderful physiological fact...'[3]

It certainly is, and modern research confirms it. In a 1988

study of American 80–102-year-olds, 62 per cent of men and 30 per cent of women surveyed said they had had sexual intercourse 'recently'. Recent physical intimacy was reported by 87 per cent of men and 68 per cent of women.[4] It should be noted, however, that these were exclusively fit and wealthy residents in California and thus not representative of the general elderly population.

Not everyone can be like one of my patients whose dying words to his wife were, 'Let's have a bit of the other'! However, all of us can, if we wish, maximise our potential for sexual intimacy for as long as possible. To do so it is important to understand how sexual function changes with age, and how we can adapt to these changes.

CHANGES FOR HIM

● In arousal

Spontaneous early morning erections and nocturnal emissions are both less common with age, and the ability to be sexually aroused generally diminishes. This particularly applies to arousal from thinking about sex (psychic stimulation), though arousal from touch (tactile stimulation) is also affected.

These changes can be profoundly disturbing, particularly to those men who have prided themselves on their previous sexual prowess. John, an HGV driver, had throughout his marriage to Joan always come to intercourse with a good solid erection almost before any foreplay had begun. When he had turned sixty, this no longer happened so spontaneously and he began to feel he was losing his virility. If his wife initiated any sexual overtures, he would now turn away in shame that he had only such a weak offering.

In this sort of situation a shared understanding by both partners that reduced arousal is a normal process and does not automatically reflect adversely on remaining a 'real man', can be enormously liberating. Indeed, the greater necessity of direct touch to maintain an erection can be turned to profit. Doubling the pressure may double the pleasure for the man, and if his wife has always hitherto struggled with his speed of arousal she may actually value the new dynamic of a sex life in which she has a chance to catch up at last. A great deal depends on taking a positive approach. Reduced psychic stimulation may for example be regarded as a bonus by many men who have battled all their adult life with the pressure to indulge in pornography.

● In sexual performance

Erections take longer to develop, are more difficult to maintain, and tend to be less hard with ageing. The time of sustainability of an erection may be reduced to a matter of minutes in the over-seventies. Ejaculation is less powerful, of shorter duration and smaller volume. The period of unresponsiveness following an ejaculation (the refractory period) also increases and may exceed twenty-four hours in seventy-year-olds.

There is considerable debate about the role that hormones play in these changes. The decline in sexual responsiveness with ageing takes place in parallel with hormonal changes, but there is no convincing evidence that it is caused by them. Some experts suggest that after a long period of sexual abstinence in men, testosterone levels may fall markedly, and sexual function can be improved by giving testosterone injections.[5] However this is controversial, and testosterone levels in the blood should always be measured by your doctor before considering such treatment.

Certainly maintaining general health is important to good sex in later years. A balanced diet and exercise will help counter the tendency to gain weight, which can make the mechanics of sex difficult otherwise. Stopping smoking is another excellent idea, as smoking impairs the circulation to the penis just as much as to other organs.

Illness is much more likely as we get older, and diseases such as diabetes, dementia and hardening of the arteries (arteriosclerosis) can have adverse effects on sexual function, in men particularly. Similarly, some 87 per cent of over-sixty-fives are taking regular medication on prescription. Many drugs can cause impotence, especially those used to reduce high blood pressure. It is well worth while for men with sexual difficulties to see their doctor for a check-up, and to review any medication.

CHANGES FOR HER

● The menopause

Between the ages of forty-five and fifty-five most women will stop having periods. Usually this is a gradual change with periods occurring at two or three-monthly intervals for a while, before eventually ceasing altogether.

Other common symptoms at this time include:

'Hot flushes' and sweats. These result from an increased irritability of the blood vessels in the skin. This is caused by a sharp decline in oestrogen production by the ovaries. Though usually lasting only seconds, 'hot flushes' can recur many times during the day and occasionally can cause profound anxiety and social embarrassment.

Skin changes The skin becomes less elastic and begins to wrinkle. The loss of fat underneath the skin means that breasts begin to shrink.

The skin of the vagina becomes less thick and it produces less lubrication in response to sexual stimulation. The combination of a thinner and drier lining can lead to both vaginal soreness and also pain on intercourse (dyspareunia) (p. 166).

Psychological Changes A full house (or perhaps a royal flush!) of the symptoms in the rather gloomy catalogue above is bound to have psychological effects in itself. In addition, loss of fertility and the permanence of this milestone of ageing may further predispose to depression and anxiety. A sense of failure may ensue, and loss of libido is not uncommon. It is a time of great vulnerability for many women.

COPING WITH THE CHANGE

Increase Your Understanding Read one of the books listed at the end of this chapter which will explain in more detail what is happening to you. Your husband may find these useful too. Don't be afraid of your feelings. 'Menopause is a time of loss and women can only go on to enjoy the next stage of life if they mourn for their lost youth as they would for a loved one, gradually letting his memory go. "There is no name, with whatever passionate emphasis of love repeated, of which the echo is not faint at last". When the echo of the past grows faint the new life can begin.'[6]

Be positive   Of course, mourning may not be necessary for you. Most changes can have positive benefits and the loss of periods may be a welcome release. 'A seventy-six-year-old woman who told us she never had any trouble with the menopause added, "Well, I guess it's true; I had what you call hot flushes, but I always associated that feeling with getting sexy and I liked the idea as I was so sexy at that time in my life. So the feeling was really kind of nice." '[7]

Hormone Replacement Therapy   Most of the symptoms of the menopause result from a declining output of oestrogen from the ovaries. They can be minimised, or even eliminated in some cases, by hormone replacement therapy. Though it is inadvisable for some specific groups of women (for example those with breast cancer) to take hormone replacement therapy, it is estimated that only 10–15 per cent of women who might benefit are actually taking it.[8] As well as relieving menopausal symptoms, it is also of proven value in preventing fractures in later life. There is also strong evidence that it reduces the risk of heart attacks and strokes.

The major disadvantage of HRT is the return of periods, but with some forms of HRT even this can often be avoided. You should discuss this with your doctor.

Other measures   The use of lubricating gels (such as K-Y jelly) can greatly ease the problem of a dry vagina. The use of oestrogen creams can also help, but these should not be inserted immediately prior to intercourse, as they may be absorbed through the husband's penis.

AGEING INTIMATELY TOGETHER

There are many ways in which sexual intimacy can be maximised in later years.

● Plan ahead

As we have seen, the mechanics of sex become slower with

ageing, and an unsatisfactory sex life in earlier years is likely to deteriorate further with ageing. Those wanting to have a rich sex life in their eighties need to maintain regular sexual intercourse when younger.

● Have a double bed

It is at this stage that a couple sometimes decide to change to separate beds or even separate rooms. This may be a perfectly sensible decision based on the fact that one partner snores, or one sleeps poorly ... But it does means that there is little chance for physical closeness or the impulse cuddling that can say so much in its own right, as well as leading naturally and delightfully to full sexual enjoyment.[9]

Taking the most of every opportunity is especially important in later years, and sexual arousal can be conveyed immediately when lying together in the same bed. The separation of just two sheets in single beds pushed together might hinder sexual activity every bit as much as two suits of armour if arthritic knees have to cross the barrier.

● Keep yourself attractive

Things that might have been considered optional in earlier years may make all the difference now. Shaving is important (ageing skin is sensitive, and contact with beard stubble may be like kissing a Brillo pad), and the use of warm baths, oils and talcs can be useful aids to intimacy.

● Be inventive

Penetrative vaginal sex may become increasing difficult and may require a change in accustomed positions to achieve. Side-by-side is often easier.

Old age may be the right time to learn new ways of expressing sexual affection and to review previously-held taboos, though this must be worked through with care and concern for each other. Massaging, mutual masturbation and oral-genital stimulation may be possibilities to explore for the first time. 'The emphasis changes from a race to the summit of orgasm, to a gentle wander around the foothills of massage, the peak being a bonus rather than a necessity.'[10]

With sufficient motiviation, a way can usually be found. 'One couple discovered that they enjoyed having intercourse in a large rocking chair, she sitting on his lap as they rocked back and forth. They were convinced that the effectiveness of the technique was responsible for the lasting popularity of the rocking chair in America. To keep off the chill when they made love, the wife did a little creative sewing on her flannel nightgown and designed a special movable flap at the back...'[11]

● Be yourselves

Don't feel pressurised by anything you have read in this chapter to perform in a particular way. You and your partner need to work out what is right for you. The expression of physical closeness is, however, an important compensation for many of the negative aspects of growing older. Make time for such intimacy, and your marriage will remain the richer for it. Repetitiveness and habit are sure and certain passion-killers at any age. The changes necessitated by ageing can, with a little imaginative thought, produce a whole range of new enjoyments for you to share together.

FURTHER READING

Roger Smith and John Studd, *The Menopause and Hormone Replacement Therapy* (Martin Dunitz, 1993).

Wendy and Sally Greengross, *Living, Loving and Ageing* (Age Concern, 1989).

LETTING GO: INTIMACY AND LOSS

For all that has been – Thanks!
To all that shall be – Yes!

Dag Hammarskjold

Losses of various kinds are an inevitable part of growing older. Failing sight, impaired hearing and poor memory, for example, all cause bereavement reactions, and can induce a marked reduction in our capacity for intimacy.

In this chapter we shall consider those losses that relate most directly to our sexual identity and activity.

HYSTERECTOMY

By the time I saw my doctor I knew that there was something seriously wrong, and that my womb would have to go. I can't describe the feelings of horror, of desolation almost that hit me when he said, "It'll have to come out, Mrs B." What was so awful was that he quite obviously thought I was silly to be upset ... I couldn't explain that it was me – the centre of my whole life – that he was wanting to slice out and throw away.[1]

Hysterectomy, the removal of the uterus, is a very common operation with more than fifty thousand performed a year in the UK. Around 20 per cent of women will have had their womb taken out by the age of seventy-five. Most will regard the procedure as much more emotionally charged than, say, the removal of the appendix, but with adequate understanding and counsel it need not leave permanent psychological scars. Indeed, in spite of the many popular myths surrounding hysterectomy, there is some evidence that sexual enjoyment can actually improve following the operation. In one study of ninety-eight women undergoing hysterectomy, 75 per cent of them reported either no change or an improvement in their sex lives afterwards.[2] The possible explanations for this finding include:

THE REASON FOR HYSTERECTOMY

Fibroids.   These large balls of muscle which grow in the womb are the commonest reason for hysterectomy; over a quarter of all women will develop them to some degree. Sometimes they cause no problems, but if they grow into the lining of the uterus they can cause both pain and heavy bleeding.

Heavy periods (Menorrhagia)   Even with an anatomically normal womb, poorly understood hormonal factors can lead to very heavy periods with large clots being passed for weeks, rather than days in severe cases. If the bleeding cannot be controlled by taking medication, a hysterectomy may be needed. A newly developed technique called endometrial ablation, which involves resection of the lining of the womb using cautery, may supersede hysterectomy for menorrhagia in the future.

Dropped Womb (Prolapse)   The muscular supports of the uterus may become loose and the womb drops down. In an extreme prolapse, the womb may become visible externally.

Pelvic Infection   With repeated attacks of sexually transmitted disease the pelvic organs can become stuck down with inflammation. This can cause severe pain, particularly on intercourse.

Endometriosis   In this condition, which again gives rise to pain on intercourse as well as painful periods, the tissue lining the womb (endometrium) appears in other places in the pelvis. This may cause surrounding tissues such as the bladder to get stuck to the pelvic organs.

Cancer   Cancer of the cervix, the endometrium or the ovaries may all necessitate hysterectomy.

With most of these conditions, the possible problems with sexual intimacy are obvious. In addition, heavy vaginal bleeding may lead to anaemia, which can further reduce libido. The anxiety and depression associated with a diagnosis of cancer also diminishes sexual desire. Thus the cure of the original condition which led to hysterectomy, can result in an enhanced capacity for love-making subsequently.

THE PHYSIOLOGY OF SEX

There is no absolute physiological reason for impairment of sexual response after a hysterectomy, whether the operation be performed vaginally or through the abdomen. The lubrication of the vagina is unaffected, and though the feeling caused by contraction of the womb during orgasm is of course absent, most women will notice no change. For a minority, however, 'the quality of orgasm is related to the movement of cervix and uterus, and for these women the intensity of the orgasm is thus diminished when these structures are removed.'[3]

Obviously time must be given for the scars to heal in the top of the vagina, but six weeks after the operation a gentle return to sexual relations should be possible in most cases.

For women who have had a hysterectomy involving the removal of their ovaries as well, the situation is rather different. In pre-menopausal women there will be a premature fall in oestrogen which may be related to reduced libido. Hormone replacement therapy, discussed in the previous chapter, is then absolutely essential to prevent heart disease (known to come on early when the ovaries are removed) and osteoporosis (loss of bone density, leading to increased risk of fractures).

PSYCHOLOGICAL FACTORS

Some women may feel more sexually active once any anxiety of becoming pregnant in later life is removed. The operation may also provide an opportunity for raising the subject of already-existing sexual difficulties, which can then be tackled appropriately. Of course, the opposite can happen, and the aftermath of a hysterectomy can be used as an excuse to terminate altogether a previously faltering sex-life.

PROSTATECTOMY

Most men over the age of fifty will get some benign enlargement of the prostate gland situated beneath the bladder and through which the urethra passes. In around 10 per cent of these men constriction of the urethra will occur. This leads to several symptoms, the first of which is usually an increasing need to get up at night to pass water (nocturia).

Other features which may follow include increased frequency of passing water, a poor stream, a sensation of not having emptied the bladder properly, and even acute retention – an inability to pass urine at all. These problems (collectively known as prostatism) lead to an increased risk of urinary infection and to back-pressure on the kidney, which can cause direct renal damage.

Prostatism may necessitate the removal of the prostate gland, as can the much rarer occurrence of a cancer developing in the gland. Though a much more extensive operation may be needed for prostate cancers, the usual method of performing a routine prostatectomy is via the urethra – the transurethral prostatectomy (TURP for short). This involves removing the gland, much like coring out an apple, by passing an instrument down through the length of the penis.

Erectile problems caused by this operation are not common (around 5 per cent), although, as with hysterectomy, the operation may focus attention on previously existing sexual difficulties and form a convenient excuse for ending sexual activity.

One very common feature, affecting up to 90 per cent of cases after the operation, is retrograde ejaculation, when the semen shoots up into the bladder instead of through the penis. Husband and wife should both be made aware of the probability of this happening after surgery.

If the operation is done for prostate cancer, various drugs which can reduce libido may be given to try and slow down or prevent the spread of the tumour. This side-effect in combination with the psychological effects of surgery in the genital area calls for great understanding and tolerance in the post-operative months.

Recently there have been great advances in new drugs and

other forms of therapy for prostatic enlargement, and the number of prostatectomies performed looks likely to fall.

MASTECTOMY

Breast cancer is the commonest malignancy in women, and its diagnosis has profound effects on intimacy. Mastectomy, the removal of the breast, is still the commonest form of treatment and following the operation many women feel devastated. 'The loss of the breast in mastectomy is a loss to the woman's body image, her views of herself as a woman, and her perception of her attractiveness to others, as well as the threat to her life itself in the malignant diagnosis associated with it.'[4]

The press furore that followed a leading gynaecologist's tentative suggestion in the *British Medical Journal* that women should consider having normal breasts removed to prevent the risk of cancer[5] suggests that, at least in our Western society, breasts are indeed considered vitally important to both sexual identity and arousal.

Careful counselling of both partners before and after the operation is essential. The Mastectomy Association may be of great value. Much positive affirmation of self-worth in spite of physical deformation must be given. For a time some practical measures may need to be taken, such as the avoidance of coital positions which emphasise the breasts.

LOSS OF A LIMB

The loss of a limb can have devastating consequences, whether through an accident, or through surgery for a disease such as diabetes or poor circulation.

The possible psychological consequences of depression or feeling incomplete ('I'm only half a man', as one of my patients put it), are compounded by the physical difficulties of love-making. Some helpful publications for those affected by such physical handicaps are listed at the end of Chapter 21.

Andrew was a fit and vibrant sixty-year-old before he was involved in a car accident. The smash so badly damaged his right leg that it had to be amputated above the knee. He coped with the initial aftermath of the operation very well, and was fitted with an artificial limb.

One evening after a meal out with his wife and some friends, they were leaving the restaurant when his false leg caught on a projecting floor tile and he fell heavily to the ground. He felt utterly humiliated by the incident. Previously he and his wife had always enjoyed intercourse, especially after evenings out, but that night he could not get an erection at all. He felt stripped of his masculinity in having had to be picked up off the floor by his wife. Sexual intimacy became impossible for months thereafter.

After talking with Andrew, it became clear that his attitude towards his accident was essentially one of total denial. He was quite determined to get back completely to normal. Initially, this attitude was a great asset and he had done exceptionally well with his rehabilitation. The fall, however, had been a stark reminder of the permanence of his disability. It could never be 'business as usual' again. Once he had learned to accept this limitation, his depression lifted – as did his erections!

INCONTINENCE

I believe that incontinence – not sex or even death – tops the list of taboo subjects. Many sex manuals don't even mention it. Yet loss of bladder control, leading to involuntary leakage of urine, is a very common problem. In 1991, the British Association for Continence Care commissioned a MORI survey in which 10 per cent of the nearly 3,000 women questioned said they had leakage of urine. In other studies, over half of women of menopausal age have been reported as suffering urinary incontinence.[6]

Leakage of urine most often occurs when muscular strain puts pressure on the bladder. Coughing, laughing and excitement can all precipitate it. Having a good chuckle while making love during a flu epidemic can thus prove disastrous! Even without the flu, things can be bad enough and incontinence can be a real wet blanket both literally and metaphorically as far as sexual intimacy is concerned.

In spite of this, it is estimated that less than half the total number of women suffering from incontinence ever consult their doctor about it. This may be because of embarrassment, or the mistaken belief that nothing can be done anyway (not to mention the fear of an unsympathetic response from the doctor).

In fact, quite a lot can be done, and a 70 per cent success rate can be achieved overall with appropriate treatment. Your doctor may perform an examination and a few simple tests to exclude causes such as a urine infection. After appropriate investigation, pelvic floor exercises and bladder training regimes may be given by a physiotherapist. Some drugs which improve bladder control may also be prescribed. For those 30 per cent of women whose continence cannot be totally restored, the use of incontinence appliances can do much to reduce the problems of wet underwear and the accompanying smell. Instruction in intermittent self-catheterisation may also help to restore self confidence and renew the potential for sexual intimacy.

LOSS OF A PARTNER

Though the grief process has been widely researched and described, there is immense individual variation in reaction to the death of a spouse.

In the bereavement crisis there is an intense longing for the lost partner. For some bereaved people this may manifest itself as an intense sexual longing as well. Yet for others, all thought of drive or need related to sexuality may be totally inhibited; the 'last thing' that is thought of. All desire may be absent and may take a long time to return. For those women whose longing for their husbands is expressed sexually as well as emotionally, the situation may be quite distressing.[7]

Comparatively little is known about the actual sexual response patterns of the bereaved. The social stereotypes of the 'merry widow' or the widower constantly searching for a new partner, may make it difficult for the bereaved to express their sexual feelings honestly.

What is certain is that the bereaved need bodily comfort and contact for self-affirmation just as much and probably more so than others. In our rather physically inexpressive culture, it is not surprising that the bereaved may believe that the yearning to be held in someone's arms can only be fulfilled sexually. Relatives and friends should be aware of such needs for physical touch, and be prepared to help meet them in ways which do not involve the obligation of sexual repayment.

In the adjustment phase following bereavement, a new relationship leading to eventual marriage is not uncommon. For those who cannot or choose not to form such new beginnings, sex manuals often recommend the use of masturbation as 'a natural, lovely way to give oneself a treat.'[8] Many bereaved would find such a suggestion incompatible with the memory of their beloved, but for others it may prove an acceptable outlet. The ambivalence of the 'help' offered by pornography is discussed in detail in Chapter 22, and in my view makes its use inadvisable even for those who have lost their life-partner.

FURTHER READING

Helen Alexander, *Bereavement. A Shared Experience* (Lion, 1992).
Mary Batchelor, *Forty Plus* (Lion, 1988).

CONTACT AGENCIES

Breast Care and Mastectomy Association, 15/19 Britten Street, London SW3 3TZ. Tel 071-867 1103.
CRUSE Bereavement Care, Cruse House, 126 Sheen Road, Richmond, Surrey TW19 1UR. Tel 081-940 4818.
Hysterectomy Support Group, 11 Henryson Road, Brockley, London SE4 1HL.

V

THE ENEMIES OF INTIMACY

18

FATAL ATTRACTION: AFFAIRS AND ADULTERY

What men call gallantry and the gods adultery
Is much more common where the climate's sultry.

Don Juan
Byron

'Adultery, when it becomes known to the spouse, is the most serious threat to the great majority of marriages. It is often the final straw – the symbolic final treason'[1] warned Henry Dicks, one of the world's leading marital therapists.

Many people, though, remain coolly indifferent to the potential dangers of adultery. The journalist, Sue Arnold, is typical in her casual dismissal of the issue. 'It looks as if fidelity is going the same way as chastity – nice idea but not practical in the circumstances ... If you can stand the pace of a double life and still have the energy to iron your husband's shirts, then bully for you.'[2]

Adultery is undoubtedly popular, and in the 1990s is becoming an equal opportunities occupation as well. Following in the wake of every fresh exposé of the latest affair of a politician or pop-star, most women's magazines run one or more generally approving features on the frequency of infidelity. A readership survey by *Cosmopolitan* indicated that 54 per cent of its married women readers had been involved in an extra-marital affair.[3] A more recent systematic survey of some six hundred white middle-class couples showed that 40 per cent of the women and 60 per cent of the men admitted to having one or more affairs.[4]

The hot passion of an affair always needs fuel to make it burn. Though the participants in it often mention the element of surprise which overtakes them – 'We didn't plan it. It just happened' – in fact the seeds of adultery were often sown months before, in a soil of emotions which may have been unconsciously prepared over decades to fertilise their growth.

THE SOIL AND THE SEEDS OF ADULTERY

The Soil

There are certain sociological factors which do not in themselves create affairs but do encourage their development or precipitate them. They constitute the soil of adultery and include:

FAMILY HISTORY AND PARENTING

Dave Carder in his perceptive and helpful book on recovering from extra-marital affairs, *Torn Asunder*, says that affairs 'rarely occur for the first time in the current generation; they have a history behind them'.[5]

Your family background can predispose you to adultery in two principal ways. First, if there has been a history of overt infidelity or divorce, this can serve as a direct pattern for you to follow. 'Millions of children are growing up accepting the marital unfaithfulness of adults as a simple fact of life'.[6] On the other hand, if an affair is hidden, it may exert its effects in more subtle ways.

Stephanie's father had a short-lived affair when her mother, Claire, was pregnant with Stephanie's younger brother. Claire had always been a fairly domineering woman, and when she found out about the affair her control over the family became absolute. She ruled it with a rod of iron from that day onwards.

She was desperately concerned that what had happened to her should never happen to Stephanie. As a result, no man was ever up to scratch in Claire's eyes as a prospective son-in-law. When Stephanie did finally marry against her mother's wishes, her husband, Carl, was subject to Claire's repeated criticism both openly and behind his back.

Claire continued to interfere in her daughter's marriage under the pretext of 'checking that everything was all right.' The resulting strain made Carl feel totally frustrated and inadequate as a husband. Stephanie eventually came to view him in that light too. It was not long before she began to be attracted to another man and fell into the very affair from which her mother had tried to protect her.

SEXUALISED SOCIAL ATMOSPHERE

As we have seen earlier (p. 65), our contemporary throw-away society is not conducive to sustaining long-term relationships. As one of my friends succinctly put it, 'Before my Christian conversion, I thought people were binnable!'

The same social factors that encourage pre-marital sex also fan the flames of extra-marital affairs. Lynn Atwater in her book, *Extra-Marital Connection,* maintains that 'The impact of pre-marital sexual experience stands out as the first factor in the path to extra-marital involvement.'[7] In Annette Lawson's UK study in the early 1980s, adultery was more common among those who had had premarital sexual involvement of any kind than in those who had not. Interestingly, she highlights premarital homosexual involvement as leading to a particularly high risk of subsequent adultery. 'None of those reporting any premarital relationship with someone of their own sex (about 4 per cent) remained faithful after marriage.'[8]

The media have an especially powerful influence in conditioning sexual thought-patterns. Marriage is usually portrayed as dull and boring, while an affair injects a much-needed shot of thrills and excitement. There is no shortage of material glamorising the affair: 'My affair helped me to get in touch with the assertive, independent, achieving and successful part of myself,' claims one happy adulterer; another testifies that 'In an affair there is always time for that special treat. Work and home worries can be forgotten.' Exposure to this slow drip-drip of justification for adultery can eventually weaken your defences and you begin to believe it.

At the same time, increasing business travel and the presence of larger numbers of career women, as well as men, on the move, all offer unparalleled opportunities for adultery to take place with little chance of being found out. A first-name-only affair in a foreign city is likely to go undetected – at least for a while.

VULNERABLE PERIODS
Though an affair can occur at any stage in a marriage – even on your honeymoon, there are certain times which provide a more fertile soil for it than others. I have already referred to periods of geographical separation but there are other danger zones where the separation is psychological.

The birth of a baby can be a highly vulnerable period. If you were already feeling neglected by your wife, the 'competition' presented by a new arrival can be the last link in the chain leading up to an affair (chap. 15).

At the other end of parenting, when the children grow up and leave home (pp. 124–6), affairs can also flourish. As spouses realise that they were giving their all to the children with little time or attention for each other, the temptation to start something with a new partner can be particularly strong.

The Seeds

Into this soil of twisted heritage, sexual desensitisation and vulnerable times, the seeds of adultery can take root and grow. Most affairs start innocently in the staff-room rather than the bedroom, and since they take a while to develop, they can be pre-empted if the danger is spotted in time and appropriate help is available.

A common seed is that of *distancing* in your marriage relationship. If you fail to communicate with each other, spending too much time on independent tasks and not sharing your hearts together, then it becomes easier for both of you to confide your deepest emotions in someone else. Many affairs really do start with the old cliché, 'My husband/wife doesn't understand me'. Sometimes an affair may be deliberately started in order to get an unresponsive spouse to hear your distress driven by their emotional deafness.

Unresolved conflict is another seed. As we have seen, conflict in marriage is quite normal and can be very positive (pp. 140–3). Anger left simmering, however, can thrust you into an affair in order to punish your spouse. In this situation 'the angry person is not falling in love with a third person; he is falling in anger against his spouse'.[9]

Poor self-image has many aspects to it. Lack of affirmation from your spouse, anxiety about waning attractiveness from ageing or disease, concern about latent homosexuality, failure at work, or depression from other causes can all result in pressure to try and raise a flagging self-esteem by having an affair. It can be particularly flattering to an older man or woman to find that they still attract a younger mate.

There may be no more sophisticated seed involved than sheer *boredom* (p. 169) and the associated desire to escape from sexual monotony. The thrill of a fresh chase often seems more exciting than the safe but predictable certainty of an existing catch.

DANGEROUS LIAISONS?

In the present moral climate, it is necessary to ask what is so harmful about adultery anyway? Though acclamation of adultery, at least in certain circumstances is increasingly common, this is still pretty much a minority view. In a recent survey in *Elle* magazine, only 2 per cent of respondents thought affairs were harmless.[10] Those who advocate open marriage will often baulk at the idea of open adultery, especially when it touches them personally. 'Even people of either sex, who have secretly been having outside liaisons, react with deep shock, anger and jealousy to the discovery that their partner has been doing the same.'[11]

This should not surprise us. As John White forcefully argues in his devastating critique of the 'New Adulterers',

if we decide, for instance, that marital partners in open marriages should share their sexuality with other friends, we make new kinds of demands on them ... We have thus added new commandments in the teeth of terrible ancient temptations: Thou shalt not be jealous. Thou shalt not be possessive of thy wife or husband. Thou shalt always be understanding of the wonderful maturing process that thy husband is undergoing in his fascination with thy neighbour Mary. For we are caught, whether we choose to ignore it or not, in a moral universe.[12]

Although the sexual pleasure of adulterous intercourse may indeed be intensely sweet, its consequences are ultimately bitter. This is because adultery is almost always a betrayal of trust, and this inevitably inflicts hurt. It also wounds for the same reason that premarital sex wounds – it is a life-uniting sexual act without the actual life-union which that very act signifies. The spouse is obviously open to hurt by this betrayal, but the 'other woman or man' is nearly always a victim too. As Reibstein and Richards point out in their book *Sexual Arrangements: Marriage and Affairs,* people rarely leave their established partners for the person with whom they commit adultery, and if the adulterous couple do marry the likelihood is that one or other of them will start another affair.[13]

The spread of AIDS is another danger of an affair. I would suggest that no wife or husband should return to a sexual relationship with their adulterous spouse until the presence of HIV or other sexually transmitted diseases has been excluded. This may sound harsh, but then AIDS is not exactly noted for its mercy either.

OUT IN THE OPEN?

If you are currently having or have had a secret affair, the question inevitably arises at some point as to whether you should tell your spouse.

The answer really depends on what you want to happen to your marriage. If the intention of the affair was to end your marriage or to punish your spouse, then you will tell them regardless – boastfully, cruelly and as vindictively as you possibly can. You would not heed my advice anyway.

If, however, you genuinely want the best possibility of recovery, and a more meaningful marriage in the future, then I would generally advise a policy of coming clean. Those who advise keeping quiet often betray the weakness of this position in their very own writings. 'Discretion, secrecy, lying and subterfuge then are the prices one has to pay to keep an affair from one's spouse and for many *these outweigh* the advantages of the affair itself. (My italics.)[14]

This is just the problem with deception. What begins as your 'little secret,' ends up as a big millstone around your neck. The sting of the affair is that at the very time you seem to have it most under control, something always crops up to prove that it controls you. The poor concentration at work, the anxiety about explaining those items on your credit-card statement, the momentary fear every time your spouse gets to the telephone first – these and a thousand other terrors like them exact a heavy toll. You feel cut up about it because you *are* cut up. Your life is divided between two lovers.

A marriage betrayed by deception will never be rebuilt while deception remains. It will not be easy to disclose the affair, though, and excuses will come flooding in. 'They won't be able to take it'. 'Their career will be ruined'. 'I won't be able to handle their reaction'. These objections need to be squarely faced and examined, but in the vast majority of cases the adverse consequences of continuing deceit far exceed the pain of revelation.

It is often helpful to write down a worse-case versus a best-case scenario of the possible consequences of disclosure before making a final decision to come clean. You will then be prepared for all eventualities. In my view it is only when there is a history of repeated domestic violence that silence may well be the best option. Adultery does sometimes lead to murder by the betrayed spouse (pp. 265–6).

THE AFTERMATH OF REVELATION

Disclosure or the discovery of an affair results in overwhelming emotional turmoil for both spouses. If the revelation comes as a total surprise to the betrayed spouse, he or she will usually experience deep hurt, bewilderment and shock. Once the affair has been confessed, it is not uncommon for the spouse to know immediately at that point who the other woman or man is without being told, even if totally unsuspecting previously.

Often, of course, the spouse has already sensed that something has been going on. In these circumstances, disclosure may bring a sense of relief at first that the nightmare of wondering is over. One patient expressed it like this, 'It wasn't being the last to know that made it so painful, it was being the first to know and having to listen to all his lies.'

Once the initial feeling of numbness or relief has gone, intense anger immediately ensues. It is important that this anger is ventilated. Couples never recover if their anger is not fully expressed. Suppressed rage will only surface again later, and the betrayed spouse needs to let the adulterer know how great is the hurt. If there is no rage at the betrayal, this may indicate to the adulterer that there was little of value in the marriage to betray in the first place.

As the anger subsides, the betrayed spouse often feels a strong need to ask lots of questions about the details of the affair. If the marriage is to survive, then everything should be told at the level the spouse wants to hear it. Though the rehearsal of every promiscuous detail is inappropriate and may produce graphic images that haunt the injured party for years, this is no time for further deception either. The whole truth is likely to be known eventually anyway, and holding back information now will merely spawn yet more suspicion, and erect further barriers to the redevelopment of trust in the marriage relationship.

Jealousy is another natural response of the betrayed spouse. This can be especially intense if the third party involved was a close friend. Such jealousy is aroused by the emotional involvement of the adulterer as much as the sexual.

The disclosure of an affair is in many ways like a bereavement. Indeed it is a bereavement. The previous marital relationship is dead and though a new one can be rebuilt, the loss of the old must be mourned if recovery is to be complete. All the classical features of a grief reaction may surface – shock, denial, guilt, depression as well as the anger already considered. It may take a long time before these feelings subside. Usually the total process of recovery is about the same duration as the precipitating affair.

It can be of immense help if the betrayed spouse realises that he or she holds the reins at this stage, assuming that the adulterer does want the marriage to continue. The spouse must come to a position of free choice, knowing that survival is not dependent on taking the adulterer back again. It is only from such a position of freedom that any real trust can ever be re-established.

The adulterer, as well as the spouse will experience severe mood swings following disclosure. There will be grief both for the loss of the lover, and for the pain inflicted upon the spouse. Depression commonly sets in and is compounded by the loss of power in the marriage relationship. In addition, there is often a deep sense of shame at the exposure of deep-seated needs which drove the affair.

As I work with couples I am struck by the utter childishness of infidelities. I say that not in a denigratory way but in a literal sense: you get a feeling that those unmet childhood needs are carried forward so that they are fully present in adulthood. The private world of the affair that the infidel and partner create for themselves is much the same world of the narcissistic infant, combined with adolescent sexual attraction.[15]

Adultery always stems from an intimacy deficit in the marriage at some point. Even if the marriage survives this affair, it will be vulnerable to a repeat performance of infidelity if the deficit is not remedied. It is therefore essential that both partners understand the message of the affair.

THE MESSAGE OF THE AFFAIR

In the film *Fatal Attraction,* Alex, the other woman, has a fascinating conversation over breakfast with her married lover.

'I was wondering why is it that all the interesting guys are married?'
'Well, maybe that's why you find them interesting – the fact that you can't have them.'

After Alex has questioned him about his marriage, she goes in for the kill.

'Sounds good,' she says.
'Yeah. I'm lucky,' he replies.
'So what are you doing here?'
'Boy, you know how to ask 'em!' he gasps.

She certainly does, and there has to be an answer, too. There is always a message in the affair – something that the adulterer needs to tell about themselves and their marriage. The spouse is often clueless as to what the message might be, and that is part of the problem. The unfaithful partner, on the other hand, is often aware of the message from the very beginning.

One of my patients came to see me specifically for a medical check-up prior to embarking on an affair that weekend. 'I've told my wife I'm going on a fishing trip,' he smiled.

'Aren't you concerned that your wife might find out?' I ventured.

'She's so wrapped up in her work she's paid no attention to what I'm doing for the past twenty years,' he replied. 'There's no reason to think she'll pay any more attention now!'

He was right. Twenty years of the unheeded message, 'You are neglecting me' had led up to that weekend affair. Other common messages include, 'I am/You are changing and we seem to be growing apart'; 'I have a secret that I have never shared with you'; 'I have always found — about you very difficult and yet you've never done anything about it'; 'I miss — that always used to make me feel good when I lived with my parents.'

Unearthing the hidden message is important because it provides both spouses with a sense of hope. The adulterer needs to feel intimately understood by someone other than the third party, otherwise he or she will run to seek refuge once more when the going gets tough again. The spouse needs to understand what it was the adulterer was getting from the affair that was absent from the marriage. Only then can she or he begin to provide it within the marital relationship. Without such a definitive change, the fear of another affair will always remain.

REBUILDING FROM THE RUINS

Few couples will be able to cope with the aftermath of adultery without outside help, and a book such as this can never be a substitute for an experienced counsellor. There are certain principles, however, which will contribute towards a complete and permanent recovery.

● Both Partners Must 'Own The Affair'

I have deliberately refrained in this chapter from referring to the betrayed spouse as the 'innocent partner', because I don't believe there ever is a totally innocent partner. It may take two to tango, but it takes three to precipitate adultery. Both husband and wife must own their parts in contributing to the affair.

Resistance of the betrayed spouse to this idea often complicates the process of uncovering the message of the affair. While the message is hidden, the spouse need not face up to her or his contribution to the affair. Men are often particularly resistant to facing up to their own responsibility in an affair, even when the husband is the partner who has been unfaithful. 'Men are more apt to blame the partner and try and protect their own self-esteem, while women are more likely to blame themselves and save the relationship.'[16]

But it is only when both spouses acknowledge their parts in the cause that they can play an active part in the recovery process. If the work of recovery is only one-sided, it is unlikely to succeed in building a stronger marriage.

● Don't Bury The Pain Alive

Even in our permissive society, 'the notion of fault dies hard'[17] when it comes to adultery. The relish with which the press so self-righteously pounce on adulterous vicars and evangelists bears witness to this in its own perverse way.

Both the disapproval of society and the desire to minimise the pain of exploration may tempt a couple to bury the affair alive. 'Let's just forget it' can be an attractive escape route, particularly for individuals who have always had difficulty in expressing anger. Unresolved, suppressed anger is, however, a common factor which drives affairs in the first place. More of the same will only reinforce to the adulterer that the message has not been heard and understood. The rage and hurt of both betrayer and betrayed need to be appropriately and fully expressed.

● Forgiveness Is A Process

Forgiveness is essential to healing the wounds of adultery, but exercising a true and deep forgiveness in such circumstances is often a far from straightforward business. 'Just as trust is the forerunner of betrayal, forgiveness can be its sequel. But how hard this is. The problem of forgiveness, or the paradox of it, is that one is not really forgiving if one can easily forgive.'[18]

Forgiveness can only be real if you know what it is you are forgiving. An instant forgiveness, which has not emerged from the painful process of expressing anger and working through the grief, is very likely to be denial masquerading as forgiveness.

Such short-cut 'forgiveness' can be very appealing. It wins the admiration of relatives and friends who feel that you are such a marvellous person to have coped so well. It boosts a strained self-esteem by encouraging the feeling, 'Well, at least I haven't done anything wrong.'

However, such a healing is only skin deep, and does nothing to rebuild intimacy and trust with your spouse. A superficial forgiveness denies your true feelings and exempts you from vulnerability. There is no room for an honest exploration together of what went wrong. Consequently you can never trust your spouse again. Your personal affirmation and nurture will still come from outside the marital relationship, and both of you will be vulnerable to further affairs in the future. A deep forgiveness can only result from the work of developing mutual intimacy once more.

● Restructuring Intimacy Takes Time

There are no instant cures, and learning to trust again is a roller-coaster ride for months or even years. The betrayer shouldn't expect immediate reacceptance, and the betrayed can't expect cast-iron guarantees that it won't happen again.

If you are both willing to start afresh, then in addition to exploring the message of the affair and what went wrong with your marriage, it is also worth reviewing what was right with it. Talk about what attracted you to each other in the first place. Look through old photos and videos together, and perhaps go back to some of those places that have special meaning for you both. The mental flashbacks of the illicit relationship will fade more quickly if you reinvest in happy memories of each other.

It is vital that you also share with each other your true selves. Part of the lure of adultery is that it allows the expression of things long repressed in the marriage. She will wear clothes for her lover that she'd never have thought of enticing her husband with. He will take his lover to places his wife has never been to, and buy her presents every week when his wife is lucky if she even gets one on her birthday. Mutual transparency about your needs to be met and your resources to meet your spouse's needs is the most sure protection against adultery that you can get.

Of course such restoration is not guaranteed. For some couples the message of the affair is that the adulterer has had enough of the marriage and wants to get out. The third party is sometimes only a 'transitional person' – a convenient stooge who is just used to get the adulterer out of an unhappy marriage with a convenient excuse, and at the same time to inflict punishment on a spouse who has been resented for years. One of the greatest ironies of infidelity in such circumstances is 'the fidelity which both betrayed and betrayer keep, after the event, to its bitterness'.[19]

Even without such compounding malice, an affair obviously constitutes a severe blow to any marriage from which it may not recover. It is frequently the last phase before separation and divorce, which will be examined in the next chapter.

FURTHER READING

James Dobson, *Love Must Be Tough* (Kingsway, 1987).

Rob Parsons, *Loving Against The Odds* (Hodder & Stoughton, 1993).

INTIMACY UNRAVELLED: SEPARATION AND DIVORCE

Since there's no help, come let us kiss and part,
Nay, I have done: you get no more of me,

Michael Drayton.
1563–1631

The decision to part company usually comes as the culmination of months and sometimes years of increasing unhappiness. Love leaches out slowly from most marriages, rather than disappearing dramatically like a conjurer's assistant from a cabinet. This gradual erosion of intimacy may go completely unnoticed by one partner. 'There are really two marriages – his and hers – inside every marital union and they do not always coincide.'[1] Thus one partner may be completely oblivious to what is all too obvious to the other. In general, husbands tend to be the less sensitive spouse in detecting the signs of terminal decline in the marriage, and the final curtain may therefore come as a totally unexpected shock to them.

Alan sounded relatively calm when he rang me during evening surgery to ask if I could leave out another prescription for his insulin. Since he had been issued a fresh supply only the week before, I enquired what had happened to it. Then he broke down totally. Choking back the tears, he told me how he had arrived home to find not only his wife and two children gone, but the house completely cleared of every last stick of furniture and fittings, including the fridge where he kept his insulin. That nightmare situation was bad enough in itself, but the thing he found most unbearable in the months that followed, was the realisation that his wife, Drena, had obviously been planning her escape for a long time, yet he had not suspected anything was wrong at all.

THE EXTENT OF THE NIGHTMARE

Alan and Drena are just two of the many casualties that make the UK's divorce rate the highest in Western Europe. One in three first-time marriages in Britain will end in divorce. In parts of the United States now this figure is one in two. In 1990 there were 153,000 divorces in England and Wales, more than double the number (74,000) in 1971 when the Divorce Reform Act became law. Marriages ending in divorce last, on average, just under ten years, but nearly a quarter collapse in under five years.

The vast majority of divorcing couples have children, so each year around 150,000 children under the age of sixteen witness their parents' marriage break-up. As a consequence, one in four children by the age of sixteen will not be living with both parents. A staggering 43 per cent of parents (mainly fathers) who do not have custody, will never see their children again. This means that around 750,000 British children never see their father.

THE BEGINNING OF THE END

Let us look at some of the reasons why so many marriages end up on the rocks.

A FALSE START
Some marriages collapse because they were built on poor foundations from the very beginning. We considered the whole subject of adverse motivations for marriage in Chapter 9. Those who see marriage as an escape from some difficulty or problem usually find that they have jumped out of the frying pan into the fire. As we saw earlier, (pp. 118–19) the emotional contraband

of unresolved childhood conflicts can be carried over into the marriage and cause havoc. Many couples who divorce only after many years of marriage, can nevertheless trace the problems leading up to parting right back to the earliest days of married life.

DISILLUSIONMENT AND DRIFTING

After the novelty of initial attraction wears off, many couples go through a stage of disillusionment before a deeper, committed love can eventually develop. Sadly, some spouses see this phase as a time to bale out of the marriage and look for someone else who appears to match up better to their ideals.

'Till death us do part' is a long time, and character and aspirations do alter over the years. Some spouses cannot adjust to the changes occurring in their mate, and the couple drifts apart. Younger marriages are particularly vulnerable in this respect as we have seen. Wives are much more acute in their ability to detect such drifting apart in the marriage. In Thornes and Collard's study for example, 80 per cent of the divorced women said their marriage problems started well before their fifth wedding anniversary, whereas only 59 per cent of their divorced husbands had acknowledged any problems by that stage.[2]

OTHER PEOPLE

Interference from outside the marriage, particularly from in-laws, can lead to severe marital tensions culminating in divorce. Falling in love with another man or woman is another common breaking-point, although, as we saw in the last chapter, affairs usually occur because of pre-existing problems with marital intimacy. A quarter of the divorces granted to wives in 1990 were on the grounds of the husband's adultery.

THE PAINS OF PARTING

Divorce is one of the most stressful of all life-events. Though the deserted partner is often tempted to fantasise about the wonderful time the other must be having, the reality is usually brutally different. Divorce involves so many losses for both partners that some mutual pain is inevitable. Let us now look at some of these areas of loss.

● Emotional

The emotional consequences of divorce follow the same pattern as an acute grief reaction. However, as one divorcee expressed it, 'It's not so much like a bereavement – more like a living death.'

This deathlike quality results from the multiplicity of emotional losses involved, and is much worse when the marriage has lasted for a long time. Not only has your actual partner gone, but also the familiar routines and rituals which give structure to daily life. 'In the marital conversation the world is not only built, but it is also kept in a state of repair and ongoingly furnished.'[3]

The continuous presence of your spouse over time enables you to link past, present and future into a meaningful frame of reference. As Nicky Hart indicates, a married couple 'share together many of life's more intimate occasions. They maintain their joint living arrangements through a pooling of resources and, besides eating and sleeping together, they are also likely to be each other's sole confessor, a confidante to soothe away the anxieties and disappointments inherent in everyday life.'[4] After divorce, the unravelling of such intimacy can bring an unbearable sense of loneliness, which society does little to ease.

● Social

Divorce is an unplanned change for which there are few chances to make any preparation, and society offers minimal support for those having to go through it.

In marriage, your spouse sees what Gorman[5] refers to as the 'backstage' of your life. The marital relationship, at its best, functions as a safe haven, where you can be yourself, and practice social skills with a generally sympathetic audience. 'Is my hair all right, darling?' and 'Do you think this sounds better?' are everyday examples of the sort of social soundings that spouses take from each other. Divorce destroys the opportunities for this kind of practice run, and social skills may consequently be considerably impaired.

Furthermore, most social networks only know how to cope with couples, not with divorcees. This is brilliantly illustrated by an incident in the popular television series, *Ever Decreasing Circles*. In one episode, Penelope Wilton turns to her screen husband, Martin (played by Richard Briers) and says, 'Let's have a dinner party'. 'Oh good, yes,' he replies, 'I'll ring Laurence-and-Virginia and Howard-and-Hilda'.

Social encounters may be embarrassing and awkward for years, as friends and family alike try to delete Howard-and-Hilda from their collective consciousness and substitute Howard-and-Henrietta instead. The decision to separate or divorce will then seldom be welcomed by others. This is partly because of the widespread stigma associated with divorce, described by one divorcee as a 'kind of moral shudder'.[6] This shudder is expressed in a variety of ways, from the widespread assumption among employers that divorcees are less reliable workers to the lower credit rating customarily given to the divorced by credit-brokers.

Family ties are obviously strained by divorce. Relatives usually take sides, and family feuds soon develop, adding to isolation of the individual divorcees. The general disapproval of others, however, also relates to the fact that people find that all outside change is invariably stressful to some degree, and they will find their own social landscape altered by a couple's decision to split up.

Overall, men experience much greater difficulty than women in overcoming this social isolation of divorce. Wives are usually the driving force in maintaining outside friendships in the marriage – remembering birthdays, organising parties, and so on. When she is no longer there, social links are severed. The precipitous drop in Christmas cards received by ex-husbands speaks for itself.

If the husband has to leave the marital home, he is generally left with fewer resources to sustain social ties than a wife in the same situation. How many divorced men keep the family address book, for example? As women are generally given custody of children, there is some incentive for them to keep up links with their former in-laws in their role as grandparents. The ex-husband on the other hand has little reason to continue to see his ex-wife's family socially.

The sexual stereotypes of the divorced in society present ex-wives and ex-husbands with different problems. While divorced women are often seen as fair game for seduction, divorced men are often seen by other men and women as a potential threat to their own marriages. Either reaction can cause great embarrassment, and generate further icy gusts in the already frozen wastelands of the divorcee's social life.

● Medical

The divorced and separated are much more prone to ill-health than their married counterparts. The emotional strain of divorce quite naturally leads to a great deal of psychological problems. Suicide and alcohol abuse may be precipitated. Anxiety states, panic disorders and depression are frequent causes of visits to the doctor during divorce proceedings. These conditions can also result in a wide variety of physical symptoms such as headaches, sweating, giddiness, diarrhoea, nausea and abdominal pain.

But it is not just in the area of mental health that divorce takes its toll. There is a substantial body of well-conducted research[7] which links divorce with both a greater incidence of many diseases and higher death rates from them. These include coronary heart disease, which is the major killer among Western diseases. The higher incidence of such heart disease among divorcees is not simply due to the fact that divorcees smoke more. In fact as Dominian comments, 'It is intriguing to note that being divorced and a non-smoker is only slightly less dangerous than smoking a packet or more a day and staying married![8]

● Financial

Divorce consumes enormous amounts of money. Relate estimated that in 1987–8 divorce in Britain cost the nation £1.3 billion[9] – a staggering £3.6 million a day in legal proceedings, local authority costs, social security benefits, NHS costs, statutory sick pay, and days lost from work. In 1991–2 legal aid costs alone for divorce proceedings amounted to £192 million.

On an individual level, financial loss for both partners is unavoidable for the simple reason that two households are more expensive to maintain than one. Wives are likely to be more affected than husbands ultimately. This is because men are still the main income earners in most households and may default on maintenance payments. Furthermore, custody of children is usually given to the wife and this increases her financial commitments while restricting her ability to earn. Some 60 per cent of women with children will draw income support from the state at some stage following divorce.

COPING WITH DIVORCE

Hurt, rage and bitterness will play their part in any unravelling of intimacy; 'only the truly indifferent will be able to part company amicably'.[10] But there are certain principles that can help to try and salvage some useful remains from the wreck of a marriage.

LEARN FROM THE PAST

There is a lot of truth in the saying that 'Those who do not learn from the mistakes of history are doomed to repeat them.' You should look at your relationship closely to try and indentify precisely what the problems were that led to your parting company. If these flaws remain undetected, they may well fracture subsequent relationships in exactly the same way. Pay particular attention to:

● **The things that drew you together at the very start of your relationship**

Kathy was an only child in a very loving, caring family with a strong emphasis on traditional family values. There was no shortage of boys who buzzed keenly around her at school, but she soon learned that most of them were only after one thing.

Sam was different, however. A soft and gentle boy from a very similar background to her own, he reminded Kathy very much of her father.

Sam and Kathy started going out together, and she liked the security he offered her – just like her Dad. Eventually they married when Kathy was just nineteen. Things went well at first but, within two years, Kathy found herself becoming increasingly frustrated with Sam. His steady, placid disposition that had once seemed so rocklike and reliable, now seemed bricklike and boring – just like her Dad had become.

Kathy realised too late that she had been attracted to Sam because she related to him well in a daughter-father role. As she had begun to develop her independence from her own father, however, so she began to distance herself from her husband as well. Kathy, the woman, was not the same kind of person as Kathy the girl and, try as he might, Sam simply could not transform into the new role now demanded of him. Kathy left him within six months and divorce soon followed. She has since happily remarried and now has two children.

● Repeated patterns of relating which proved destructive

Marital therapists categorise various pathological patterns of relationship between partners. These are often given literary names such as the 'Doll's House' marriage or the 'Babes in the Wood' marriage. Sarah Litvinoff in *The Relate Guide to Starting Again*[11] helpfully discusses these patterns in much more practical terms. She examines the patterns of rescuer and rescued, mutual selfishness, illusory unity, idol and worshipper, martyrdom, and superficiality. All of these are common barriers to intimacy which will recur if not identified.

In looking at where the relationship went wrong, try and focus on the part *you* played in the process. After all you, not your ex-spouse, are the one who has to rebuild your future. Fixing attention on his or her faults only produces blame, fixing on yours can produce hope for change.

AVOID LOVE ON THE REBOUND

When you are hurting it is natural to seek immediate comfort. Divorce leaves you very vulnerable, and it can be very tempting to fall into the first pair of arms that open to welcome you. Multiple short-lived sexual liaisons often occur at this time, but entering into a new intimate relationship soon after a separation presents two equal and opposite dangers.

The first is that you will get less than the best, especially if your new romance starts on the basis that any new relationship is better than none. The second danger is that you will give less than your best if you have not fully worked through the emotions left simmering from your divorce. This takes at least a year for most divorcees, and two years or more is not at all unusual.

Second marriages are even more likely to end in divorce than first-time marriages, so great care should be taken before making this move. In the aftermath of divorce, time is best given to concentrating on self-development, and building a confidence and happiness which is not dependent on an immediate second romance. Then, if a subsequent intimate relationship should lead to remarriage, it will stand a much greater chance of success.

DON'T BE MALICIOUS

No one can predict how they will react to divorce until they have to go through it. We all behave unpredictably under pressure. 'Even now when I look back I can scarcely believe that I could have done some of the things that I did. I can actually remember crawling through a hedge at three o'clock in the morning with a pair of field glasses to spy on her. Can you imagine it! ... I find myself acting like a lunatic.'[12]

When you are in the throes of divorce, it is easy to behave badly not out of any intentional vindictiveness but because of totally overwhelming emotions which are difficult to handle. Nevertheless there are spouses who feed their bitterness as diligently as a snake-charmer cares for his cobras. I have known, for example, a husband who took his wife on holiday, and then abandoned her in a single room at one hotel, having booked himself in at another with his lover. I have known a wife falsely accuse her husband of sexually abusing their grandson in order to try and punish him, and blacken his reputation as much as possible during divorce proceedings.

I understand the depths of passion and hatred that provoke both these and the many other acts of pure malice that I all-too-frequently encounter in my clinical practice, but I also see the effect they have upon the perpetrator. Sure, such acts often do maim the person they were intended to hurt, but it is the instigator of malice who is eaten away by their hatred as if it were a cancer. Bitterness reaps its own reward eventually. Don't succumb to it.

So far I have focused on the effects of divorce on the divorcing couple themselves. If children are involved the situation is yet more emotionally fraught and tense.

CHILDREN AND DIVORCE

Around two-thirds of divorces in Britain are between couples with children under sixteen, and a third of the 150,000 or so children involved each year are under five. Though parents may choose to divorce each other, children always have this crisis forced upon them. There may well be excellent reasons for getting divorced, but don't fool yourself that 'It's best for the kids' is one of them. It never is.

Judith Wallerstein and Joan Kelly showed in their famous study[13] in the late 1970s, that most children would have preferred their parents to have stayed together, no matter how conflictual their relationship. Subsequent research has confirmed this finding.[14] Though some children do indeed adapt to their parents' break-up with remarkable courage and fortitude, the vast majority are badly traumatised emotionally and are much more likely to encounter serious problems than their peers from intact families.

On the whole, the children of divorced couples do less well at school and tend to be more aggressive and disobedient. Later on there is an increased chance of violence and other forms of delinquent behaviour including drug abuse. Let us look at these problems in greater detail.

THE EMOTIONAL FALLOUT

No two children will react to divorce in exactly the same way, but there are nevertheless some commonly recognised patterns in different age groups.

Pre-School Age   Fear and bewilderment are the hallmarks of the reaction at this age. Youngsters up to three years old have a limited understanding of what is going on, and react by crying fretfully and clinging to one or other parent. They may also suffer disturbed sleep and throw tantrums more frequently.

Slightly older children are also more tearful and may become overtly aggressive. They are usually highly anxious and insecure as they become aware that something is wrong. They can easily misinterpret situations and if, for example, daddy's sudden departure coincides with the child's being particularly naughty, they may blame themselves for having driven daddy away. There is, however, considerable debate about the frequency of such misinterpretations. Frightening fantasies of the fate of the missing parent can also occur. Regression of speech and toilet training and disrupted sleep are also frequent disturbances.

Six- to Eight-Year-Olds   Sadness and longing characterise their reactions. Children of this age can be very moody and withdrawn. They will fantasise wistfully about the possibility of the absent parent's returning home. Older children may actually go so far as to devise schemes to try and reunite the parents. They may, for instance, pretend to be ill in the hope that the missing parent will visit them.

At the same time there is often anxiety that the remaining parent may also disappear, and there will be no one left to look after them. A desperate need to please may become such a fixation that they are afraid to ask questions about the situation. At the same time they may feel very angry at what has happened, but cannot express their rage for fear of driving the custodial parent away.

Nine- to Twelve-Year-Olds   This group respond with more overt anger and express deep loyalties. They can understand the seriousness of the situation but lack the emotional maturity to handle it. They often feel compelled to take sides in order to resolve their confusion. One parent may be fiercely blamed for having broken up the family. Alternatively, this anger may be displaced on to siblings or find expression in lying, violent outbursts or running away from home.

Teenagers Withdrawal and anguish often form the key motifs in their response. They tend to ease their pain by throwing themselves into hobbies, and emotionally investing in other people. Their teachers may notice that they engage in a lot of extra-curricular activities and are reluctant to go home at the end of the day. The fantasy world of videos or computer games may provide another avenue of escape. Alternatively, intense relationships with boyfriends or girlfriends are pursued eagerly in an attempt to find security.

In the long term, it seems that children under five at the time of their parents' divorce are most likely to suffer the worst effects. The reasons for this are far from clear. It may be that children of this age are more vulnerable because they have less understanding of what is happening to them at the time. Alternatively, since divorce, as we have seen, is a cause of economic and social loss, it is the younger children who have to live through these consequences for a longer period of time. There is certainly some research data suggesting that the standard of living achieved in adult life may be directly reduced as a result of parental divorce in childhood.[15]

Having considered all these problems, it is important to emphasise that divorce does not automatically mean that your children will become poor, delinquent or psychological wrecks. Every case is different, and many children prove remarkably resilient and grow up without any of the aforementioned catastrophes. As divorce lawyer Ken Crispin wisely points out in this context, 'Children are not little computers whose future is dependent upon parental programming. They ultimately must decide for themselves. This is true for all children whether their parents are divorced or not.'[16]

Even so, there remain some key areas where experience and research have clearly shown that divorcing parents can either make life easier or much harder for their children, depending on how the divorce is handled.

HEALING THE HOLOCAUST
Parenting after divorce is difficult for both the single parent with custody, and the parent who has left or been driven out. What steps should be taken by divorcing parents to minimise their children's pain?

● **Tell The Children**

Many divorcing couples try to keep their children in the dark about what is happening, believing that the less said the better. This is not so, however.

Most children are pretty perceptive and there comes a time when they are unlikely to believe that there is nothing wrong any more. Unwarranted dismissal of their concern may provoke wild speculation and even more anxiety in the child than if they knew the truth. Besides, truth is an essential component of any intimate relationship. 'When your parents have parted, and your life is shifting, you desperately need some solid ground. The truth is solid. When you can trust your parents to tell you the truth you know you have at least one foot on safe ground.'[17]

The truth needs to be told in a way that your children can understand. It should also be couched in language that reduces their anxieties, rather than put in words which further your own ends. For example, when your ten-year-old son asks why Daddy doesn't live at home any more, it is more helpful to reply, 'Daddy thinks he loves someone else more than Mummy,' than to bite back with, 'The scum has abandoned you for that blonde tart who works in the fish-shop.'

This brings me to my next point.

● **Don't Encourage Hatred**

If you feel bitter and angry about your ex-spouse, it is only natural for you to want those close to you, including your children, to feel the same way, but if you yield to the understandable temptation to give your children instruction in hatred, they may well try out what they have learnt on their teacher one day.

It is better to try and separate in your mind the two roles of ex-spouse and yet continuing parent that your former partner now plays. Your children don't have to hate your ex in order to love you. Though you may no longer need him or her as a spouse, your children continue to need both partners.

● Allow Each Other A Parenting Role

Much of the trauma of divorce upon children results from the disrupted parenting when one parent disappears. Custody is given to the mother in some 90 per cent of cases. Within two years of separation, less than half of fathers have regular access to their children and a third have no contact at all.

Children who maintain contact with both parents after divorce, suffer less emotional disturbance in terms of both its intensity and duration. Hess and Camera's research has suggested that this still applies even when there is continuing conflict between the parents.[18] They further showed that it is the duration, not the frequency of visits to the non-custodial parent that is the most crucial. As a visiting father explains, '... a good landmark for a reasonable relationship is when the parent is able to express their feelings to the child when they are angry about something with the knowledge that they will be together long enough to "make it up." The Saturday parent seldom feels safe enough to do this and may be afraid that their anger might sever the very thin strand which links them to their child.'[19]

● Avoid Early Sexual Liaisons

For some individuals divorce can act like a cork out of the bottle of their libido. Frenetic and transient sexual encounters bubble up effortlessly and spill all over the place. Wallerstein and Kelly[20] reported that the children in their study – especially those between seven and eleven – viewed with dismay the appearance of their mother's multiple lovers in rapid succession. Some of these children reacted with overwhelming jealousy, others became preoccupied with sexual fantasies and soon acquired a veneer of sexual sophistication. 'Sometimes they combined this precocity with a fine disdain for adults who seemed to them to have so little control of their impulses and to be so vulnerable to hurt.'[21]

This in part may provide an explanation as to why children who have experienced a parental divorce are more likely to become involved in sexual relationships at an earlier age than their peers whose parents are together (p. 66).

In order to try and avoid these difficulties, some parents will try and continue their sexual liaisons well away from the children, but this subterfuge is rarely completely successful, and the need for secrecy may foster a resentment against the child who becomes increasingly viewed as an impediment to mother's happiness rather than a source of it.

A succession of lovers will also have obvious implications, tending towards denial of access to the other parent. The fear of the children's spilling the beans can lead to access being unreasonably blocked. When, however, parents can summon the will to work together to ensure their children enjoy a continuing relationship with both of them, the benefits for the children are incalculable.

ENDGAME

We have seen that the emotional, social, medical and financial costs of divorce are likely to be high for any divorcing couple. In addition, for those couples with children the sad effects of divorce may reverberate on through the next generation. Having duly considered all of this, however, we must recognise that marriages do take place which should never have been embarked upon to start with, and initially appropriate unions can irretrievably break down later on. Not every marriage on the critical list can be saved by intensive care, and merely to keep trying indefinitely may be no more effective than ventilating a corpse. Even then there are precedents for resurrection, of course, but they are extremely rare!

If every possible avenue of help has been tried, yet without success, there is little point in endlessly perpetuating an intractably destructive pattern of marital relationship. Though divorce always entails a measure of failure, it can actually be a courageous decision in some circumstances, particularly in the face of repeated domestic violence. We will consider this further in the next chapter.

FURTHER READING

Helen Garlick, *Which Guide To Divorce* (Hodder & Stoughton, 1992).

Caroline Nystrom, *Mike's Lonely Summer: A Child's Guide Through Divorce* (Lion).

CONTACT ORGANISATIONS

National Council for One-Parent Families, 255 Kentish Town Road, London NW5 2LX. Tel 071-267 1361.

National Family Conciliation Council, Shaftesbury Centre, Percy Street, Swindon SW2 2AZ. Tel 0739-514 055.

Relate, Herbert Gray College, Little Church Street, Rugby CV21 3AP. Tel 0788-573241.

SHOUT QUIETLY OR YOU'LL WAKE NEXT DOOR: DOMESTIC VIOLENCE

> The notion that a man's wife is his PROPERTY, in the sense in which a horse is his property ... is the fatal root of incalculable evil and misery.

Frances Power Cobbe (1878)
Wife Torture in England

TROUBLE IN PARADISE

In writing a book that emphasises the pleasures of marital intimacy, I am nevertheless aware that many a marriage does turn out to be a living hell. Close proximity under the same roof provides the ideal environment for domination and envy as much as for partnership and intimacy. Getting close enough for affection also means being near enough to be assaulted.

Such assaults are nearly always committed by men. In one report,[1] 95 per cent of all incidents of battering of a spouse were committed by the husband. In those few cases where wives did resort to violence it was almost always in self-defence. Thus domestic violence is primarily a problem of violent husbands (though a recent study[2] has challenged this generally accepted view). I know all too well the heartache and despair such men cause, since part of my work involves caring for the battered wives who take refuge in the Women's Aid centre near my surgery.

Determining the exact incidence of domestic violence is not an easy matter. There is no single central source of information in the UK that can be used to make an estimate. In addition under-reporting is likely to be a major problem in any survey. I well remember seeing a young woman in casualty, who had clearly been beaten up and we suspected her husband had done it. When asked how she had received these terrible injuries, she replied in all earnest, 'The washing machine jumped up and hit me.'

Given this bias towards under-reporting, it is disturbing that in an anonymous survey of 620 women attending a hospital casualty department for any cause, 35 per cent of them reported having been struck by their intimate partner.[3] The myth that domestic violence is a rare and inconsequential occurrence was finally exploded by the pioneering study of Straus et al.[4] They found that one in six couples had engaged in acts of domestic violence within the previous year, and 25 per cent reported them at some point in the marriage.

Such violence affects all social strata. 'Despite a common notion that wife-beating prevails mostly among blue-collar workers, it is no less common among the white-collar classes and the professional elite.'[5] We have certainly had for example a judge's wife stay in our local refuge. The incidence of violence in wealthier homes is more difficult to determine, however, since such abused wives may be able to afford a hotel as a sanctuary rather than fleeing to a Women's Aid centre.

THE VIOLENT HUSBAND

WHAT MAKES MEN ABUSE THEIR WIVES?
No single explanation is likely to account fully for such a common and multi-faceted problem as domestic violence. Several or all of the following factors may combine to precipitate violent outbursts.

● The Violence Within
In his book of this title, the Swiss psychiatrist Paul Tournier contends that we all have an innate tendency towards violence. 'Well brought-up, reasonable, kindly people, gentle as lambs, can suddenly break out into brutal violence, in thought, words or deeds – and it happens more often than you would imagine. The sheep suddenly turns into a wolf.'[6]

This terrifying metamorphosis is usually triggered by a power conflict. Sandra Horley, the director of the Chiswick Family Rescue Centre touches on a central theme when she claims, 'Domestic violence is systematic and purposeful – it is about power and control'.[7] Many men view their marriage as a power-base rather than a partnership, and cannot see any way of exercising power other than through violence. They have no alternative means of expressing themselves. The desire to dominate others is by no means exclusive to men, but it is easier for them, rather than women, to impose it. 'Physical violence is an example of this desire put into motion. It becomes a means of taking another person's life into one's hands, usurping the divine prerogative of judgement and misusing it.'[8] In marriage, as in all other areas of life, the one who tries to play God ultimately becomes more like a demon.

There are many factors that will influence whether or not this potential violence within all of us is triggered in our marriages or not.

● Social Factors

There are two main areas where social factors increase the likelihood of domestic violence. First, since violence is often a response to stress and frustrated ambitions, socially constricting circumstances will predispose to wife-battering. Unemployment, bad housing and poverty have all been identified as contributory factors.

Second, many researchers[9] have suggested that it is also the role expectations of men in Western society that lead to frustration which boils over into domestic violence. Men are seen as the breadwinners, and are expected to be successful, but the means of fulfilling such expectations are not always forthcoming, and the husband's resulting tension and humiliation is taken out on his wife. Harris and Bologh[10] found that even husbands in well-paid jobs with a relatively egalitarian relationship with their wives still found themselves in conflict between the demands of their work and the ideals they or their wives wanted in their marriage. The perceived injustice in this double-bind caused them increasing anger leading to violence.

This enables us to see how the excesses of rampant materialism can redispose to violence every bit as much as the deprivations of poverty. The wife who expects to have everything, and then blames her husband when her dream-home doesn't materialise as quickly as she would like will provoke considerable friction in her husband. The staff at our local Women's Aid Centre say this is a recurring motif; frequently they see what they describe as 'the designer curtain syndrome'. A battered wife will arrive at the refuge having left important documents and everyday essentials like a toothbrush at home, yet tightly clutching her video-recorder in her arms.

● The Dark Side of the Family

There has been an increasing tendency in recent years to explain wife-battering as simply a domestic version of the treatment women have always received in the wider community. 'The family is seen as a microcosm of an unequal society. Domestic violence thus becomes a symptom of the more general demonstration of male violence, a demonstration of the male ethos and the male domination of women.'[11]

It seems beyond question that wife-abuse is much more common in marriages where the husband adopts an autocratic role. The book, *Behind Closed Doors: Violence in the American Family* sent shock waves throughout America when it was published in 1980. Its authors concluded that wife-battering is much commoner in 'homes where power is concentrated in the hands of the husband. The least amount of battering occurs in democratic homes.'[12] Similarly, sociologist Kersti Yllo[13] found that the incidence of wife-battering in symmetrical relationships was only a third of that in marriages where the husband was the dominant partner.

The financial arrangements of a marriage are a good indicator of where the distribution of power is. Husbands often use the control of money as part of a more general attempt to subordinate their wives. Over three-quarters of the battered wives in one study named money as the main problem area.[14] Evason[15] in her 1982 survey found that the abused wife more often had the type of husband who gave her money only as and when he saw fit. Marriages in which husband and wife shared a joint account were much less likely to be violent ones. This study also confirmed that violent husbands were much more likely to see themselves as 'master of the house'. Any attempt on the part of the wife to assert herself was seen as undermining his position, and she was promptly 'put in her place'.

● Psychological Disturbance

Many early studies sought to explain domestic violence on the basis of mental illness in the husbands concerned. Gayford's[16] 1975 study concluded that wife-abusers were pathologically jealous and immature. Leonora Walker lists among the batterer's typical characteristics 'insecurity, a need to keep the environment stable and non-threatening, jealousy and possessiveness.' Harris and Bologh[17] have suggested that these husbands are insecure about their masculinity and beat their wives in order to prove that they are real men.

Abusers then tend to have low self-esteem and be suspicious, envious individuals. In spite of such traits Richard Gelles concludes that the proportion of men who batter 'and suffer from psychological disorders is no greater than the proportion of the population in general with psychological disorders'.[18] Though psychological disturbance may explain some isolated cases, it does little to aid our understanding of the phenomenon of wife-battering as a whole.

● The Demon Drink

Alcohol abuse is widely assumed to have an important part in contributing to domestic violence. Dominian refers to it as 'probably the commonest antecedent of violence'.[19] In fact, the evidence on this is rather more equivocal. Certainly in studies such as Gayford's,[20] around half of the wives surveyed said they were only struck when their husbands were under the influence of drink. Emerson and Russell Dobash,[21] however, found that only a quarter of their sample said their husbands were drunk during assaults. They concluded that drinking in itself was insignificant as a *cause* of domestic violence.

It seems more likely that alcohol abuse is a condition that co-exists with wife-battering but is not a primary cause of it. Gelles suggests that 'Individuals who wish to carry out a violent act become intoxicated in order to carry out the violent act.'[22] In other words, the desire to abuse is already present before the alcohol is consumed.

● The Sins of The Fathers

The concept of inter-generational transmission of violence stems from two main elements. Through witnessing violence in the parental home, children learn that violence is an appropriate way of resolving conflict in their own intimate relationships. If the children themselves are also physically abused, this will contribute to the low sense of self-worth that predisposes to wife-battering. 'It stems from the small child who equates blows with attention and the only affectionate gesture from brutal parents.'[23]

The duty officer at our local refuge is rarely surprised by anything, but even she was astonished when she saw the tiny daughter of a new resident run up to her mother shouting, 'Smack me, Mummy. Smack me.' When my colleague raised her eyebrows questioningly, the mother responded immediately 'That's what we call love in our family. It's the only way to get attention.'

Children brought up in violent homes are severely affected emotionally and behaviourally by what they both witness and experience. They learn quickly to tune in to anger as an emotional response, and are slow to perceive non-violent alternatives. Research such as the carefully designed study by Widom[24] has provided dramatic support for the concept of the inter-generational cycle of domestic violence. Physical abuse as a child led to significantly greater violent behaviour in later life. However such a link is not universal nor an inevitable one.

● The Evil That Men Do

It is far easier to describe the nature of domestic violence than to account for its origins. Black eyes, bruised arms, knocked-out teeth, lacerations, dislocations, fractures – you name it and it happens.

The violence tends to escalate in both frequency and severity over time. If wife-abuse occurs at all, it happens often and the resulting injuries may be very serious. One of our refuge residents was attacked with a brick-hammer by her husband. Sexual abuse, including rape, frequently forms a part of the pattern. Pregnancy is a particularly vulnerable time for any couple (pp. 202–3), and the violent husband is much more likely to attack his wife when she is pregnant. This may result from sexual frustration, or jealousy of the unborn infant.

Leonora Walker[25] has described a cyclical pattern of domestic violence comprising three phases. First is the *'tension-building'* phase in which relatively minor episodes of abuse occur, which the wife learns to avoid by keeping out of his way or blaming herself. She does not allow herself to show her anger towards him. In the *'acute battering'* stage the husband loses all control and the violence escalates to a climax. During this phase the wife will often become overtly angry but is battered nevertheless. Following the severe outburst, comes the phase of *'contrition'*. The abuser belatedly recognises that he has gone too far, and tries to make up. He becomes placid and kind for a while, and attempts to manipulate 'forgiveness' from his wife. The wife convinces herself that all will now be well. 'The traditional notion that two people who love each other will overcome all kinds of odds against them prevails.'[26] Sadly this evanescent fantasy soon evaporates as the cycle of abuse starts all over again.

Though Walker sees this third phase as crucial – the time in which the wife's victimisation is made complete, not all researchers are convinced of its importance or even in some cases its existence. Certainly as the violence accelerates there is less and less likelihood of even a semblance of regret by the husband, though there is often some temporary remorse after early battering episodes.

Acute batterings are much more likely at times of maximal contact between spouses, so evenings and weekends are particularly frequent flashpoints. Ultimately such violence may be fatal. The husband may strike once too often and actually kill his wife, or she may turn and kill him. 'Being a victim of violence does not turn one against violence. On the contrary, it tends to be a powerful pro-violence learning experience.'[27]

'People tend to get murdered at night on a Friday or Saturday'[28] states forensic pathologist, Prof. Michael Green. Since 60 per cent of murders are committed by a close family member, in particular the spouse, it is little wonder that 'looking forward to the weekend' is no consolation to those families locked in the descending spiral of domestic violence.

In spite of the horrific nature of such physical violence, many affected wives and those who work with them say that the effect of 'mental violence' is more difficult to deal with. 'The cuts and bruises heal in months; the psychological damage takes years' one counsellor told me. She cited the case of a woman who had never actually been struck by her husband. However, because he considered her to be pretty poor in her performance in bed, he made her sleep on the floor every night. When she finally summoned up the courage to break free from his tyranny and came to the refuge, she could not believe that she was to have a bed of her own. Her self-esteem was so ravaged that she felt unworthy of such a luxury.

THE BATTERED WIFE

● The Scapegoat: Why Is She Blamed?

As we have seen in the previous section, domestic violence is predominantly a problem of violent husbands. It is therefore one of the saddest indictments of the sexism of psychiatry that, in the literature, women are frequently considered to be responsible for the violence. 'What did you do to provoke him?' is a frequent opening gambit by the profession which causes despair and bewilderment to many a battered wife.

Much of the tendency to blame the wife stems from the enormous influence of Freud, who taught that masochism – sexual pleasuring through suffering, pain or humiliation, formed part of the normal feminine psychology. He described it as 'the preferred state'.[29] The tendency within psychiatry to blame the victim is also shamefully illustrated more recently by Gayford's insensitive and derogatory stereotypes of battered women such as 'Fanny the Flirt' and 'Go-Go Gloria'.[30]

We all tend to feel helpless and vulnerable when faced with meaningless violence. Blaming the victim may be a defence mechanism to make us feel less vulnerable, and to avoid having to ask difficult questions about ourselves. It means that we can ignore the problem and not feel guilty in doing so. We can at the same time avoid being contaminated by contact with the victim. If the battered wife is to blame why should we go out of our way to help her?

The problem is that the myth of masochism just does not stand up to close examination as a satisfactory explanation for wife-abuse. Far from provoking their husbands or 'asking for it', most battered wives simply do not understand what triggers the violence. If they did they would be the first to avoid it.

● The Prisoner – Why Does She Stay?

If masochistic pleasure is not the answer, what is it then that keeps the battered wife from leaving her violent husband?

The staff at our local refuge were unanimous in their answer. 'All the women here really love their man. If they could only stop his violence, they'd go back.' Even in the most violent relationship there are lulls between the storms. During these intervals when the husband does offer some love and affection a 'traumatic bonding'[31] occurs. The wife becomes emotionally attracted to the loving rather than the abusing side of her husband.

Violent men are often master manipulators. They know how to play the game, and will gauge exactly how much pleasure reinforcement is needed in order to keep their wife captive. Walker suggests that by being taken in by this, the wife is 'selling herself for the few moments of phase-three loving', the contrition phase, (p. 265) and hence becomes 'an accomplice to her own battering'.[32] Far from gaining pleasure from brutality then, the pleasure that makes the wife stay is found then in the 'loving' phase of the marriage.

Another reason why women stay in violent relationships is fear. Fear of the unknown if they leave and fear for their own lives or those of their children; 40 per cent of female homicides are perpetrated by the husband, and if the wife threatens to leave him or actually does so, her chances of being murdered ihcrease substantially.

Wives also stay because their resistance is broken down by the husband's 'conjugal terrorism'.[33] The battered wife's existence resembles that of the terrorist's captive. Their husbands often isolate them from friends or outside family members and keep them in a position of total economic dependence.

Other reasons suggested by Vicki Moss[34] for the wife staying in the relationship include the lack of an alternative support network ('the more responsible question to ask then is not "Why does she stay?" but "What in our community is keeping her there?" '[35]), and misplaced religious convictions about keeping the family together at all costs.

● The Victim – What Should She Do?

Abused wives should not just silently submit to their torture. To yield is not a loving act, but a participation in wickedness. There is also some evidence that merely accepting the violence without any resistance, may encourage more violence.[36] However it has been shown in one survey that 'forty-one per cent of married women who were attacked by their husbands or ex-husbands but did not call the police were assaulted again within an average of six months, compared with fifteen per cent of women who alerted police'.[37]

Battered wives need to seek protection and expert help in dealing with their desperate plight. Most police forces have a special unit for helping the victims of domestic violence, and are more than willing to assist. Alternatively, there are networks of Family Rescue Centres where battered women can not only take refuge but obtain expert guidance. Health visitors are another useful channel of information and advice.

It has taken a long time for the problem of wife abuse to be recognised and for appropriate help to be organised. In our increasingly violent society, I wonder if similar centres will be needed for husbands threatened with violence also? One of our Women's Aid Centre staff told me they did have a call recently from a man with his two children, who was terrified to go back home because of his wife's violent behaviour. 'He had previously rung several other refuges and they had laughed at him. I didn't laugh at him. I knew how desperate he was.'

CONTACT AGENCIES

Chiswick Family Rescue, PO Box 855, London W4. Tel 081-995 4430 (Crisis Line), 081-747 0133 (Office).

Women's Aid Federation 52–54 Featherstone Street, London EC1Y 8RT. Tel 071-251 6537.

21

SATURDAY NIGHT FEVER: ILLNESS AND DISEASE

After years of hardly a cross word, we quarrel: harsh, unpleasant, unloving things are said by both of us. The cancer is threatening to tear us apart.

Jeremy Warburg
A Voice At Twilight

ILLNESS AND INTIMACY

The effects of illness in undermining our capacity for emotional and sexual intimacy should never be underestimated. They can be devastating. This is because ill health touches us at all levels of our being. The physical effects alone of disease on sexual intimacy may be far from straightforward.

If you are involved in a car accident which seriously damages your penis or vulva, the sexual implications of such an injury are readily apparent. Many common diseases, though, such as diabetes, or arteriosclerosis can also directly impair male genital function. Drugs used to treat conditions such as high blood pressure may have the same effect. With other conditions the difficulties are more indirect, but none the less incapacitating. Sex is an energetic business and you need to be reasonably fit to enjoy it, or even be able to do it at all. The breathlessness from angina or chronic bronchitis and emphysema, for example, may render intercourse impossible. So too can the chronic pain and limitations on mobility resulting from arthritis.

Neurological conditions can be particularly detrimental to sexual intimacy. Multiple sclerosis, for example, may paralyse below the waist completely, thus robbing the sufferer of sensation and movement simultaneously. It can also, in common with other conditions such as a stroke, affect the part of the brain relating to sexual desire. Neurological carnage in different parts of the brain can cause other problems with intimacy too. Partial or complete paralysis of an arm for instance, will greatly reduce the ability to embrace and caress. Furthermore, the absence of sensation from the affected limb, gives a distorted sense of bodily proportion.

A low body image altogether may occur and this can cause relationship difficulties, particularly in those who previously prided themselves on their former physical prowess. 'There is nothing so additionally disabling as to look back upon happy memories, and to know those memories are out of present-day reach for all time. The despair, depression, resentment and frustration are all too likely to disrupt future satisfactory sexual activity.'[1] Severe body-image problems often result when sexual organs are removed. This subject is dealt with more fully in Chapter 17.

The concept of body-image is just one example of the subtle interplay between the physical and the psychological. Some aspects of specific mental illnesses are considered in the next section, but most physical sickness gives rise to some form of psychological reaction. Anxiety, fear and depression can follow any illness, and make sexual enjoyment very difficult as a result. As marital counsellor, Joyce Huggett, shares,

> It happened to us one occasion. I slipped a disc playing badminton and a few months later sustained back injuries in a car crash. The two accidents meant that for over a year we were unable to have intercourse. When my back was better, I wanted to enjoy sex again but I was afraid of the pain it might cause. The fear made me tense and unresponsive.[2]

Such a reaction is not uncommon.

Pre-existing fears and anxieties may, of course, be made worse by illness. Jack was a very insecure man in his late twenties, who had always worried that he couldn't satisfy his wife's sexual needs adequately. When he developed an orchitis – an inflammation of his testicles, as a complication of adult mumps, he became completely impotent afterwards even though mumps orchitis does not cause impotence. The fact that he temporarily had something physically wrong with his genitals was enough to tip the balance, given his already fearful predisposition.

There are also social and family factors connected with illness that can disrupt your marital intimacy. Sickness in a child or elderly parent, can lead to anxieties and also practical concerns for their welfare, which can drown your own needs as a couple for closeness. When your spouse is ill, physical separation by hospitalisation can present obvious problems which may be compounded by financial worries about protracted sick-leave from work, and so on.

Space does not permit a detailed consideration in this book of how to tackle problems of sexual intimacy presented by specific diseases and disabilities. Some comprehensive texts which deal with this in detail are recommended at the end of this chapter. As in tackling so many enemies of intimacy, however, giving time to each other and maintaining good communication are essential.

A particularly important specific skill in dealing with illness, is to learn to give and receive sexual pleasure in alternative ways that are appropriate to your new situation. This often requires considerable mental as well as physical adjustment. 'Not only must past conditioning leading to sexual orgasm be unlearnt – often a painful and difficult procedure – but a whole new set of conditioning procedures ... has to be learnt.[3] Alan Riley, a former editor of the *British Journal of Sexual Medicine,* cites the case of a man, who having sustained a serious injury to his penis, subsequently found stimulation of his prostate gland by his wife's finger in his rectum was a pleasurable substitute for penile stimulation. Similarly she came to enjoy cunnilingus as a substitute for penetrative sex.[4]

I have focused in this section on how illness leads to marital stress. But, of course, marital stress can also lead to illness. One study[5] has shown that 30 per cent of patients who attended their doctor's surgery had marital problems, of which a half were severe.

Joanna came to see me with a history of persistent nausea for the previous two months. She was not pregnant, and a full battery of blood tests followed by X-rays and various scans showed no demonstrable cause. I referred her for a second opinion. Before she was seen by the specialist, however, her husband came to see me. During the course of this consultation, as he told me how there was no love left between him and Joanna and he was thinking of leaving her, the possible cause for her unexplained symptom became apparent. The specialist found nothing wrong with her medically, and when Joanna's husband eventually left, so did her nausea.

MENTAL ILLNESS

When you are physically unwell, there is usually a great deal of understanding and sympathy forthcoming from the majority of other family members. Mental illness, however, still has a great deal of stigma attached to it. For instance, it is much less acceptable to be off work with the strained emotions of an acute anxiety state, than with strained tendons resulting from a tennis match. Similarly the broken spirit of the depressed commands less tolerance than the broken leg of the injured. This general climate of misunderstanding and disapproval makes it more difficult to cope with mental illness not least in the marriage relationship. Let us briefly consider three common psychiatric conditions which frequently damage marital intimacy.

THE BLACK DOG – DEPRESSION

Depression is a very common condition. Current estimates suggest that about one in twenty adults suffers from a depressive illness at any one point, with up to 70 per cent of these going untreated.[6]

Depression, not surprisingly causes considerable marital stress and makes intimacy very difficult. The classical features of depression – low mood, anhedonia (inability to experience pleasure), poor or increased appetite, loss of energy, sleep disturbance (whether insomnia or sleeping all the time), inability to concentrate, low self-esteem and guilt, slowing down or getting more fidgety, and suicidal thoughts – all constitute a formidable barrier to a fulfilling marriage even without the additional problem of reduced libido which affects well over two-thirds of sufferers from depression.

Depressed people tend to withdraw from all social interaction including their marriage, which further reduces the opportunity for emotional and sexual intimacy. This reclusiveness may understandably be misinterpreted by the spouse as a sign of diminished affection towards them. This contributes further to the spiral of unravelling intimacy between husband and wife.

It is important for couples in such a situation to recognise that the sexual and emotional difficulties have arisen from the depression, which requires appropriate treatment. Unfortunately depressive illnesses often go undetected for some time, and even when they are recognised there is still widespread misunderstanding regarding treatment. In a recent article, Prof. Andrew Sims, the then President of the Royal College of Psychiatrists, reported that among the general public, 'only 46 per cent viewed antidepressants as effective, and 78 per cent, against all the evidence, regarded antidepressants as addictive'.[7]

In fact, antidepressants are not at all addictive, and moreover they are effective in alleviating depression in around 70 per cent of patients who are treated with them. I would recommend that if you have marital difficulties which you suspect may be related to depression, you seek expert medical help promptly.

THE ASPEN LEAF – ANXIETY AND STRESS

Anxiety and stress are strange emotions. A certain level of them is quite normal from time to time in life, and they can be our allies to spur us into necessary action. Too much of them, though, can be destructive – reducing us to an indecisive, quivering heap of jelly.

As we have seen throughout this book, there are plenty of areas for stress to develop in marriage, such as gender-roles, having a child, sexual difficulties, and so on. Stress originating outside the marriage relationship may also cause problems within it.

It is important to try and spot the early warning signs of anxiety and stress-related illness, some of which are identical to those of depression – a condition which frequently coexists with anxiety. Such signs include the commencement of, or increase in, smoking and drinking, loss of appetite or comfort eating, insomnia, irritability and easy loss of temper, feeling tense, lack of concentration, inability to cope with work and loss of libido. Physical symptoms such as trembling, palpitations, sweating, diarrhoea, breathlessness, giddiness and tingling of the hands, feet or around the mouth are also very common. The anxious person always has a sense of being driven. They find it difficult to relax and just sit still and enjoy things. Intimacy soon withers in such an unsettled climate.

Ricky was a very successful businessman. He could sell anything and everything. As his talent became increasingly recognised by his firm, he was asked to do more and more. At first his wife, Sandra, was very pleased with Ricky's rapid promotion but gradually things began to turn sour.

Ricky was always in a hurry. He never enjoyed sitting down for meals any more. He was always flying round the house looking for things he'd mislaid. He went to bed late, tossed and turned all night, and not surprisingly looked tired all day. He rarely spent any time with the children and even when he did his mind was elsewhere. As time went on, he took longer and longer to do the simplest task. He lost much of his interest in sex, and when he did make love to his wife, he was usually thinking of his next deal.

One evening Sandra turned to him and said, 'You will have a breakdown if you carry on like this.' A week later, while driving to work along the motorway, he suddenly panicked in his car. He pulled on to the hard shoulder, unable to drive any farther, and the police had to escort him home. After this episode he was incapable of work. This prompted him to get psychiatric help, and after four months of treatment he made a gradual recovery. Since then he has not been promoted further in his firm, but he and Sandra are much happier together.

In the treatment of anxiety, the dangers of the addictive potential of many tranquillisers are now well recognised, so most patients suffering from mild anxiety will be treated with relaxation techniques and counselling. If drug therapy is needed, there is an increasing tendency to use the antidepressant group of drugs which, as we have already noted, are entirely non-addictive. Where tranquillisers are prescribed they should usually be taken only for short periods of five days or less.

HOOKED ON THE BOTTLE – ALCOHOL ABUSE

Alcohol abuse makes a major contribution to marital problems. It has been estimated that twice as many marriages complicated by alcohol abuse break down in comparison with the rate in the general population[8]. Divorce is not the only problem. Alcohol abusers are more susceptible to many diseases, and have a higher mortality rate from them. They have more fatal accidents as well, and have a high suicidal rate leaving behind them a trail of widowed spouses. Domestic violence, as we have seen, is also associated with alcohol abuse (pp. 263–4). Finally, alcohol dependency gives rise to many problems with sexual intimacy.

Though many people believe that alcohol is an aphrodisiac, clinical experience has consistently shown that excessive alcohol use is associated with many forms of sexual dysfunction.

It is well known that alcohol excess makes it more difficult for men to obtain and sustain an erection. Wilson,[9] in a comprehensive review of the effects of alcohol on sexual function, also states that it takes longer to ejaculate and there is reduced pleasure and less intensity of orgasm the more intoxicated with alcohol a man becomes. For women, too, studies have shown a suppressing effect of alcohol on sexual functioning, with greater difficulty in reaching orgasm. However, if a climax was reached, women in contrast to men reported more pleasurable orgasms at higher levels of intoxication.[10]

Quite apart from the physical affects of alcohol, Jensen considers that 'the sexual problems of alcoholics have their roots mostly in psychological and interpersonal relations'.[11] Among these he includes a sense of low self-esteem, a feeling of constant malaise and tiredness with reduced capacity for intimacy, and changes in the power balance of the relationship with the spouse as the alcohol abuser becomes increasingly incompetent.

The social damage inflicted on the marriage by alcohol addiction also does little to enhance loving responses between husband and wife. The alcohol abuser usually performs poorly at work, and may eventually be dismissed. Thus unemployment and family poverty are added to strains upon the marriage. Dominian graphically describes how the alcohol abuser becomes cut off in other areas.

> The husband, who gets drunk in social situations both at home and when visiting friends, is an acute embarrassment to his wife. He causes a scene by talking too much, too loudly, making rude interruptions, attacking friends and relatives and – in the end – becoming incapable of functioning. He has to be carried to the bedroom and is not a pretty sight. The embarrassment is particularly acute if the alcoholic is the wife.[12]

The treatment of alcohol problems is often difficult and lengthy. The alcohol abuser will usually have to engage in some form of detoxification programme either in hospital or as an out-patient. The spouse will need to examine the marital relationship carefully to see if they have contributed albeit unintentionally to the alcohol abuser's habit. By clearing up that vomit, or by making that excuse telephone call to the boss, spouses may spare the drinkers the consequences of their actions and so delay the day when they actually seek help. Sometimes it takes a crisis to turn the tide. 'The turning point came two months ago when he got into a pub brawl. The police charged him with disorderly conduct. He didn't drink from that night and called Alcoholics Anonymous a week later.'[13] Some useful support networks for both alcohol abusers and their spouses are listed at the end of this chapter.

SEXUALLY TRANSMITTED DISEASES

On a global scale, sexually transmitted diseases (STDs) are the commonest type of infectious disease. In the UK alone there has been a five-fold increase in attendance at STD clinics over the past twenty-five years. At least 50 per cent of those who attend, however, are eventually found free from any STD following examination and investigation. Obviously, then, there is a great deal of worry in the community at large about the possibility of having an STD. Such anxiety as well as the effects of the diseases themselves have obvious implications for sexual intimacy. The rarity of premarital virginity (pp. 65–75) and the frequency of postmarital infidelity (p. 229) are key contributors to the escalating rates of many of these STDs. Until such patterns of behaviour change, increasing numbers of couples will continue to face the problems presented by these conditions.

It is not my intention here to give a comprehensive survey of STDs. I shall, however, outline the important features of some of the more common conditions. AIDS is considered in detail in Chapter 24.

GENITAL HERPES

Genital herpes, along with genital warts, has caused the largest increase in numbers of attendances at STD clinics in the last decade. From the early 1960s when the incidence of genital herpes began to rise sharply, the media have generated a sensationalist approach to the disease, homing in on its recurrent nature, 'incurability', its potential for infection in the absence of symptoms, and the transmission of the disease from mothers to newborn children, possibly leading to blindness. Let's take a less emotionally charged look at this all too common condition.

What Is Genital Herpes? Genital infection with herpes simplex virus (HSV) is caused by two viruses – HSV2 which is the type most commonly involved in genital infections, and HSV1, which more commonly affects the face (giving a 'cold sore'), but also causes around 20 per cent of all genital infections. The infection is transmitted by any intimate contact, not just penile vaginal penetration. The rise in HSV1 infections may be due to an increase in the practice of oral sex. Herpes infection of the throat and pharynx is often transmitted by this means also.

Symptoms in both men and women usually take two to ten days to develop after infection has occurred. Either virus gives rise to multiple painful ulcers on any part of the genitalia. These take two to three weeks to resolve completely, and may be associated with painful glands in the groin, fever, headache and muscle or joint pains. In those who have already been exposed to the virus (by having had a cold sore, for example) the infection is usually less severe.

Recurrent infections are a unique and troublesome feature of the disease. HSV2 infections tend to recur more frequently than those caused by HSV1, but with either virus the recurrences are less severe and shorter than the original attack. Frequency of recurrence is unpredictable, but many sufferers will have four or more attacks a year. Such recurrences may be heralded by a burning, tingling sensation in the affected area. This problem often causes much more distress than the actual recurrent attack itself. The psychological impact of genital herpes can be profound and lead to much anxiety and stress.[14]

How Should It Be Dealt With? All patients with suspected genital herpes should attend an STD clinic for confirmation of the diagnosis. There is no entirely satisfactory treatment, but in recent years the anti-viral drug, acyclovir, has greatly helped management of the condition. Acyclovir tablets are taken five times a day and are only available on prescription, but they do shorten the duration of attacks. Patients with very frequent recurrences may take acyclovir continuously for several months to try and prevent such frequent attacks.

There are several other important points about genital herpes infection. There is considerable evidence that it is linked with the development of cancer of the cervix, so any woman at risk in this way should have annual smear tests. It is possible to transmit the infection to the baby in childbirth so special precautions must be taken during the delivery to try and minimise this risk.

The use of a condom and avoidance of intercourse when symptoms are present will reduce the chances of spread. Since the disease can be passed on despite these precautions, it is understandable that in a marriage where one partner has had herpes, it can be a real impediment to sexual intimacy. Fear of infecting the other partner can result in impotence, vaginismus or other sexual problems.

Accurate information about the disease is vital in such a situation and many couples find it a relief to learn that herpes infection can in some cases be relatively trivial. The unaffected partner can also have a blood test to see if they have antibodies to HSV. If they do, then their chances of having a significant attack of genital herpes are not very great. Even if they have no antibodies present, there is around a 50 per cent chance of any contracted infection being completely without any symptoms.

CANDIDIASIS ('THRUSH')
Genital infection with the fungus, Candida albicans, is a very common condition in women, although only around 10 per cent of cases are thought to be sexually transmitted. In men, however, symptomatic genital candidiasis often appears to be contracted sexually.

Vulval infection is more common in diabetics, the overweight and during pregnancy. Contrary to popular belief, there is no evidence that candida infection is greater in those women on oral contraceptives. Vaginal irritation is the main symptom, accompanied usually by a white cheesy discharge. Pain on passing water and also during intercourse is also common.

In men, irritation of the glans penis and prepuce occurs in symptomatic infections. Moist red patches appear on the surface of the glans and, in severe cases, it may be impossible to retract the foreskin. Pain on intercourse may again occur.

The usual treatment for vulvo-vaginal thrush is a combination of anti-fungal cream and pessaries. Canesten, one of the most popular treatments, can be obtained over the counter from chemists. Several other types are available on prescription only. There are also treatments involving tablets taken by mouth. Whatever treatment is given to the woman, it is important that the husband or sexual partner is also treated with an anti-fungal cream as otherwise reinfection may occur.

TRICHOMONIASIS

Trichomonas vaginalis is another fairly common cause of vaginal infection and 10–50 per cent of cases may have no symptoms at all. In those that do develop symptoms, the most common feature is a plentiful, yellow, frothy and smelly discharge. In severe cases there may also be redness around the vulva and pain on intercourse.

It is treated with a course of an antibiotic called metronidazole. Though in men trichomoniasis is a rare cause of NGU (see below) it usually gives no symptoms. The sexual partner of a woman with trichomonas infection however should also be treated with metronidazole to reduce the incidence of reinfection. Because trichomonas is associated with the presence of other STDs, especially gonorrhoea, the male partner should also be investigated for these other conditions when possible.

NON-GONOCOCCAL URETHRITIS

Non-gonococcal urethritis (NGU), also known sometimes as non-specific urethritis (NSU) is now three times more common than gonorrhoea, and has shown an increasing incidence ever since statistics were first available in 1952.

It is caused by a variety of organisms of which the commonest is Chlamydia trachomatis. As would be expected from a wide range of responsible culprits, the incubation period varies from a few days to six weeks.

Usually men with NGU notice a mucousy discharge from the penis, particularly in the early morning. The discharge is not usually profuse. Pain on passing water may occur and there may be discomfort at the tip of the penis.

Most cases of NGU respond rapidly to a course of an antibiotic such as tetracycline, but around 10 per cent of cases suffer numerous recurrences.

The female sexual partner of a man with NSU must be investigated and treated. Usually Chlamydia infection gives rise to no symptoms at all in women, but around 10 per cent of untreated cases will develop non-gonococcal pelvic inflammatory disease – a common cause of subsequent infertility (chap. 14).

PELVIC INFLAMMATORY DISEASE

Pelvic inflammatory disease (PID) is the term describing any infection of the pelvic organs from the cervix upwards. Chlamydial and gonococcal infection are the commonest types, and 30–40 per cent of cases involve more than one organism.

PID may give rise to severe lower abdominal pains or, on the other hand, attacks may be relatively silent. Infection with chlamydia in particular, causes tubal damage out of all proportion to the apparent insignificance of the infection. Infertility rates resulting from PID are amazingly high as we have seen (pp. 185–6), especially in recurrent infections. Pain on intercourse can also be a very distressing problem with PID.

Treatment is with a two-week course of metronidazole and another antibiotic such as tetracycline simultaneously. Women who have had one attack of PID are prone to reinfection, and the risk of an ectopic pregnancy is also increased six-fold after a single attack.

SAFE SEX AND STDs

There has been so much emphasis on AIDS in the past decade that other STDs can easily be forgotten. Few people are aware for example that syphilis, the sexual scourge of a previous generation, is on the increase in the UK and USA once more.

Complacency and sex are a dangerous combination. Even safe sex practices (pp. 315–17), such as non-penetrative sex, do not necessarily prevent the spread of such STDs as crabs (pubic lice), warts, scabies, herpes and hepatitis. There is a sense then, in which safe sex is a myth – except when it is between two uninfected partners who are faithful to each other for life.

FURTHER READING

Michael Adler, *ABC of Sexually Transmitted Diseases* (BMA, 1990).

Sue Atkinson, *Climbing Out Of Depression. A Practical Guide For Sufferers* (Lion, 1993).

David Bullard and Susan Knight, eds, *Sexuality and Physical Disability* (C.V. Mosby, 1981).

Gaius Davies, *Stress* (Kingsway, 1988).

Robert Kolodny, William Masters and Virginia Johnson, *Textbook of Sexual Medicine* (Little, Brown & Co, 1979).

Greg Wilkinson, *Depression* (BMA, 1989).

CONTACT AGENCIES

Association To Aid The Sexual and Personal Relationships of the Disabled, 286 Camden Road, London N7 0BJ. Tel 071-607 8851.

Stress and Life Trust, The Istana, Freezeland Lane, Bexhill-on-Sea TN39 5JD. Tel 0424-219133.

Alcoholics Anonymous, PO Box 1, Stonebow House, York. Head Office tel 0904-644026. Local branch numbers listed in area phone books.

Al-Anon Family Groups, 61 Great Dover Street, London SE1 4YF. Tel 071-403 0888.

Herpes Association, 41 North Road, London N7 9DP. Tel 071-609 9061.

22

PROMISES, PROMISES! PORNOGRAPHY

> Sometimes when the wrappings fall
> there's nothing underneath at all.
>
> Steven Sondheim
> *Follies*

A POPULAR PASTIME

'My husband and I quite often hire a sexy video to watch together in the evenings. I find it really turns me on,' remarked Sue during the course of a clinic consultation with me. Many today would share her experience, and who can blame them? The publicity machine of the pornography industry works very effectively, and it is impossible to escape its seductive sell completely, even if we wanted to – and many people don't.

Whether it is in the corner shop or on the highway hoardings, the imagery of either breasts or beefcake assaults us daily. The range of media involved is expanding continually too – pornographic telephone chatlines and computer games adding to the ever-increasing proliferation of magazines, books, films and videos.

The target audience is also widening. 'They are bronzed, topless and desirable' – reads the front cover of a magazine in the teen section of my local library. The surprise is that they are also male! This is not *Playboy,* but a magazine aimed at young girls. Traditionally the sole prerogative of men, pornography for women is growing fast in popularity. At the same time, pornographic material for either sex is aimed at an increasingly younger sector of the population. In a 1989

Cosmopolitan survey of nearly 4,000 women[1] the average age of first contact with pornography was fourteen and a half. For males this age is considerably lower, many boys becoming involved as young as seven.

PORNOGRAPHY AND INTIMACY

Many of the sociological and moral arguments both for and against pornography lie outside my immediate concern here and have recently been comprehensively reviewed elsewhere.[2] The popular view that pornography may actually be of positive therapeutic value for some people, however, is obviously of great importance in any consideration of potential allies or enemies of intimacy.

Some sex therapists do indeed maintain that exposure to pornography can be helpful in treating certain sexual dysfunctions. One has even written a paper rather wonderfully entitled 'Therapeutic Uses of Obscenity'! For example, Peter Dally, a consultant psychiatrist, in his brief section on pornography in one popular sex guide maintains, 'Aids to sexual excitement and arousal such as pornographic videos and stories are now widely available and used, and are especially helpful to couples whose taboos are still strong.'[3]

As we shall see later (p. 292), the scientific evidence for such claims is highly equivocal and often misrepresented. John Court, Professor of Psychology at Flinders University, Australia, rightly points out. 'We must distinguish between the legitimate presentation of sexual information to those who need it, and the gross distortions of sexuality found in pornography.'[4] This is an important distinction. Sexually explicit material in itself does not necessarily constitute pornography. Indeed, parts of this book are highly explicit, but few readers are likely to regard it as pornographic, as I have made it very clear that my aim is to educate and inform, not to exploit or degrade.

Some sex manuals however do blur this distinction. Many of the 18-rated video sex manuals fall into this category. In a perceptive review of several such titles, Tristan Davies observed,

'Their popularity (and boy are they popular) may have something to do with our New Age interest in "interpersonal relationship skills" i.e. how in the era of Aids one can have sex and not die, either literally or of boredom. But I suspect their appeal is rather more basic.'[5]

Davies quite rightly implies that there is a difference between arousal which enhances a relationship, and that which only gratifies self-centred desire. As a US civil rights ordinance makes clear, in pornography 'women are presented dehumanised as sexual objects, things or commodities';[6] relationship and mutuality are absent. My only quibble with this definition is that it does not make it clear that men also can be degraded by such representation as sexual objects. Pornography is not just a feminist concern.

Of course many couples who buy pornographic materials do so because they are dissatisfied with their sexual experience, and hope to find suggestions which will help to improve the quality of this area of their lives together. Though it may well be an adjunct to getting turned on, in my view pornography will never enrich intimacy because of its intrinsically damaging psychological effects. One professor of psychology, Earl Wilson, has gone so far as to state his opinion that far from being therapeutic, pornography ultimately contributes to 'sexual insanity'.[7] How does it do so?

THE PROBLEM WITH PORNOGRAPHY

Sex associated with viewing pornography is inevitably going to be deficient sex for a wide variety of reasons. This is because it is:

SEX WITHOUT REALITY
The world of pornography is a fantasy world of stereotypes. The women are all stunningly beautiful and ample-breasted, the men all have the physique of a Greek god – one American group of male strippers is actually called Adonis.

'It is the mythical world of the totally sensuous woman or the supremely virile man. Each page is designed to lead people to believe that the next page will present the ultimate body.'8 It is a private world of fantasy which severs our links with the real world.

While superficially stimulating, the negative aspects of such unreality can be devastating. In the presence of such sexual perfectionism, how will you ever measure up? Your contours will never be as curvy (or alternatively your biceps never as bulging). Unwittingly, those who feed on pornography, starve their own sense of self-worth, and depression is a very common sequel to such a diet.

The other obvious problem with ingesting such fantasy is that your partner will never match up to the gold standard of the pornographic idols either. How can anyone who actually has to comb hair, or, even worse, cut toenails, ever compete with such perfection?

Matthew had been involved in watching pornographic videos for many years before he met and eventually married Samantha. When making love, he had great difficulty in caressing Samantha's back because she had two small moles on the skin overlaying her spine. Touching these blemishes was an instant turn off for him, because previously he had never had to face up to the reality of such human imperfection in his fantasy world. It was only when, with appropriate counselling and support, Matthew eventually stopped watching pornography that the moles gradually ceased to be a problem to him.

SEX WITHOUT RELATIONSHIP

Pornography is a poor model for intimacy. 'Men who read or view pornography are in search of the _ultimate_ without the intimate.'9 The sexual partners portrayed in porn are never married. Indeed relationship is so peripheral to the entire proceedings that they are lucky if they even know each other's names!

Pornography is concerned only with sensations, not with relationships, and encourages their experience in isolation from the relationships to which they properly belong. It brings us into a world of irresponsibility where we can experience the emotional and even the physical accompaniments of love-making without a partner, and without any demand being made on all the other aspects of our personalities that we find being developed in a healthy marriage relationship.'[10]

Even watching such material together as a couple, inevitably focuses erotic attention on someone else's partner, not your own. It is counter-productive to intimacy because it suggests that what you don't have may be better than what you do.

A further danger is that sexual arousal may become so exclusively associated with the violent, the forbidden or the inaccessible, that increasing difficulty is experienced in enjoying intercourse with your own husband or wife, who is accessible. The loneliness of the long-distance porn-masturbator is desperate indeed.

SEX WITHOUT RELEASE

There is no comparison between the orgasm and warm afterglow of intimate love-making, and the brief thrill and guilt-ridden aftermath of sexual stimulation from pornography. The use of pornography does seem to be universally associated with guilt, particularly in the early stages. At the very least, pornographic magazines are usually stashed under the bed, rather than given pride of place on the coffee-table.

As an expert witness testified before the US Attorney General's Commission on Pornography,

The myth about pornography is that it frees the libido and gives men an outlet for sexual expression which liberates mind and body. This is truly a myth. I have found that pornography not only does not liberate men, but on the contrary is a source of bondage. Men masturbate to pornography only to become addicted to the fantasy. There is no liberation for men in pornography.[11]

Guilt is a hard taskmaster, and it can cripple your ability to function normally and relate closely to others. My own clinical experience tallies with that of Wilson when he writes,

> As a therapist, I have found guilt over sexual behaviour is a common cause of mental disturbance. Many who are active in the type of sexual life promoted by pornography seem to have lost something. The more sexually active they are, the less they enjoy it! One person lamented, 'I seem to be dying inside.'[12]

The addictive potential of pornography is beyond dispute. As one author puts it, 'were pornography not a kind of mental addiction, an enthralled fantasy, who would seriously credit its "ideas"?'[13] Such 'ideas' include a sense of excitement and escape from the humdrum of everyday routine, an illusion of both sexual prowess and personal power, a temporary relief from feelings of unattractiveness and loneliness as well as an intense if fragmentary sense of personal pleasure. As Corrine Sweet indicates, 'These intense feelings can create a compulsive or addictive "pull" towards using pornography repetitively.'[14]

SEX WITHOUT RESPECT

For self   In addition to its guilt-inducing potential, pornography lowers self-esteem in several other ways. It feeds the powerful myth that sex is the most supremely important thing in life. Therefore, if you are not engaging in it as often as possible, you are missing out. This constant feeling of deprivation is another predisposing factor for depression.

The fixation of pornography on the sexual also hinders the development of other areas of the personality which could raise self-esteem. The hours wasted in the pursuit of sexual fantasy could be better invested in other more truly creative areas of interest.

By his mid-teens, Jonathan was totally hooked by pornography. Occasionally he would make determined attempts to break free from it, and during one of these, he threw all his porn magazines into a sewage ditch, but when the addictive urge overcame him again a few hours later, he climbed into the ditch to recover them. The stench from the escapade which permeated his clothes as he walked home, seemed to him pungently to represent his feelings about himself. He sought professional help and eventually overcame his addiction. In the recovery process, he rekindled his neglected musical talent. This led to his joining a jazz band, through which he eventually met his future wife.

The other barrier to self-respect raised by pornography is its emphasis on sexual performance as opposed to sexual pleasing – on technique rather than context. This can foster both strong feelings of inadequacy and the fear of failure. The well-known psychologist, Rollo May, writes:

> It is not surprising then, in this preoccupation with techniques that the questions typically asked about an act of love-making are not, 'Was there passion or meaning or pleasure in the act?', but 'How well did I perform?' Take for example what Cyril Connolly calls the 'tyranny of the orgasm', and the preoccupation with achieving a simultaneous orgasm, which is another aspect of the alienation. I confess that when people talk about the 'apocalyptic orgasm', I find myself wondering, why do they have to try so hard? What abyss of self-doubt, what inner void of loneliness, are they trying to cover up by this great concern with grandiose effects?[15]

For the opposite sex 'The problem for women is men's use of pornography and how it affects their attitudes and behaviour. How can women be taken seriously in society if they are portrayed as pieces of meat, and the objects of men's lust and desire?'[16]

When pornography stereotypes women as simply being available for sex, it decreases men's perception of their potential for true intimacy involving relationship. This effect has been well documented from several research studies. Zillman and Bryant[17] for example exposed college students to 'standard' non-violent pornography for one-hour sessions over six consecutive weeks. In both this study and several later ones involving a wider sample of a city population,[18,19] subjects following such exposure reported the trivialisation of rape as a criminal offence, an increased acceptance of sexual infidelity, and a decreased satisfaction with their partner's physical appearance and the partner's expressions of affectionate behaviour. These results led Zillmann and Bryant to consider that the regular viewing of commonly available sexually explicit material encourages an increased level of callousness towards women in general, and leads to decreased satisfaction with existing sexual relationships; and diminished love for the existing partner.

James Weaver and his colleagues[20] have demonstrated that even transient exposure to standard pornography can lead to increasing dissatisfaction with an existing sexual partner. Similar results have been reported by other researchers.[21]

Nigel Williams graphically illustrates the everyday human (or should that be inhuman?) face of such academic laboratory research in his book *False Images:*

> As we sat in the train at Manchester station three young football fans came into the compartment each carrying a pornographic magazine. As they sat down in the seats behind us we could hear them talking about the contents of the magazines. Then a very attractive young woman joined the train and sat level with my companion and me. One of the fans looked up from his magazine and said to the others in a sniggering tone, 'Cor, look, a woman'. It is hard to convey in the printed word the degree of sexual undertone he managed to invest in that short phrase. I know if I had been that young woman I would have felt very intimidated by those young men.[22]

SEX WITHOUT RESTRAINT

As we have seen, the addictive potential of pornography is high. Many who get involved with it find themselves being drawn ever deeper into a well of obsession and misery. What began as a search for personal intimacy ends in an agony of mental imprisonment.

Thus, while some psychiatrists may still confidently claim

that 'there is no convincing evidence that porn has undesirable consequences for society or the individual'[23] such assertions are increasingly difficult to maintain.

The 1985 US Attorney General's Commission on Pornography[24] (which the pornography industry has fought tooth and nail to discredit), was unanimous in its finding of a causal link between pornography and sexual violence. The Minneapolis hearings of 1983 also received testimony from many experts as to the harm inflicted by pornography.

For example, Bill Seals, a full-time worker with sex offenders, stated that such offenders used pornography 'as a stimulus to their sexually acting out. The sexual insecurity of sex offenders is reinforced by porn'.[25] Floyd Winecoff, a psychologist, testified before the hearing that with regard to pornography, 'ultimately men lose because they never experience the true intimacy that comes from . . . opening up with someone . . . Pornography portrays a fantasy of social communion, but in reality it leads to the desperation that leads me to abusiveness.'[26]

In this country, Ray Wyre, the former Director of the internationally famous Gracewell Clinic, with all his twenty years of experience in dealing with sex offenders, can confidently assert, 'In the course of my work I have developed a model which identifies the patterns which predictably operate in the cycle of sexual abuse. I have discovered that pornography can and does function at every stage in that cycle of abuse.'[27]

The truth of such remarks is well illustrated by the extreme but by no means unique case of Ted Bundy. He was a convicted serial killer and rapist. In an interview recorded the night before his execution in 1989 he stated:

> I'm no social scientist and I haven't done a survey ... but I have lived a long time in prison now. And I've met a lot of men who were motivated to commit violence just like me. And without exception every one of them was deeply involved in pornography.[28]

Admittedly the risk of such an extreme escalation is very small for most people, and at first sight this seems a far cry from hiring a blue film from the local video shop. But is it really so unconnected? Heavy consumption of common forms of pornography fosters an appetite for stronger materials.[29] Can we even think of taking the slightest chance if we are truly searching for intimacy with our partner? As Diana Russell so powerfully argues, 'What was considered hard-core in the past has become soft-core for the present. Where will all this end? Will we as a culture forever refuse to read the writing on the wall?'[30]

It seems incredible that the 1990 Home Office report into pornography in the UK did not consider much of the recent research outlined above. Yet even the authors of this report who generally felt that the evidence of the adverse effects of pornography was far from clear-cut, did concede that 'There is a good deal of justification for the association of pornography with social ills in the public mind.'[31] John Court showed prophetic insight in 1981 when he wrote, 'The evidence linking cigarette smoking to lung cancer ... was once open to debate, but has now achieved high credibility. Evidence identifying harmful effects of pornography is I claim moving in the same way to become increasingly convincing.'[32]

FROM FANTASY TO INTIMACY – OUT OF THE NET

If you have not entered the twilight world of pornography I trust I have given sufficient reason for you to continue to avoid it. If you are already entangled in the net, I would like to offer some principles to help you escape.

● Take control of your thought life

This is not easy, but with practice it can be done over a period of time. Learning to recognise those thought patterns associated with pornography is the first step. Conscious action should then be taken to stop those thoughts as soon as they begin. This process can be facilitated by reminding yourself of the damage that pornography has already done to you, and will continue to inflict unless the cycle of addiction is broken.

Exaggeration must also be firmly controlled. For example, use of pornography often leads to the thought, 'We will never be able to have a good sex life without porn again.' This needs to be acknowledged as totally untrue, and replaced by a thought such as, 'Our appreciation of each other will only have a chance to grow once we are free from pornographic stimulation.' Fixing thoughts on future positive gains can greatly help in overcoming present struggles.

● Be ruthless about fantasy

'I do not agree with the arguments that fantasy is something that happens in your head and behaviour is something else. In my experience fantasy and behaviour are directly connected.'[33]

Strong addictions require radical measures. For a time it may be necessary for you to avoid anything which remotely stimulates living in fantasy. Paperback romances and TV soap operas, which may be harmless for most people, can be a dangerous diversion for those locked in unreality. I usually advise my patients caught in the pornography trap not to read or watch such things at all for a while.

● Focus on each other

There are many steps that can be taken to improve an ailing sex life without getting involved with pornography. Various ways to enhance sexual excitement without the use of porn are given in Chapters 12 and 13.

● Make yourself accountable

Pornography is like quicksand, and few can pull themselves out without help. Confiding about the problem with someone else and making yourself accountable to them can be invaluable. Great care however should be taken in choosing the right person. Unfortunately, those in greatest need often have the fewest friends in a position to help, and professional counsel may need to be sought.

Many men desperately need to do the very thing they find

so difficult – to get in touch with their sexual feelings and attitudes.[34] Men's groups, such as those recently described by McCloughry,[35] may help in this process.

A BETTER WAY

Pornography is a cul-de-sac that ultimately ends in frustration and deceit. There is a better way. As Prof. Court concludes,

> To reject pornography is to take a stand for sex as a special way to expressing and deepening interpersonal commitment. Pornography fails to understand sex as a sacred gift intended for joy, intimacy and deep fulfilment in a loving, lasting relationship.[36]

Those who come to understand and appreciate sex as such a gift will find such ecstasy within it that the transient thrill of pornographic fantasy will pale into insignificance by comparison.

FURTHER READING

Tom Minnery, (ed.), *Pornography: A Human Tragedy* (Living Books, 1986).

23

SKELETONS IN THE CUPBOARD: CHILD ABUSE

I want to make love to you without any ghosts in the bed.

Ariel Dorfman
Death and The Maiden

Naomi has a very pretty face, yet her eyes betray her inner pain. Not that they are easy to see. She never looks at me for long, but usually gazes at the floor as we speak.

She can't sit still for long. She wrings her hands throughout the consultation and always hovers on the edge of her seat as if ready to fly out of the door at a moment's notice. I don't think I've ever seen her visibly relaxed.

No matter what the weather, summer or winter, she always comes dressed in at least one thick, baggy sweater with an anorak on top. She tells me that she feels more comfortable like that. It hides the fact that she's a girl. She wishes she wasn't for, perhaps, if she'd been a boy, her father would not have sexually abused her.

THE ICEBERG OF ABUSE

I would say that the fallout from child sexual abuse is by far and away the commonest sexual problem that I have to deal with in my clinical practice. The subsequent damage from such abuse on the child's intimate relationships in later life is usually catastrophic. What then is child sexual abuse, and how does it differ from the legitimate expression of affection?

Child sexual abuse occurs whenever a child is deliberately involved in or exposed to sexual stimulation or a sexual act which they do not completely understand and which is inappropriate for their age, emotional development and role within the family.

In short, the abuser exploits the child for sexual self-gratification. When the abuser is a family member, the term incest is usually applied, though for the *legal* definition of incest to be fulfilled actual intercourse has to have taken place. Physical contact does not have to take place for sexual abuse to occur. For example, the exhibition of the genitals by an adult to a child for the purpose of sexual arousal constitutes abuse and such incidents can be extremely distressing to a child. 'Sexual' games between young children of similar ages where there is neither coercion nor embarrassment may be quite acceptable, but the filming of such activity for sexual stimulation of paedophiles is abuse.

There is a definite line between the expression of tenderness and torment, between affection and abuse. Even a young child senses the differences between being lovingly kissed or cuddled, and being sexually stimulated. An aroused and guilty adult behaves in a very different manner. Children instinctively turn away when the contact goes too far from normal.

For adults, a good gauge of the appropriateness of your behaviour with children is whether you would want to be seen in public. If there is a need for secrecy then the boundary is crossed. Abuse begins when your insistence stifles the child's expression of discomfort.

The exact prevalence of child sexual abuse is hard to determine accurately. Children tend to keep such experiences a secret, and most estimates are therefore based on adults' recollection of their childhood abuse. In Diana Russell's survey of over 900 women in San Francisco,[1] 38 per cent reported at least one episode of sexual abuse before the age of eighteen. This study excluded non-contact experiences of abuse such as exhibitionism. Had these been included, the number of women abused before the age of eighteen would have risen to an astonishing 54 per cent.

In the UK there are no national statistics for the number of new cases of child sexual abuse each year, but statistics from the National Society for the Prevention of Cruelty to Children give a total of more than 6,700 new cases a year, and this figure is likely to be an underestimate. It is a sobering thought that around one in four girls and one in twelve boys will have been sexually abused by the age of sixteen.

THE ABUSER AND THE ABUSED

Children of any age can be the victims of sexual abuse. In 1991 the mean age at the time of reporting of abuse was ten years and two months and 18 per cent were under five. As we have already noted, girls are three times more likely to be sexually abused than boys.

The abuser is usually male and in 80–95 per cent of cases is known by the child. 'Child abuse is not really about nasty strangers luring away your daughters. The slogan, 'Say "No" to strangers' is wide of the mark. Abuse is about perpetrators in your family and in your home.'[2] Abusers include fathers, brothers, uncles and cousins as well as that 'nice man next door'. Dr Diana Riley gives a thumbnail sketch of the average child sexual abuser –

He is commonly between 20 and 40, married, a father, leading a normal social life, enjoying the respect of his colleagues and friends, and often holding a position of trust and authority in relation to children – in short a person apparently above suspicion.[3]

One particularly notorious child-pornography case actually involved a professor of paediatrics in a famous London teaching hospital. He has since been dismissed from his post.

Recently it has become clear that female abusers are far from rare. In 1992 it was reported that of a total of 8,600 children counselled by Childline – a voluntary telephone helpline – nearly one in ten had been abused by a female. At the Great Ormond

Street clinic for child abusers around 5 per cent of patients are women.[4]

The duration of child sexual abuse ranges from an isolated incident to sequential exploitation which can go on for years before it is detected. There are several factors which increase the risk of sexual abuse occurring in a family:

Family history of sexual abuse   Many abusers have themselves been physically or sexually abused as a child.

Marital Problems   There is often poor marital communication and minimal levels of intimacy. The father may often feel rejected by his wife, and use this as a justification for abuse.

Alcohol   Excessive drinking reduces the capacity to control behaviour (pp. 277–8).

Child Pornography   This can never act merely as a 'safety-valve' 'both because children in it are being abused, and because the paedophiles use it to ... make them feel they are normal. In that way it lowers their inhibitions about abusing children rather than preventing them from doing so.'[5]

THE MARK OF THE BEAST – RECOGNISING THE SIGNS OF CHILD SEXUAL ABUSE

The correct recognition of child sexual abuse can sometimes be difficult even for trained experts. While there are very few signs which give absolute proof, however, there are many pointers which *may* indicate that sexual abuse is occurring. These clues fall into three main groups:

● Physical
– Genital injuries or bleeding.
– Bites, burns or bruises on other parts of the body.
– Signs of sexually transmitted disease, such as a vaginal discharge or genital warts.
– Pregnancy, especially in young girls and when there is uncertainty about the identity of the father.
– Abnormal enlargement of the vaginal or anal openings.

- Wetting pants or pain on passing water.
- Soiling of pants or recurrent constipation.
- Self-mutilation.

● General emotional and behavioural

- Unexplained accumulation of money or sweets.
- Disturbed sleep patterns and nightmares.
- Anorexia or overeating.
- Clinging to mother and refusing to play.
- Poor concentration and learning problems.
- Reluctance to change clothes for PE, etc.
- Anxiety, tearfulness, aggression.
- Running away from home.
- Suicidal attempt.

● Sexual

- Explicit preoccupation with sex in play or conversation.
- Sexual knowledge inappropriate for child's age.
- Frequent masturbation.
- Sexually provocative behaviour with adults.
- Hinting about sexual activity or secrets.

I should stress that there may be good reasons other than sexual abuse for many of these features, but any suspicion that your child is being sexually abused must be taken seriously.

Children rarely lie about sexual abuse although, over the years, I have become wary of accusations *arising for the first time* when divorce proceedings are already under way. Unfortunately, children can be coached by a vengeful parent into making false statements. Outside these circumstances, however, your child should *always* be believed.

Any child disclosing such a secret has shown great courage in doing so, and should be listened to carefully with as little interruption as possible. She (or he) should be thanked for sharing with you, and promised your support and help. Under no circumstances should the child be blamed or criticised in any way.

Once a child has reached the stage of revealing the abuse, if help and support are not forthcoming further damage will be done as the child then feels an even greater isolation. Your next move should be to inform the proper authorities who will take the next necessary steps. The duty social worker at your local social services department, the NSPCC, your GP, health visitor, or the the police are all appropriate agencies to contact for further help. The local authority will automatically have to be notified by the other agencies.

PREVENTING SEXUAL ABUSE

There is no way that prevention can ever be 100 per cent effective, but there is much that you can do to reduce the risk for your child.

MAKE TIME FOR YOUR CHILD

Time spent in playing and communicating generally with your child is never wasted. When any crisis develops, your children need to know that you will listen to them and that you respect them.

In particular you should respect their trust and confidences in you in the same way that you would an adult's.

Do not be afraid to apologise to your child if you are at fault over a particular issue.

Being open about sexual matters with your child is very important. It is, for example, by seeing parents naked and unashamed at home, that children can be helped to sense the difference between this and the unhealthy nakedness involved in exhibitionism.

PROTECT YOUR CHILD

I have already stressed that preventing child sexual abuse involves much more than refusing sweets from strangers. Having said that, your child should be told about not accepting gifts from or going off with people they don't know. They should avoid going to places such as public loos on their own.

Baby-sitters, child-minders and nannies should be thoroughly checked before being left alone with your children.

TEACH YOUR CHILD SELF-PROTECTION

You should tell your child that their body does not belong to anyone else but them. If anyone tries to touch them in a way that frightens or upsets them, you should tell them to say 'No' in a loud voice. If they are being hurt, stress that it is all right for them to yell and scream, and to run away.

You should encourage them to tell you if anyone touches them in such a way – even if that person is a family member or friend. Explain the difference between a good secret (like a surprise party), and secrets that should never by kept (like if an adult asks you to kiss or hug them secretly).

LOOK AFTER YOURSELF

It is when you are under stress yourself, that you are less likely to be sensitive to your children's needs. Your child will be aware of your anxiety or preoccupation and may feel less free to open up to you. If you are going through a difficult time, then talk to your children about it in terms they can understand. This will help to keep the lines of communication open.

GHOSTS IN THE BEDROOM – THE LATER CONSEQUENCES OF ABUSE

When I first met Robert, he was absolutely frantic with fear. He had developed a large painful abscess which clearly needed surgical treatment. His wife Amanda, had insisted that he went to the local hospital where he was seen as an emergency. The casualty sister rightly thought that the abscess would need to be lanced and drained. When the doctor arrived however, Robert screamed at the sight of him and ran out of the hospital terrified.

His terror was far more extreme than the natural anxiety that anyone requiring urgent surgery would feel. Amanda recognised this and eventually she persuaded Robert to see me. Over the course of many months, Robert, little by little, began to unfold his story. As a boy he had been both physically and sexually abused by his father. Eventually his father was found out and Robert was taken into a children's home where, tragically, history repeated itself and he was subjected to repeated sexual abuse by the doctor to the home. He had never told anyone about this, not even his wife.

The consequences of child sexual abuse can be hidden for years and then suddenly surface with volcanic ferocity, and they did for Robert. Such eruptions may take many forms in the adult survivors of child sexual abuse. The underlying pressures include:

GUILT AND SHAME

Child sexual abusers are often unable to admit that they are doing wrong, or that they inflict suffering on the child. Their trump card is complicity – making the child feel that she asked for it, that she is as guilty as the abuser. Victims approaching puberty are particularly likely to feel that they were in some way responsible for what happened to them. The pleasure experienced by the children, either sexually or in terms of the attention or treats received, may add to the guilt they feel.

Sexually provocative behaviour in children is quite natural. Little girls need to know they can win their daddy's heart by fluttering their eyelids at him, but it is the responsibility of adults to let children know such behaviour can be expressed safely. When the adult is seductive and sexually arousing in return, it is never the child's fault.

CONFUSION AND LACK OF TRUST

It is little wonder that most victims of child sexual abuse have difficulty in forming strong adult relationships. The sense of betrayal is often overwhelming, especially when the abuser is a father or other close family member. The non-abusing parent may also be blamed for not having detected the child's suffering.

The child is often emotionally torn apart by the mixed feelings they experience towards an abusing parent. One child poignantly sums up the dilemma in a poem:

> If they take my devil-Daddy
> They take my lovely daddy too.[6]

Sylvia Frazer, an adult survivor, describes the torment even more graphically in her book *My Father's House:* 'I unscrew my head from my body as if it is the lid of a pickle jar. From now on there will be two of me – a child who knows, and a child who dares not know any longer.'[7]

DENIAL AND DISPLACEMENT

As Sylvia Frazer illustrates, children have an incredible ability to blot out what they can't cope with. Denial is such a basic psychological defence mechanism against bad feelings, that many women and men find it very hard to recall fully their experiences of abuse.

Clulow and Mattinson go so far as to say,

> As therapists we have over the years become suspicious of the adult patient who too openly and easily confesses incestuous experience, putting this as the first and foremost cause of all their problems. When incest is the genuine major cause of sexual and relationship problems, it usually emerges only slowly ... When, as it were, it is flaunted as *The Problem,* it is more often being used as a defence against a deeper underlying one.[8]

Denial is not usually a totally effective solution, however, and the problem of child sexual abuse often gets displaced into other areas. Many sexually abused girls develop a wide variety of psychosomatic symptoms and conditions such as chronic fatigue syndrome, migraine and irritable bowel.

LOW SELF-WORTH

'Think of the lowest thing in the world. Whatever it is I'm lower.'[9] Such thoughts are very common among child abuse victims. This savaging of self-worth has several origins.

First, as we have seen, there is a *false sense of guilt* arising from the child's inability to see the abuser as the guilty one. Second, there is the *fear of blame and rejection* if the secret should become known. The third and possibly the most crushing blow to a strong sense of self-worth, stems from the abuser's domination over the victim. The *sense of powerlessness* against such alien invasion of their bodies cripples many victims for years. They feel weak and incapable throughout life and are very prone to clinical depression.

ANGER

Not every victim is overtaken by passivity and hopelessness. Some are gripped by anger. It is true that such anger may compound depression, 'Hating takes up so much energy, so much concentration, that there's very little left to do anything else.'[10] But for others, their anger fires them to excel.

Though sexual abuse in childhood makes some survivors timid, it makes others tough. 'If I can survive that, I can survive anything,' becomes their motto. Such a motive often drives a ruthless passion for success at any price.

MARITAL AND SEXUAL PROBLEMS

The victims of child sexual abuse experience a distorted sexuality which profoundly affects their attitude to their own bodies and leaves them suspicious of the motivation behind any subsequent sexual attention. The possible damaging effects of this include:

Promiscuity Those who have received confusing signals about the difference between caring love and exploitative sex often end up being used as a sexual object. Relationship formation is difficult and multiple sexual partners are often used as a substitute for personal intimacy.

Pornography Addiction Peter Baker suggests that male abuse victims tend to be attracted to pornography that is reminiscent of the way in which they have been maltreated. 'It is as if their minds are trying to push the painful memory to the surface and expel it, although they are never quite succeeding.'[11]

Homosexuality Many writers such as Meiselman[12] comment on the possible relationship between lesbianism and sexual abuse in earlier life. Revulsion against men may have a part to play in the development of homosexual attraction in some women.

Poor Partner Choice   Sexually abused girls are more likely to get involved with a partner who has either been abused or is an abuser. They tend to create 'a self-fulfilling prophecy. They expect to find men untrustworthy and they marry men who are just that.'[13]

Cycle of Abusing   Poor parental models, unresolved conflicts, unsuitable partners and other factors all combine to increase the risk of the victims of sexual abuse becoming its perpetrators on their own offspring. '... similar types of child abuse may be handed down to the third and fourth generation. We found that many parents tried hard to avoid perpetuating their abuse but under conditions of stress they reverted to treating their children as they had been treated.'[14]

Fear of Sexual Intimacy   Sex may become so identified with feelings of fear, shame or disgust that the enjoyment of sex as an adult becomes impossible. Lack of libido, vaginismus, anorgasmia and many other sexual problems (chap.13) may arise from the memories of sexual abuse in childhood which live on to haunt the large room of the adult mind.

PHOENIX FROM THE ASHES

A thriving and integrated sexuality can arise even from the emotional ashes of child sexual abuse. The process is not easy however. 'It is like dealing with a cancer that has spread throughout a victim's body and is now needing to be removed one speck at a time. But relief is possible.'[15]

If you are the victim of sexual abuse, acknowledging that the abuse has occurred and facing up to the memories are essential first steps. The knowledge that others have been through this experience and found healing from its scars can be of great benefit and the books listed at the end of this chapter may be useful.

It is likely that you will need to share your pain with someone else. This involves a costly trust on your part and you should choose your counsellor with care. There will probably be a great deal of anger and frustration which your confidant will have to contain. Your GP or health visitor may be a good place to seek initial advice, and there are some useful agencies listed at the end of this chapter.

If you are married to a victim of sexual abuse who has shared that secret, you may find a great relief initially in understanding why your partner behaves as she (or he) does. Subsequently, however, resentment against the abuser (if known) usually has to be dealt with. Patience, sympathy and respect for your partner are essential in helping the recovery process.

Finally you may have sexually abused a child yourself. If so, you need to admit that this is wrong and that you need help in overcoming it. A useful contact address is given below.

FURTHER READING

For Parents
Maxine Hancock and Karen Burton Mains, *Child Sexual Abuse: A Hope for Healing* (Highland Books, 1990).

For Children
Michelle Elliott, *Feeling Happy, Feeling Safe* (Hodder & Stoughton, 1990).

CONTACT AGENCIES

Childline, Freepost 1111, London EC4 4BB.
Freephone 0800-1111.

National Society for the Prevention of Cruelty to Children, 67 Saffron Hill, London EC1N 8RS. Tel 071-242 1626.

For Abusers
Gracewell Clinic, 81 Walker's Heath Road, King's Norton, Birmingham B38 0AN. Tel 021-433 3888.

24

LOVED TO DEATH: AIDS

''Scuse me', said the Elephant's Child most politely, 'but have you seen such a thing as a Crocodile in these promiscuous parts?'

Rudyard Kipling
Just So Stories

The grim spectre of AIDS casts its dark shadow over each of the ages of intimacy discussed in this book. Babies and infants do not escape. It has been estimated that there are now 10,000–20,000 children infected with the AIDS virus in the United States alone. Pregnant mothers who are infected have a 20–50 per cent risk of passing the infection on to their children. Children may also become infected as a result of sexual abuse (chap. 23).

From adolescence to middle age, the relevance of AIDS is self-evident, but even the elderly are not exempt from its chilling touch. Over the past year I have personally counselled several pensioners who have consulted me because of their fears that they might have the virus.

AIDS, then, is no respecter of age. In global terms there is also no doubt that AIDS is the deadliest enemy of intimacy. The World Health Organisation currently estimates that 14 million people worldwide are infected with the AIDS virus,[1] and predicts that by the year 2000 this number will have risen to 30–40 million. Past predictions have tended to over-estimate greatly the rate of spread of the AIDS virus, but even if this latest prediction should again prove exaggerated, the current figures give no reason for complacency. A missionary surgeon writing in the *British Medical Journal* personalises the popular feeling which exists in many countries in the light of such alarming statistics. She laments, 'We would all be happy and optimistic about the future if AIDS was not here. AIDS is not just another disease, it has changed life and death in Africa. It dominates the medical and social scene.'[2]

By April 1993, the statistics indicated that around 30,000 people were infected with the HIV virus in the UK, and there had been a total of some 8,000 actual AIDS cases, of whom over half had died. In the US in 1993 about 4,000 new AIDS cases were being diagnosed each month.

It is not my aim here to give a comprehensive account of this devastating disease. There are already many excellent books which do this. In this chapter, I shall mainly focus on those aspects of AIDS which are of particular relevance to sexual intimacy in Western society.

WHAT IS AIDS?

AIDS, short for Acquired Immune Deficiency Syndrome results from infection with Human Immunodeficiency Virus (HIV). There are three principal stages of the infection:

Asymptomatic During this phase which may last from months to years, infected individuals usually have no symptoms. They both look and feel perfectly well, yet are, however, infectious to others.

Early Illness In this stage various symptoms can develop, including persistently swollen lymph glands, weight loss, night sweats, fever, fatigue and diarrhoea.

AIDS The body's immune defence mechanism has now been so damaged by HIV that normally rare infections and cancers invade and eventually cause death. Pneumocystis carinii pneumonia is the commonest infection involved in the UK and USA. Kaposi's sarcoma, which affects the skin, is the commonest cancer.

The AIDS virus may also directly attack brain cells, producing symptoms such as loss of balance and poor co-ordination of movement, depression, personality changes, loss of memory and dementia.

The average time from infection with HIV to the development of AIDS is ten years. Many experts believe that almost all those infected with HIV will eventually go on to develop AIDS in time.

I should emphasise that all the individual symptoms mentioned above can be caused by many diseases other than AIDS, and the presence of one or several of these features does not automatically mean you need to seek medical investigation for AIDS.

THE AIDS HAZE

There is relatively little argument about the facts I have presented so far. But, even so, only yesterday I read a book published as late as 1993 which was still suggesting that AIDS might not be caused by HIV!

However, it is usually when the discussion moves on to talk about the transmission and prevention of AIDS that the fog really descends. The AIDS haze is still pretty thick in many parts of Britain today. Few people are unaware of the disease, but many are misinformed and confused about it.

A survey of five hundred eleven-to-thirteen year-olds carried out in 1992 showed that 70 per cent first heard of AIDS through a television programme. Only one in ten heard about it from parents or school. The survey suggested that such piecemeal TV information encouraged misplaced fears and prejudice. 'One in five children said they would avoid social contact with children carrying the AIDS virus ... some thought it could be passed on by sharing cutlery, crockery, toilet seats or food.'[3]

The reason for such reluctance to talk frankly about AIDS is not hard to identify. AIDS strikes at the heart of the two greatest areas of human vulnerability – our sexuality and our mortality. Sex and death meet together in a potent cocktail of social taboos. No wonder we find it difficult to face the truth about AIDS.

Threatened with the prospect of death on a vast scale, human emotions understandably run high. A wide assortment of pressure groups – political, sexual, commercial, racial and religious, all have vested interests in making capital out of their own interpretation of the AIDS epidemic. This problem is further complicated by the fact that our knowledge of the nature of the disease is advancing all the time and some of our earlier concepts rapidly become outdated.

Given these provisos, let us look at some aspects of AIDS as we currently understand it.

STRAIGHT ANSWER TO A GAY QUESTION?

How is the AIDS virus spread?

HIV has been isolated in many body fluids, including saliva, sweat, tears, urine, breast-milk, and secretions from the vagina and cervix, but the greatest concentrations are found in blood and semen, and they therefore constitute the principal means of transmission.

There is no evidence that HIV is spread by coughs, sneezes or casual contact such as shaking hands. It is spread either sexually or by receiving infected blood. Those most at risk from infection by the latter route are mainlining drug addicts who share needles, or people receiving blood transfusions in parts of the world where donors are not screened adequately for the presence of HIV. Much more controversial is the question of who is at most risk from sexual transmission?

It is becoming increasingly clear that AIDS risk is directly related to sexual behaviour rather than sexual orientation, and 90 per cent of all new HIV infections worldwide are now among heterosexuals. On a global scale, 70 per cent of all HIV infection to date was acquired heterosexually. 'AIDS is no more a gay disease than German measles is German.'[4] Almost a half of the one million adults infected worldwide in 1992 were women.

It is when we examine the relative risk of sexual behaviours, listed at the end of this chapter, that we see why, in the West, AIDS is predominant among male homosexuals.

Anal intercourse, though by no means exclusive to homosexuals (up to one in ten women in the UK and USA practise it), it is particularly prevalent in this group and is a very high risk behaviour. This is thought to be because the lining of the anus in the receptive partner is likely to be traumatised, and thus be more readily open to infection. This risk is compounded by the fact that homosexuals in the past have been much more likely than their heterosexual counterparts to have multiple partners (p. 92).

Although initially the changing sexual practices among male homosexuals were reducing the incidence of HIV infection in the gay community, there is recent evidence[5] that it is on the increase here again in Britain, particularly in London.

It seems that the price of life is eternal vigilance, not a temporary change of behaviour. What, then, can we all do, irrespective of sexual orientation, to minimise the risk of HIV infection by our sexual activity?

A CRUCIAL CHOICE

The first step is to acknowledge the danger. Tanya, a glamorous twenty-year-old patient of mine typifies an attitude still currently widespread in Britain today. She came to see me requesting an HIV test.

'Have you been at special risk?' I asked her.

'Oh, yes,' she replied nonchalantly. 'My boyfriend is from East Africa and is bisexual.'

'And have you had unprotected sex with him?'

'Yes, many times.'

'May I ask why you have done that when you are obviously aware of the risk you were running?'

'Well,' she said, 'You never think at the time it could possibly happen to you.'

The main take-home message of this chapter is that it *could* happen to you if you choose the wrong partner. In Africa, 90 per cent of infections are transmitted between men and women, and 30 per cent of women with AIDS were virgins when they married and have been faithful wives ever since marriage.

Nothing could be plainer than the following statement issued by the World Health Organisation:

> ... the most effective way to prevent sexual transmission of HIV is to abstain, or for two uninfected individuals to be faithful to one another. Alternatively, the correct use of a condom may reduce the risk significantlly.[6]

I have discussed in detail the rationale of extra-marital abstinence in Chapter 6, but will explore further in the next section the other two main points of this WHO guildeline.

THE FREEDOM OF FAITHFULNESS

A British actress recently advised the American public to 'sleep with anything that has a pulse'.[7] As we have seen, if you choose to follow her advice, both you and 'anything' you sleep with may not have a pulse in a few years time.

This actress, and many like her, presumably think that for 'two uninfected individuals to be faithful to one another' is a rather boring recipe for life's sexual banquet. In fact, nothing could be farther from the truth. Claire Rayner, the dynamic doyenne of Britain's agony aunts, has this to say in her book *Safe Sex*,

> It is far from romantic flim-flam to say that the happpiest lives are likely to be built on a relationship that has moved from slow and gentle courtship, taking each step one at a time and slowly, rather than the all-at-once bound that has been fashionable for the past few years, to permanent commitment sealed with a public statement of some kind (a wedding, in other words).[8]

She goes on to say that lifelong monogamy not only protects against AIDS, but it can be great fun as well. Notice though that it is *lifelong* monogamy that protects, not serial monogamy – taking one partner at a time.

Most people who have only one sexual partner at a time, rightly do not consider themselves unduly promiscuous, but you have only to have intercourse with, say, your sixth partner already to be involved in a sexual network of 46,656 people – assuming that all your partners have also had six previous sexual relationships as well. Serial monogamy is risky behaviour.

There is yet one more important point to emphasise. It is lifelong monogamy with an *uninfected* partner that is safe. 'If most heterosexual intercourse involving infected people took place in stable relationships *long-term* partners would be the most at risk...'[9] Regular sex with an infected partner holds very high risks, even if condoms are used. This is a further reason to get to know your partner really well before embarking on a sexual relationship, or you may well be literally entrusting your life in having intercourse together.

If you or your prospective sexual partner have engaged in activity which puts either of you at risk, an HIV test should be considered.

CONDOM CAPERS

When reducing the risk of AIDS is mentioned, most people think first of condoms rather than faithfulness. Well, if faithfulness is rejected, condoms do offer some protection, and they should, of course, be used. Whether they are truly safe, however, is highly debatable.

At a recent AIDS conference, not one of the eight hundred sexologists and other experts present raised their hand when asked if they would trust a condom to protect them during intercourse with a known HIV infected person.[10] Small wonder, when the failure rate of condoms in preventing pregnancy can be as high as 13–15 per cent per year. It must also be remembered that conception can only occur on seven or eight days of each cycle at most, but HIV can be transmitted by an infected individual *every single time* they have intercourse.

Often the suggestion is made that it's not condoms that are unreliable, but the people who use them. A recent survey from

Manchester of people experienced in using condoms reported that '52 per cent of respondents had experienced condoms' bursting or slipping off in the previous three months'.[11] The author of this study commented, 'We do the public no favours by promoting the idea among medical staff that it is all the fault of the user when things go wrong.'[12]

One correspondent in the *British Medical Journal* even went so far as to suggest that 'refusal to talk about the failure rate of condoms is irresponsible and may be even legally liable. Telling young people to reduce their risk to one in six is no better than advocating Russian roulette. Both are fatal eventually.'[13]

The regular use of condoms does indeed reduce the risk of HIV transmission but it in no way constitutes a truly safe option.

SAFER SEX OR SAFE SEX?

Many people actually equate the term 'safe sex' with condom use. Safe sex, however, refers to sex which doesn't mix body fluids. Safe sex keeps the penis outside the other partner's body. It involves only so called 'dry sex activities', such as caressing and mutual masturbation.

There are many books, such as the popular *Stronger Love, Safer Sex* by Celia Haddon and Thomson Prentice which give fuller details of such safe sex activities, but though there is in these books much helpful material, such as I have considered in Chapter 12 to enhance your love-making, the frustrating restrictions and limitations which 'safe sex' imposes are also clearly apparent.

For example, Haddon and Prentice write about 'having to put some clothes back on and walk out',[14] and making 'an excuse to go to the lavatory and relieve ourselves there by masturbation'.[15] They also emphasise various other restrictions, such as where the penis can and can't go during your time of sexual intimacy. Even more illuminating is their observation that 'the penis tends to find its way into its *natural* place, the vagina'[16] (my italics). Such a statement seems to betray an underlying awareness that there is at least an element about 'safe sex' which is not natural?

Dr Patrick Dixon, one of Britain's leading authorities on AIDS, so rightly comments on this subject that

> many pamphlets tell us how wonderful 'safe sex' is. They say how fulfilling and lovely it is just to rub bodies together and have a cuddle ... The pamphlets condemn people to a lifetime of nonsense. *'A hundred and one ways to have fun with a condom.'* How lovely. How stupid when the alternative is so simple ...[17]

To choose an uninfected partner with whom to share a mutually faithful relationship is the only way to an abandoned, anxiety-free sex-life.

TO TEST OR NOT TO TEST?

That is the question asked sooner or later by anyone who has been, or is currently at risk of HIV infection.

The 'AIDS test' does not in fact test for AIDS as such, but is a blood test to detect infection with HIV. The body recognises HIV as an invading enemy and tries to neutralise it by producing substances called antibodies. Though these antibodies are ineffective in actually killing HIV, they do indicate the presence of the virus, and HIV antibody testing has been of invaluable help in our understanding of the extent of spread of the infection.

An HIV test can be obtained through your general practitioner, or alternatively from the Sexually Transmitted Diseases department of your local hospital. At the time of writing, the establishment of specific community HIV testing centres is also being considered by the Department of Health.

The HIV antibodies which the test detects, take between three weeks and three months to appear after infection has occurred. HIV testing, though, like any other biological test, is not 100 per cent reliable. False negative results are extremely rare, but it is important to realise that there are case of AIDS who have never shown up as sero-positive even on repeated testing.

False positive results do sometimes occur as well, particularly in blood from haemophiliacs which does not clot in the normal way. If a positive result is obtained, the laboratory will usually do a confirmatory test using an independent method from the first test.

There are several compelling reasons why you should consider being tested if you are or have been at risk of HIV infection.

TO PREVENT SPREAD OF THE VIRUS
If you are infected, knowing the fact may provide the all-important motivation to adapt your sexual behaviour to minimise the risk of infection to your partner. If you truly love that partner, you both need to know if you are sero-positive.

If you are a woman you run the additional risk of transmission of the virus to your children if you are infected. Again, the knowledge that you are HIV positive should prompt particular care over contraceptive measures.

TO ASSIST EARLY DETECTION OF COMPLICATIONS OF HIV INFECTION
Some of the infections affecting HIV-positive individuals are rare in everyday medical practice. There have been several instances of patients dying of such infections when doctors were slow in making the correct diagnosis because both they and the patient were unaware of the presence of HIV.

TO MINIMISE PROGRESS OF THE DISEASE
Though at the time of writing AIDS is incurable, there is much that can be done to try and slow the progress of the disease if it is detected in the early stages. A recent study concluded decisively, 'People who are unaware of their serostatus ... are more likely to die during the month in which AIDS is diagnosed than people who are aware of their infection.'[18]

There are some negative aspects of having the test. Difficulties may have been experienced in the past with some companies in obtaining a mortgage or life insurance,[19] even if the test is negative. These attitudes are changing rapidly, however, and the insurance world is gradually realising that having an AIDS test is often a sign of responsibility rather than an indicator of recklessness. If you have a negative test, and a lifestyle questionnaire reveals that you have never injected drugs or had a gay lifestyle, there should be no problem.

Other attitudes are slower to change in society, however, and the stigma of a positive result can often lead to rejection rather than compassion. People with HIV are no more immune to prejudice than they are to opportunistic infection. 'You turn on the television or open a newspaper and in the context of an item on AIDS, you will see yourself described in terms which make it clear that in society's eyes, you are finished.'[20] Dismissal from work, exclusion from a circle of friends, and rejection by the family can all adversely affect the capacity for intimacy, quite apart from the disease itself.

The knowledge of a positive test can be an overwhelming experience for some people. In the early days of testing, before extensive counselling facilities were the norm, some suicides did follow a positive result. Extensive follow-up and support is essential for those having to face life with HIV infection.

BEYOND AIDS

A colleague of mine regularly begins one of his lectures with a slide on which is written, 'Where there's hope, there's life'! This is so true. It is vital to stress that having a positive result is not an automatic death sentence. Though, as mentioned above, there are some experts who believe that almost all those infected with HIV will eventually develop AIDS, present studies indicate that it takes ten years for 50 per cent of HIV-infected individuals to develop symptoms.[21]

Even in the absence of HIV infection, life still has 100 per cent mortality. This book has focused on one of the greatest gifts that life has to offer – the joy of inter-personal intimacy. But human intimacy, no matter how deep and satisfying, cannot answer all the needs of our hearts. Neither can such intimacy last for ever.

AIDS forces us to look afresh at our mortality as well as our morality. 'As my doctor once commented, many people with AIDS become what they always wanted to be. Perhaps, but I still worry about the black bag at the end...'[22]

As Patrick Dixon powerfully challenges us,

> AIDS confronts us at the very root of our being and at the end of the day leaves us with choices about how we respond, not just to AIDS and those who are dying from it, but also to the ultimate issue: What is the meaning of life? What is the meaning of *my* life?[23]

It also begs the question, 'What is the meaning of my sexual life?'

> A society founded on a libertarian concept of sexual freedom must be vulnerable to that freedom's being abused. If such an ill-conceived 'freedom' results in death and illness we must not be surprised when some start to question whether it was worth anything in the first place.[24]

It is as a result of my own such questioning that I have written this book. I hope it will stimulate you to re-evaluate the meaning of your own sexual experience. In the final analysis, the Author of sex is the one who knows best how it should be expressed. I believe that only in following the Maker's instructions, can we discover a more satisfying sexuality and a deeper intimacy that exceeds even our wildest dreams.

CONTACT AGENCIES

National AIDS Helpline, Freephone 0800-567 123.
AIDS Care, Education and Training (ACET), PO Box 1323, London W5 5TF. Tel 081-840 7879.

SAFE SEX AND DEGREES OF RISKY SEX

Safe
Dry kissing
Massaging and caressing the body away from genital area
Solo masturbation
Sex with an uninfected partner

Low Risk
Mutual masturbation
Vaginal intercourse using a condom
Cunnilingus

High Risk
Wet kissing
Vaginal intercourse without a condom
Fellatio
Anilingus
Fisting (insertion of hand or fist into rectum)
Anal intercourse with or without a condom

Very High Risk
Sex with an infected partner with or without a condom
Injecting drugs with shared needles or syringes.

POSTSCRIPT – BECOMING ONE FLESH

As in an Indiana Jones film, after dealing with so many enemies, we can't end without a final look at the goal of our quest.

The most precious treasure that sexual intimacy affords is the glorious possibility of two people becoming one flesh. Man does not live by orgasm alone; our sexual capacity is indissolubly linked with our personhood. Human sexual union means so much more than mere genital interaction – pleasurable though that may be. When two people engage in sexual intercourse, a spiritual interaction – albeit both unseen and unacknowledged, also takes place between them. The two become one flesh. This unseen union may occur as a result of a sexual encounter between two people in an otherwise uncommitted relationship. When such a relationship subsequently breaks up, both partners' capacity for intimacy is inevitably damaged.

However, when this 'one flesh' experience occurs within a committed relationship in which both partners have devoted themselves unconditionally to the other, it results in enhanced intimacy. It is the 'one flesh' element that gives such a deep and wonderful dimension to sexual ecstasy.

> It is surely this which explains the profound mystery of heterosexual intimacy, which poets and philosophers have celebrated in every culture. Heterosexual intercourse is so much more than a union of bodies; it is a blending of complementary personalities through which, in the midst of prevailing alienation, the rich created oneness of human being is experienced again.[1]

Satisfying human intimacy can be found independently of sexual intercourse (as the celibate writer of the above quotation exemplifies!), but if such intimacy is sought through a sexual relationship, it will only be found there within the mutual life-commitment that becoming 'one flesh' demands. This is the ultimate goal. I pray that this book will help many of you to achieve it.

REFERENCES

INTRODUCTION

1   Susan M. Daniels, 'Crucial issues in sexuality and disability', in *Sexuality and Physical Disability*, eds David Bullard and Susan Knight (C.V. Mosby, 1981) p. 9.

CHAPTER 1: GENDER IDENTITY

1   Milton Diamond, 'A critical evaluation of the ontogeny of human sexual behaviour', *Quarterly Review of Biology*, 1965, 40, 147–75.
2   J. McGlone, 'Sex Differences in Human Brain Asymmetry: A Critical Survey', *Behavioural and Brain Sciences*, 1980, 3, 215–63.
3   C. de Lacoste-Utamsing and R.L. Holloway, 'Sex Differences in the Fetal Human Corpus Callosum', *Human Neurobiology*, 1986, 5, 93–6.
4   William Byne and Bruce Parsons, 'Human Sexual Orientation – The Biologic Theories Reappraised', *Arch Gen Psych*, 1993, 50, 228–39.
5   Robert Stoller, *Sex and Gender. On the development of masculinity and femininity* (Hogarth, 1968).
6   John Money, *Man and Woman, Boy and Girl. Differentiation and Dimorphism of Gender Identity from Conception to Maturity* (John Hopkins University Press, 1972).
7   Eleanor Maccoby and C. Jacklin, *The Psychology of Sex Differences* (Stanford University Press, 1974).
8   Glenn Wilson, *The Great Sex Divide* (Peter Owen, 1989) p. 37.

9   Diana Halpern, *Sex Differences in Cognitive Abilities* (Erlbaum Associates, 1986).
10 John Bancroft, *Human Sexuality and its Problems* (Churchill Livingstone, 1985) p. 16.
11 Leonard Le Sourd, *Strong Men, Weak Men* (Hodder & Stoughton, 1991) p. 29.

CHAPTER 2: SEXUAL ANATOMY

1   Daniel C. Goldberg et al, 'The Grafenberg Spot and Female Ejaculation: A Review of Initial Hypotheses', *Journal of Sex and Marital Therapy*, 1983, 9, 27–37.

CHAPTER 3: SEXUAL BEHAVIOUR AND SEX EDUCATION

1   Lynda Madaras, *What's Happening to my Body. A Growing-up Guide for Parents and Sons* (Penguin, 1984), p. 15.
2   Ronald and Juliette Goldman, *Show Me Yours*, (Penguin, 1988), p. 225.
3   *Unplanned Pregnancy* (Royal College of Obstetricians and Gynaecologists, 1972).
4   Thomas Szasz, 'The Case Against Sex Education', *British Journal of Sexual Medicine*, December 1981.
5   Robert Kolodny, William Masters and Virginia Johnson, *Textbook of Sexual Medicine* (Little, Brown and Co., Boston, 1979), p. 71.
6   Robert A. Lewis, 'Parents and Peers', *Journal of Sex Research*, 1973, 9, 156–70.
7   Josh McDowell, *How To Help Your Child Say No To Sexual Pressure*, (Word, 1988), p. 99.
8   Lynda Madaras, op. cit., p. 32.

CHAPTER 4: PUBERTY

1   Ronald and Juliette Goldman, *Show Me Yours* (Penguin, 1988), p. xxvi.

CHAPTER 5: SOLO SEXUALITY

1   P.H. Gebhard and A.B. Johnson, *The Kinsey Data* (Saunders, Philadelphia, 1979).
2   ibid.
3   M. Hunt, *Sexual Behaviour in the 1970s*, (Playboy Press, Chicago, 1974).
4   Philip Cauthery, Andrew Stanway and Penny Stanway, *The Complete Book of Love and Sex* (Arrow, 1983). pp. 264–7.
5   Thomas Blackburn, *A Clip of Steel*. Quoted by Arthur Marshall in *Girls will be Girls*, (Hamish Hamilton, 1974), p. 146.
6   Paul Francis, *Masturbation – Lonely Love*, (Going Public, Cardiff, 1991), p. 1.
7   Derek Llewellyn-Jones, *Understanding Sexuality*, 3rd edn, (OUP, 1988) p. 35.
8   Philip Cauthery, Andrew Stanway and Penny Stanway, *The Complete Book of Love and Sex*, (Arrow, 1983), p. 267.
9   Derek Llewellyn-Jones, ibid.
10 John Bancroft, *Human Sexuality and its Problems*, (Churchill Livingstone, 1985), p. 120.
11 Una Kroll, *Sexual Counselling*, (SPCK, 1980), p. 43.
12 William Kraft, *Sexual Dimensions of the Celibate Life*, (Gill & Macmillan, 1979), p. 153.
13 Shere Hite, *The Hite Report*, (Talmy Franklin, 1976), p. 6.
14 John White, *Eros Defiled*, (IVP, 1978), p. 37.
15 Lewis Smedes, *Sex in The Real World*, (Lion, 1979), p. 155.
16 Jack Weir, 'The Psychology of Sex', in *Sex and Your Health*, ed. James Bevan (Mandarin, 1990), p. 216.
17 Lewis Smedes, ibid., p. 154.

CHAPTER 6: VIRGIN TERRITORY

1　Michael Schofield, *The Sexual Behaviour of Young People*, (Longman, 1965).

2　Christine Farrell, *My Mother Said...* (Routledge & Kegan Paul, London, 1978).

3　Alexander Gunn, 'Treating Teenagers', *BMJ*, 1992, 304, 1320.

4　Health Education Authority, *Young Adults' Health and Lifestyle: Sexual Behaviour*, 1990.

5　David Phillips, *Changing Sexual Lifestyles of Young People* (RCGP Members' Handbook, 1992), p. 300.

6　Quoted in Celia Haddon and Thomson Prentice, *Stronger Love Safer Sex*, (Papermac, 1989), p. 135.

7　Gerhard Hauer, *Longing For Tenderness*, (Editions Trobisch, 1983), p. 75.

8　Gunter Schmidt, in John Bancroft, *Human Sexuality and its Problems*, (Churchill Livingstone, 1985), p. vi.

9　J. Kantner and M. Zelnik, 'Sexual experience of young unmarried women in the US', *Family Planning Perspectives*, 1972, 4, 9–18.

10　Ronald and Juliette Goldman, *Show Me Yours*, (Penguin, 1988), p. 225.

11　C. Hall, *Independent*, 21 July 1992: 2.

12　Alex Mellanby et al., 'Promoting Sexual Health', *BMJ*, 1992, 305, 363.

13　Josh McDowell, *Why Wait?* (Here's Life Publications, San Bernardino, 1987), p. 40.

14　Phillip Schofield, *Sunday Mirror Magazine*, 3 May 1992, 40.

15　Bent Claesson, *Boy Girl – Man Woman*, quoted by Joyce Huggett, in *Life In a Sex-Mad Society*, (IVP, 1988), p. 43.

16　Quoted in Alexander Lowen, *Love and Orgasm* (Macmillan, 1975), p. 317.

17　Ira Reiss, 'The Sexual Renaissance', *J Soc Issues*, 1966, 22, 123.

18　Jack Weir, 'Sex in Society', in *Sex and Your Health*, ed. James Bevan, (Mandarin, 1990), p. 304.

19　Alex Comfort, quoted by Joyce Huggett in op. cit., p. 22.

20　Paul Vaughan, *The Pill On Trial*, (Pelican, 1972), p. 185.

21 Alex Mellanby et al., 'Teenagers, Sex and Risk Taking', *BMJ*, 1993, 307, 25.

22 Jack Dominian, *Sexual Integrity*, (DLT, 1987), p. 79.

23 Arthur Miller, *The Crucible*, (Heineman, 1956), p. 50.

24 Lewis Smedes, *Sex in The Real World*, (Lion, 1979), p. 122.

25 A.H. Goldman, 'Plain Sex', *Philosophy and Public Affairs*, 1977, 6, p. 278.

26 Jack Dominian, op. cit., p. 70.

27 Lewis Terman, *Psychological Factors in Marital Happinesss* (McGraw Hill, 1938), p. 324.

28 David Shope and Carlfred Broderick, 'Level of Sexual Experience and Predicted Adjustment in Marriage', *J Marriage Family*, 1967, 29, 424–7.

29 Robert Athanasiou and Richard Sarkin, 'Premarital Sexual Behaviour and Postmarital Adjustment', *Arch Sex Behav.*, 1974, 3, 207–25.

30 William Reevy, 'Premarital Petting Behaviour and Marital Happinesss and Prediction', *Marriage and Family Living*, 1959, 21, p. 354.

31 John Bancroft, *Human Sexuality and its Problems*, (Churchill Livingstone, 1985), p. 141.

32 *Population Trends*, (HMSO, 1992).

33 *The Independent*, 20 June 1992: 1.

34 Robert Athanasiou and Richard Sarkin, op. cit., p. 221.

35 Katharine Trevelyan, *Fool in Love*, quoted by David Phypers, *Christian Marriage in Crisis* (Marc Europe, 1985), p. 67.

36 Walter Trobisch, *Living With Unfulfilled Desires* (Editions Trobisch, 1980).

37 Philip Cauthery, Andrew Stanway and Penny Stanway, *The Complete Book of Love and Sex*, (Arrow, 1983), p. 83.

38 Lynda Madaras, *What's Happening To My Body? A Growing Up Guide for Parents and Daughters*, (Penguin, 1989), p. 259.

39 Jack Dominian, op. cit., p. 64.

40 John White, *Eros Defiled*, (IVP, 1978), p. 51.

41 Jonathan E. Fielding, 'Adolescent Pregnancy Revisited', *New Eng J Med*, 1978, 299, 893–6.

42 John Bancroft, *Human Seuxality and Its Problems*, (Churchill Livingstone, 1985), p. 376.

43 F. Shah, J. Kantner et al., 'Unprotected Intercourse Among Unwed Teenagers', *Fam Plan Perspect*, 1975, 7, 39–41.

44 John Coleman and Leo Hendry, *The Nature of Adolescence*, (Routledge, 1990), p. 147.

45 Marsha Goldsmith, 'Silent Epidemic of Social Disease Makes Experts Raise Their Voices', *JAMA*, 1989, 261, 3509–10.

46 Michael Adler, *ABC of Sexually Transmitted Diseases*, (BMA, 1990).

47 D.C.G. Skegg et al., 'Importance of the male factor in cancer of the cervix', *Lancet*, 1982, ii, 581–3.

48 WHO Statement for World AIDS Day, 1 December 1991.

49 David Weis, 'Reactions of College Women To Their First Coitus', *Medical Aspects of Human Sexuality*, 1983, 17 (2), 60.

50 Mary Calderone; quoted by Robert Collins in 'A Physician's View of College Sex', *JAMA*, 1975, 232, 392.

51 Donald Orr et al., 'Premature Sexual Activity as an Indicator of Psychosocial Risk', *Paediatrics*, 1991, 87, 141–7.

CHAPTER 7: HOMOSEXUALITY

1 Peter Hill, *Adolescent Psychiatry*, (Churchill Livingstone, 1989), p. 210.

2 Lorraine Trenchard and Hugh Warren, *Something To Tell You*, (London Gay Teenage Group, 1984), p. 39.

3 Alfred Kinsey et al., *Sexual Behaviour in The Human Male*, (Saunders, 1948).

4 J. Gagnon and W. Simon, *Sexual Conduct: The Source of Human Sexuality*, (Aldine, 1973).

5 David Forman and Clair Chilvers. 'Sexual Behaviour of Young and Middle-Aged Men in England and Wales', *BMJ*, 1989, 298, 1137–42.

6 J. Billy et al., 'The Sexual Behaviour of Men in the United States', *Fam Plann Perspect*, 1993, 25, 52–60.

7 Frederick Kenyon, 'Female Homosexuality', in John Loraine, *Understanding Homosexuality*, (MTP, 1974), p. 85.

8   Edward Eichel and J. Gordon Muir, 'Homosexuality in The US', *BMJ*, 1993, 307, 61.

9   Judith Reisman and Edward Eichel, *Kinsey, Sex and Fraud*, (Huntingdon House/Nova, 1990).

10 Gershon Legman, *The Horn Book: Studies in Erotic Folklore and Bibliography*, (University Books, 1964), p. 125.

11 Donald West, *Homosexuality Revisited*, (Duckworth, 1977), p. 261.

12 John Hart, *So You Think You're Attracted To The Same Sex?* (Pelican, 1984), p. 15.

13 John Hart, op. cit., p. 66.

14 F.J. Kallman, 'Comparative twin study on the genetic aspects of male homosexuality', *J Nerv Ment Dis*, 1952, 115, 283.

15 J. Michael Bailey and Richard C. Pillard, 'A Genetic Study of Male Sexual Orientation', *Arch Gen Psych*, 1991, 48, 1089–96.

16 J. Michael Bailey, Richard C. Pillard et al., 'Heritable Factors Influence Sexual Orientation in Women', *Arch Gen Psych*, 1993, 50, 217–23.

17 William Byne and Bruce Parsons, 'Human Sexual Orientation: The Biologic Theories Reappraised', *Arch Gen Psych*, 1993, 50, 228–39.

18 Michael King and Elizabeth McDonald, 'Homosexuals Who Are Twins. A Study of 46 Probands', *Br J Psych*, 1992, 160, 407–19.

19 Dean Hamer et al., 'A Linkage Between DNA Markers on the X Chromosome and Male Sexual Orientation', *Science*, 1993, 261, 321–7.

20 *The Times*, 12 March 1969.

21 Simon LeVay, 'A Difference in Hypothalamic Structure Between Heterosexual and Homosexual Men', *Science*, 1991, 253, 1034–7.

22 Kenneth Klivington, quoted by David Gelman et al., 'Born or Bred?', *Newsweek*, 24 February 1992, p. 50.

23 William Byne and Bruce Parsons, op. cit., p. 228.

24 Richard Pillard, quoted by David Gelman et al., op. cit., p. 48.

25 Frederick Kenyon, 'Studies in Female Homosexuality', *Br J Psych*, 114, 1337.

26 P.M Davies et al., 'The Sexual Behaviour of Young Gay Men in England and Wales', *AIDS Care*, 1992, 4, 259–72.

27 Irving Bieber, *Homosexuality: A Psychoanalytic Study*, (Basic Books, 1962).

28 M. Siegelman, 'Parental Background of male homosexuals and heterosexuals', *Arch Sex Behav*, 1974, 3, 3–18.

29 Alan Cooper, 'Aetiology of Homosexuality', in *Understanding Homosexuality*, ed. John Loraine, (MTP 1974).

30 Elizabeth Moberly, *Psychogenesis. The Early Development of Gender Identity* (Routledge and Kegan Paul, 1983).

31 Elizabeth Moberly, *Homosexuality. Towards a New Christian Ethic*, (James Clarke, 1983).

32 Peter Hill, *Adolescent Psychiatry*, (Churchill Livingstone, 1989), p. 209.

33 Elizabeth Moberly, *Homosexuality*, op. cit., p. 2.

34 John Bancroft, *Human Sexuality and its Problems*, (Churchill Livingstone, 1985), p. 167.

35 Charles Socarides, *Beyond Sexual Freedom*, (Quadrangle: New York Times Books, 1975).

36 John Green and David Miller, 'Male Homosexuality and Sexual Problems', *Br. J. Hosp Medicine*, 1985, 33, 353.

37 Elizabeth Moberly, *Homosexuality*, op. cit., p. 42.

38 Jack Dominian, *Sexual Integrity*, (DLT), p. 26.

39 Andrew Kominsky, *Pursuing Sexual Wholeness*, (Monarch, 1990).

40 Jeanette Howard, *Out of Egypt – Leaving Lesbianism Behind*, (Monarch, 1991).

41 E. Mansell Pattison, 'Ex-Gays: Religiously Mediated Change in Homosexuals', *American J. Psych* 1980, 137, 12.

42 George Weinberg, *Society and The Healthy Homosexual*, (Alyson, 1991).

43 John White, *Eros Defiled*, (IVP, 1977), p. 110.

44 Alex Davidson, *The Returns of Love* (IVP, 1970), p. 51.

45 Oliver O'Donovan, *Transsexualism and Christian Marriage*, (Grove, 1982), p. 6.

46 Elizabeth Moberly, *Homosexuality*, op. cit., p. 37.

47 Pierre Berton, quoted by Letha Scanzoni and Virginia Mollenkott in *The Comfortable Pew* (SCM, 1962).

48 John Green and David Miller, 'Male Homosexuality and Sexual Problems', ibid.

49 Elizabeth Moberly, *Homosexuality*, ibid.

50 Alan P. Bell and Martin S. Weinberg, *Homosexualities. A study of diversities among men and women*, (Mitchell Beazley, 1978).

51 John Bancroft, *Human Sexuality and its Problems*, (Churchill Livingstone, 1985), p. 173.

52 A Hyatt-Williams, 'Problems of Homosexuality', in *Aspects of Sexual Medicine*, (BMA, 1976), p. 63.

53 Alan P. Bell and Martin S. Weinberg, *Homosexualities*, ibid.

54 Alex Davidson, op. cit., p. 49.

CHAPTER 8: ROMANCE, ATTRACTION AND PARTNER CHOICE

1 Anonymous, quoted in Richard Griffiths, *Courtship*, (Grove Books, 1978), p. 17.

2 William Shakespeare, *The Merchant of Venice* II. vi. 36–7.

3 Richard Griffiths, ibid.

4 August B. Hollingshead, 'Cultural factors in the selection of marriage mates', *Am Soc Review*, 1950, 15, 619.

5 Alfred C. Clarke, 'An examination of the operation of residential propinquity as a factor in mate selection', *Am Soc Review*, 1962, 17, 17.

6 Jack Dominian, *Marital Pathology*, (BMA, 1982), p. 14.

7 Robin Skynner and John Cleese, *Families and How To Survive Them*, (Methuen, 1983).

8 R.F. Winch, *Mate Selection: A Study of Complementary Needs*, (Harper, 1959).

9 Philip Cauthery, Andrew Stanway and Penny Stanway, *The Complete Book of Love and Sex*, (Arrow, 1983), p. 364.

10 Erich Fromm, *The Art Of Loving*, (Unwin, 1975), p. 30.

11 Erich Fromm, op. cit., p. 26.

CHAPTER 9: COURTSHIP AND ENGAGEMENT

1   Philip Cauthery, Andrew Stanway and Penny Stanway, *The Complete Book of Love and Sex*, (Arrow, 1983), p. 60.
2   Judson T. Landis, 'The Pattern of Divorce in Three Generations', *Social Forces*, 1956, 34, 213.
3   John White, *Eros Defiled*, (VIP, 1977), p. 53.
4   George Elliot, *Middlemarch*, (Penguin Classics, 1985).
5   Helen Garlick and Jane Stuart, *The Good Marriage*, (Simon & Schuster, 1990).
6   *Population Trends*, (HMSO Publications, 1992).
7   Alfred Demaris and Gerald Leslie, 'Co-habitation with the future spouse; Its influence upon marital satisfaction and communication', *Journal of Marriage and the Family*, February 1984, p. 83.
8   E. Mansell Pattison. 'Living Together: A poor substitute for marriage', *Medical aspects of Human Sexuality*, 1982, 16, 79.
9   E. Mansell Pattison, op. cit., p. 78.
10 E. Mansell Pattison, op. cit., p. 86.
11 C.S. Lewis, *The Four Loves*, (Fontana, 1963), p. 95.

CHAPTER 10: MARRIAGE

1   G. Gorer, *Sex and Marriage In England Today*, (Nelson, 1971).
2   Milton Erickson in *Changing Couples*, ed. J. Haley (Triangle, 1985).
3   Jack Dominian, *Make or Break*, (SPCK, 1984), p. 49.
4   Elizabeth Bott, *Family and Social Network*, (Tavistock, 1971).
5   Christopher Clulow and Janet Mattinson, *Marriage Inside Out*, (Pelican, 1989), p. 7.
6   A. Stephenson, *Archetype: A Natural History of The Self*, (Routledge & Kegan Paul, 1982).
7   Christopher Clulow and Janet Mattinson, op. cit., p. 25.
8   Jack Dominian, *Introduction to Marital Problems*, (Fount, 1986).
9   Jack Dominian, *Marital Pathology*, (BMA, 1979).

10 B. Thornes and J. Collard, *Who Divorces?*, (Routledge & Kegan Paul, 1979).
11 C. Walker, *Equalities and Inequalities In Family Life*, (Academic Press, 1977).
12 Alfred Lord Tennyson, *The Princess*, V. 427.
13 George F. Gilder, *Sexual Suicide*, (Bantam, 1975), p. 46.
14 Margaret Mead, *Male and Female*, (Penguin, 1962), p. 88.
15 Betty Friedan, *The Second Stage*, (Sphere, 1983), p. 145.

CHAPTER 11: INTIMATE COMMUNICATION

1 Stephen B. Levine, 'Psychological Intimacy', *Journal of Sex and Marital Therapy*, 1991, 17, 259–68.
2 op. cit., p. 268.
3 Shere Hite, *Women and Love*, (Viking, 1987), p. 5.
4 Joyce Huggett, *Growing Into Love*, (IVP, 1982), p. 82.
5 Sven Wahlroos, *Family Communication*, (Macmillan, 1974), p. 159.
6 Roy McCloughry, *Men And Masculinity – From Power to Love*, (Hodder & Stoughton, 1992), p. 189.
7 Deborah Tannen, *You Just Don't Understand*, (Virago, 1991).
8 Sarah Litvinoff, *The Relate Guide to Better Relationships*, (Vermilion, 1992), p. 108.
9 Joyce Hugget, *Two Into One*, (IVP, 1981), p. 90.
10 Christopher Clulow and Janet Mattinson, *Marriage Inside Out*, (Pelican, 1989), p. 85.
11 Celia Haddon and Thomson Prentice, *Stronger Love, Safer Sex*, (Papermac, 1989), p. 121.

CHAPTER 12: INTIMATE INTERCOURSE

1 Jack Dominian, *Marital Breakdown*, (Pelican, 1971), p. 81.
2 Domeena C. Renshaw, 'Intimacy and Intercourse', *Medical Aspects of Human Sexuality*, 1984, 18, 73.

3   Alex Comfort, *The Joy of Sex*, (Quartet, 1992), p. 36.
4   Dagmar O'Connor, *How to Make Love to the Same Person for the Rest of Your LIfe and Still Love It*, (Virgin, 1993), p. 17.
5   Alex Comfort, op. cit., p. 34.
6   John and Janet Houghton, *A Touch of Love*, (Kingsway, 1991), p. 97.
7   Rufus Fernando and Lakshman Samaranayake, 'The Infection Risk of Oral Sex', *Journal of Sexual Health*, 1992, 2, 26–9.
8   Derek Timmins, 'Infections Acquired by Oro-Genital Contact', *Br. J. Sexual Med*, 19, 100–2.
9   Robin Skynner, *One Flesh – Separate Persons,* (Constable, 1976).
10 Alex Comfort, *The Joy of Sex*, (Quartet, 1975), p. 118.
11 Celia Haddon and Thomson Prentice, *Stronger Love, Safer Sex*, (Papermac, 1989), p. 101.
12 Sarah Litvinoff, *The Relate Guide To Sex In Loving Relationships*, (Vermilion, 1992), p. 189.
13 Clifford and Joyce Penner, *The Gift of Sex*, (Word, 1989), p. 175.
14 Dagmar O'Connor, op. cit., p. 73.
15 John and Janet Houghton, op. cit., p. 122.

CHAPTER 13: SEXUAL PROBLEMS

1   William Masters and Virginia Johnson, *Human Sexual Inadequacy*, (Churchill Livingstone, 1970), p. 369.
2   E. Frank et al., 'Frequency of Sexual Dysfunction in "Normal" Couples', *New Eng J Med*, 1978, 299, 111–15.
3   David Mace, *Sexual Difficulties In Marriage*, (National Marriage Guidance Council, 1983), p. 2.
4   Liz Hodgkinson, *Sex Is Not Compulsory*, (Columbus Books, 1986).
5   David Mace, op. cit., p. 15.
6   Paul Brown and Carolyn Faulder, *Treat Yourself to Sex*, (Penguin, 1989), p. 165.

7 Keith Hawton, *Sex Therapy – A Practical Guide*, (OUP, 1991), p. 41.
8 Christopher Clulow and Janet Mattinson, *Marriage Inside Out*, (Pelican, 1989), p. 93.
9 Dagmar O'Connor, *How to Make Love to the Same Person for the Rest of Your Life and Still Love It*, (Virgin, 1993), p. 162.

CHAPTER 14: CONTRACEPTION, ABORTION AND INFERTILITY

1 John Guillebaud, *Contraception. Your Questions Answered*, (Churchill Livingstone, 1987), p. 26.
2 Ibid.
3 Germaine Greer, *Sex and Destiny*, (Picador, 1985), p. 111.
4 Ingrid Trobisch in her Preface to Mary Shivanandas, *Natural Sex*, (Hamlyn, 1980).
5 Mary Shivanandas, op. cit.
6 Frank J. Rice et al., 'The Effectiveness of the Sympto-Thermal Method of Natural Family Planning: An International Study', presented at First General Assembly of the International Federation for Family Life Promotion, in Colombia, 23 June 1977.
7 Germaine Greer, op. cit., p. 133.
8 Susannah Frankel, 'Is that an Amoeba Between your Legs?', *Independent*, 9 October 1992.
9 John Bancroft, *Human Sexuality and Its Problems*, (Churchill Livingstone, 1983), p. 384.
10 Julia Mosse and Josephine Heaton, *The Fertility and Contraception Book*, (Faber & Faber, 1990), p. 211.
11 Germaine Greer, op. cit.
12 Geraldine Howard, 'The Quality of Marriage Before and After Vasectomy', *British Journal of Sexual Medicine*, Sept 1979, pp. 13–14, 57.
13 John Guillebaud, *The Pill*, (OUP, 1980), p. 20.
14 James Owen Drife, 'One In Three', *BMJ*, 1991, 303, 653.

15 Julia Mosse and Josephine Heaton, op. cit., p. 345.
16 Jane Kilvington, 'The Main Forms of Contraception', in *Sex and Your Health*, ed. James Bevan (Mandarin, 1990), p. 49.
17 Una Kroll, *Sexual Counselling* (SPCK, 1980), p. 117.
18 Julia Mosse and Josephine Heaton, op. cit., p. 350.
19 Christopher Clulow and Janet Mattinson, *Marriage Matters*, (Penguin, 1989), p. 127.
20 Miriam Deeny, 'Abortion In The First Trimester', *BMJ*, 1992, 305, 1503.
21 Ann Winterton, 'The Abortion Act 25 Years On', *BMA News Review*, October 1992, p. 15.
22 Philip Ney, 'Relationship Between Abortion and Child Abuse', *Can J Psychiatry*, 1979, 24, 617.
23 Francis A. Schaeffer, quoted by E.R.M. Saunders in 'Abortion In the First Trimester', *BMJ*, 1992, 305, 1222.
24 Joan Raphael–Leff, 'Infertility: Diagnosis or Life-Sentence?' *British Journal of Sexual Medicine*, Jan 1986, p. 29.
25 Christopher Clulow and Janet Mattinson, op. cit., p. 131.
26 Diane and Peter Houghton, *Coping With Childlessness*, (Unwin, 1987), p. 88.

CHAPTER 15: PREGNANCY AND PARENTHOOD

1 Richard P. Perkins, 'Sexuality During Pregnancy', *Clinical Obstetrics and Gynaecology*, 1984, 27, p. 714.
2 Dennis J. Munjack and L. Jerome Oziel, 'Sex and Pregnancy', *Br J Sexual Med*, 1979, Oct, p. 19.
3 Richard P. Perkins, op. cit.
4 Christopher Clulow, quoted in David Cohen, 'The Baby Came But the Sex Went', *Independent*, 8 July, 1992, p. 14.
5 ibid.
6 J. Swanson, 'The Marital Sexual Relationship During Pregnancy', *J Obs and Gynaecol Nursing*, 1980, 9, 267.
7 Sheila Kitzinger, 'Sexuality In Pregnancy', *Br J Sexual Med*, 1982, March, p. 46.

8 D.A. Solber et al. 'Sexual Behaviour In Pregnancy', *New Eng, J Med*, 1973, 288, 1098.

9 C.J. Falicov, 'Sexual Adjustment during First Pregnancy and Post Partum', *Am J Obstet Gynecol*, 1973, 117, 991–1000.

10 Quoted in David Cohen, op. cit.

11 J. Butler and N. Wagner, 'Sexuality During Pregnancy and The Postpartum Period', in R. Green (ed.) *Human Sexuality: A Health Practitioner's Text*, (Ballimore, Williams and Wilkins, 1975).

12 Richard P. Perkins, 'Sexuality In Pregnancy: What Determines Behaviour?', *Obstet Gynecol*, 1982, 59, 189.

13 Richard P. Perkins, 1984, op. cit., p. 711.

14 P. Bray et al., 'Orogenital Sex as A Cause of Non-Fatal Air Embolism in Pregnancy', *Obstet Gynaecol*, 1983, 61, 653.

15 Lynn Faulds Wood, *Telegraph Family Supplement*, 29 January 1993, p. 14.

16 E. Le Masters, 'Parenthood as Crisis', *Marriage and Family Living*, 1957, 19, 352–5.

17 A. Oakley, 'The Baby Blues', *New Society*, 5 April 1979.

18 Katherine Dalton, 'Prospective Study Into Puerperal Depression', *Br J Psych*, 118, 689–92.

19 A. Oakley, *Becoming a Mother*, (Martin Robertson, 1979).

20 A. Macfarlane, *The Psychology of Childbirth*, (Fontana, 1977).

21 J. Richman et al., 'Gender Roles, Social Support, and Postpartum Depressive Symptomatology', *J of Nerv and Mental Dis*, 1991, 179, 139–47.

22 Alan J. Riley, 'Sex After Childbirth', *Br J Sexual Med*, 1989, May, p. 185.

23 G.H. Barker, 'The Unkindest Cut of All', *World Med*, 16, 40.

24 R. Kumar and K. Robson, 'Maternal Sexuality during First Pregnancy and After Childbirth', *Br J Obstet Gynaecol*, 1981, 88, 882–9.

25 Robin and Celia Piper, *Telegraph Family Supplement*, 1 January 1993.

CHAPTER 16: AGEING AND INTIMACY

1   Paul Brown and Carolyn Faulder, *Treat Yourself to Sex*, (Penguin, 1989), p. 186.
2   Trevor Stammers, 'What Is At the Root of Ageism?', *Care of The Elderly*, 1992, 4, pp. 228–90.
3   W.H. Long, *Sane Sex and Sane Sex Living*, (Eugenics Publishing Co, New York, 1915), p. 164.
4   Judy G. Bretchneider and Norma L. McCoy, 'Sexual Intercourse and Behaviour in Healthy 80–102-year-olds', *Arch Sex Behaviour*, 1988, 17, 109–29.
5   Pat Lloyd and Paul Brown, 'The Later Years and Sexual Satisfaction', in *Sex and Your Health*, ed. James Bevan (Mandarin, 1990), p. 108.
6   James Willocks, *Essential Obstetrics and Gynaecology*, (Churchill Livingstone, 1978), p. 140.
7   Phillip Sarrell and Lorna Sarrell, *Sexual Turning Points*, (Macmillan, 1984).
8   *Independent*, 3 June 1992, p. 16.
9   Mary Batchelor, *Forty Plus*, (Lion, 1988), p. 147.
10 John Kellett, 'Sex in the Elderly', *BMJ*, 1989, 299, 934.
11 Ruth Westheimer, *Good Sex* (Warner, 1983).

CHAPTER 17: INTIMACY AND LOSS

1   Suzie Hayman, *Hysterectomy* (Sheldon Press, 1991), p. 3.
2   T. McFarlane and J. Kincey, 'Aspects of Doctor-Patient Communication and Their Relevance to Psychological Reaction to Hysterectomy', presented at meeting of West Midland Division of Psychology, Birmingham, 6 May 1981.
3   L. Zussman et al., 'Sexual response after Hysterectomy-Oophorectomy: Recent studies and Reconsideration of Psychogenesis', *Am J Obstet Gynaecol*, 1981, 140, 725–9.
4   Beverley Raphael, *Anatomy of Bereavement*, (Hutchinson & Co, 1984), p. 292.
5   James Owen Drife, 'Are Breasts Redundant Organs?', *BMJ*, 1992, 304, 1060.

6 David Holmes, 'Incontinence', *General Practitioner*, 26 June 1992, p. 45.

7 Beverley Raphael, op. cit., p. 201.

8 Pat Lloyd and Paul Brown, 'The Later Years and Sexual Satisfaction', in *Sex and Your Health*, ed. James Bevan (Mandarin, 1990) p. 110.

CHAPTER 18: AFFAIRS AND ADULTERY

1 Henry Dicks, *Marital Tensions*, (Routledge Kegan Paul, 1967).

2 Sue Arnold, 'Between The Shirts', *Elle*, Sept 1992, p. 68.

3 L. Wolfe, *The Cosmo Report*, (Corgi, 1982).

4 Annette Lawson, *Adultery: An Analysis of Love and Betrayal*, (OUP, 1990).

5 Dave Carder with Duncan Jaenicke, *Torn Asunder: Recovering From Extramarital Affairs* (Moody Press, Chicago, 1992), p. 95.

6 John White, *Eros Defiled*, (IVP, 1978), p. 89.

7 Lynn Atwater, *Extra-Marital Connection: Sex, Intimacy and Identity*, (Irvington, 1982), p. 31.

8 Annette Lawson, op. cit., p. 364.

9 Lewis Smedes, *Sex in The Real World*, (Lion, 1979), p. 184.

10 Angela Neustatter, 'Infidelities', *Elle*, Sept 1982, p. 62.

11 Henry Dicks, ibid.

12 John White, op. cit., p. 79.

13 Janet Reibstein and Martin Richards. *Sexual Arrangements: Marriage and Affairs*, (Mandarin, 1993).

14 Philip Cauthery, Andrew Stanway and Penny Stanway, *The Complete Book of Love and Sex* (Arrow, 1983), p. 93.

15 Dave Carder, op. cit., p. 98.

16 Christine Kell, 'The Management of Sexual Jealousy', *Br J Sex Med*, July 1990. p. 205.

17 Annette Lawson, op. cit., p. 37.

18 Christopher Clulow and Janet Mattinson, *Marriage Matters*, (Penguin, 1989), p. 141.

19 J. Hillman, 'Betrayal', in *Loose Ends: Primary Papers in Archetypal Psychology*, (Spring Publications, Zurich, 1975).

CHAPTER 19: SEPARATION AND DIVORCE

1   Jessie Bernard, *The Future of Marriage*, (Yale University Press, 1982).

2   B. Thornes and J Collard, *Who Divorces?* (Routledge and Kegan Paul, 1979).

3   P. Berger and H. Kellner, 'Marriage and the Construction of Reality', *Diogenes*, 1964, 46, 13–14.

4   Nicky Hart, *When Marriage Ends. A Study In Status Passage*, (Tavistock, 1979), p. 52.

5   E. Gorman, *The Presentation of Self in Everyday Life*, (Doubleday, 1959).

6   Alfred Alvarez, *Life After Marriage: Scenes from Divorce*, (Fontana, 1983).

7   Summarised in Jack Dominian, 'Marital Breakdown and Health', *Update*, 1985, 31, 809–16.

8   Jack Dominian, op. cit., p. 813.

9   Relate, 'Family Policy Briefing No. 3', 1990.

10   Christopher Clulow and Janet Mattinson, *Marriage Matters* (Penguin, 1989) p. 159.

11   Sarah Litvinoff, *The Relate Guide To Starting Again*, (Vermilion, 1993).

12   Ken Crispin, *Divorce – The Forgivable Sin?*, (Hodder & Stoughton, 1988), p. 177.

13   Judith Wallerstein and Joan Kelly, *Surviving The Breakup: How Children and Parents Cope With Divorce*, (Grant McIntyre, 1980).

14   Summarised in Jacqueline Burgoyne et al., *Divorce Matters*, (Pelican, 1987), pp. 131–6.

15   S. Maidment, *Child Custody and Divorce*, (Croom Helm, 1984).

16   Ken Crispin, op. cit., p. 206.

17   Sarah Litvinoff, op. cit., p. 104.

18   R. Hess and K. Camera, 'Post-Divorce Family Relationships as Mediating Factors in The Consequences of Divorce for Children', *Journal of Social Issues*, 1975, 35, p. 79.

19   Jacqueline Burgoyne et al., op. cit., pp. 137–8.

20   Judith Wallerstein and Joan Kelly, op. cit., pp. 106–7.

21   ibid.

CHAPTER 20: DOMESTIC VIOLENCE

1   'Report to the Nation on Crime and Justice: The Data', United States Dept of Justice, 1983, Bureau of Justice Statistics.
2   Sue Smith et al., 'Adult Domestic Violence', *Health Trends*, 1992, 24, 97–9.
3   Appleton, 'The Battered Wife Syndrome', *Ann Emerg Med*, 9, 84–91.
4   Murray A. Straus et al., *Behind Closed Doors: Violence in The Amercican Family*, (Anchor Press, 1980).
5   Brooks Jackson, *The Wall Street Journal*, 25 February 1985.
6   Paul Tournier, *The Violence Within* (Harper & Row, 1978), p. 40.
7   Sandra Horley, *Telegraph Family Supplement*, 4 March 1993.
8   James Alsdurf and Phyllis Alsdurf, *Battered into Submission*, (Highland, 1990), p. 50.
9   Summarised by Lorna J. Smith in *Domestic Violence*, (HMSO, 1990).
10 R.N. Harris and R.W. Bologh, The Dark Side of Love: Blue and White Collar Wife Abuse, *Victimology*, 10, 242–52.
11 Lorna J. Smith, op. cit., p. 27.
12 Murray A. Straus et al., op. cit., p. 193.
13 Kersti Yllo, 'The Status of Women, Marital Equality, and Violence against Wives', *Journal of Family Issues*, 1984, 5, p. 312.
14 J. Pahl, *Private Violence and Public Policy*, (Routledge & Kegan Paul). 1985.
15 E. Evason, *Hidden Violence*, (Farset Press, 1982).
16 J. Gayford, 'Wife Battering: A Preliminary Survey of 100 cases', *BMJ*, 1975, 1, 194–7.
17 R.N. Harris and R.W. Bologh, op. cit.
18 Richard Gelles, 'An Exchange/Social Control Theory', in *The Dark Side of Families*, eds David Finkelhor et al. (Sage, 1985), p. 152.
19 Jack Dominian, *An Introduction To Marital Problems*, (Fount, 1986), p. 134.
20 J. Gayford, op. cit.
21 Emerson Dobash and Russell Dobash, 'The Nature and Antecedents of Violent Events', *Br J Criminology*, 24, 269–88.

22 Richard Gelles, *The Violent Home*, (Sage, 1974).
23 Erin Pizzey, *Scream Quietly or the Neighbours Will Hear*, (Pelican, 1979), p. 148.
24 C.S. Widom, 'The Cycle of Violence', *Science*, 1989, 224, 160–6.
25 Leonora Walker, 'Battered Women and Learned Helplessness', *Victimology*, 2, 525–34.
26 Leonora Walker, *The Battered Woman*, (Harper & Row, 1979), p. 152.
27 Murray A. Straus, 'Victims and Aggressors In Marital Violence', *American Behavioral Scientist*, 23, 691.
28 Michael Green and Tina Gough, 'Monday is A Quiet Day for Murder', *BMA News Review*, May 1993, p. 19.
29 Susan Brownmiller, *Against Our Will*, (Simon & Schuster, 1975), p. 315.
30 J. Gayford. Ten Types of Battered Wives, *Welfare Officer*, 25, 5–9.
31 Donald Dutton, 'Traumatic Bonding', *Victimology*, 1981, 6, 139–55.
32 Leonora Walker, 'The Battered Woman Syndrome Study', in *The Dark Side of Families*, eds David Finkelhor et al., (Sage, 1985), p. 152.
33 Steven Morgan, *Conjugal Terrorism: A Psychological and Community Treatment Model of Wife Abuse*, (R. & E. Research Associates, 1982), p. 30.
34 Vicki Moss, 'Battered Women and The Myth Of Masochism', *Journal of Psychosocial Nursing*, 1991, 29, 19–23.
35 James Alsdurf and Phyllis Alsdurf, op. cit., p. 28.
36 Megan Jobling, 'Battered Wives: A Survey', *Social Services Quarterly*, 1974, 47, p. 82.
37 'US Says Women Who Report Abuse Lower Odds They'll be Attacked Again', *Minneapolis Star and Tribune*, 18 August 1986.

CHAPTER 21: ILLNESS AND DISEASE

1 Michael Craft, 'Sex, Marriage and Handicapped People', *Br J Sex Med*, April 1978, p. 16.

2   Joyce Huggett, *Two Into One?*, (IVP, 1981), p. 82.
3   Michael Craft, op. cit.
4   Alan J. Riley, 'Physical Problems That May Affect Sexuality', in James Bevan (ed.), *Sex and Your Health*, (Mandarin, 1990), p.67.
5   J. Renst et al., 'Marital Problems in General Practice', *Sexual And Marital Therapy*, 1987, 2, 2.
6   Robert Priest, 'A New Initiative on Depression', *Brit J Gen Practice*, 1991, 41, 487.
7   Andrew Sims, 'The Scar That is More Than Skin Deep: The Stigma of Depression', *Brit J Gen Practice*, 1993, 43, 30–1.
8   E. Oppenheimer, *Marriage and Health*, (Marriage Research Centre, 1984).
9   G. Terence Wilson, 'Alcohol and Sexual Function', *Br J Sex Med*, Feb/Mar 1984, pp. 56–8.
10 ibid.
11 Soren Buus Jensen, 'Sexual Customs and Dysfunctions In Alcoholics', *Br J Sex Med*, Nov 1979, p. 34.
12 Jack Dominian, *An Introduction To Marital Problems*, (Fount, 1986), p. 122.
13 Quoted by Wendy Wallace in 'A Glass or Two Too Many', *Telegraph Family Supplement*, 23 October 1992.
14 Serena Haywood et al., 'Recurrent Herpes and Psychological Damage, *Br J Sex Med*, 1993, 20, 25–7.

CHAPTER 22: PORNOGRAPHY

1   What You Feel About Pornography, *Cosmopolitan*, March 1990, pp. 8–12.
2   Catherine Itzin, ed., *Pornography*, (OUP, 1992).
3   Peter Dalley, 'Sex in Society', in *Sex and Your Health*, ed. James Bevan (Mandarin, 1990), p. 321.
4   John Court, *Pornography – A Christian Critique*, (IVP, 1990), p. 46.
5   Tristan Davies, *Daily Telegraph*, 30 May 1992.
6   Andrea Dworkin and Catherine Mackinnon, 'Pornography

and Civil Rights', (Organizing Against Pornography, 1988), p. 138.

7   Earl Wilson, *Sexual Sanity*, (IVP, 1984), p. 71.

8   ibid.

9   Roy McCloughry, *Men and Masculinity*, (Hodder & Stoughton, 1992), p. 173.

10 Richard Griffiths, *Art, Pornography and Human Value*, (Grove Booklets, 1976), p. 21.

11 'Pornography and Sexual Violence: Evidence of the Links'. (The Minneapolis Hearings), *Everywoman*, 1988, p. 127.

12 Earl Wilson, op. cit., p. 78.

13 Susan Griffin, *Pornography and Silence*, (Women's Press, 1981), p. 20.

14 Corinne Sweet, 'Pornography and Addiction', in Catherine Itzin, op. cit., p. 181.

15 Rollo May, *Love and Will*, (Dell, 1969), p. 44.

16 Catherine Itzin and Corinne Sweet, 'What Should We Do About Pornography?', *Cosmopolitan*, November 1989, p. 8.

17 Dolf Zillmann and Jennings Bryant, 'Pornography, Sexual Callousness and the Trivialization of Rape', *Journal of Communication*, 1985, 32 (4), pp. 10–21.

18 Dolf Zillmann and Jennings Bryant, 'Effects of Prolongued consumption of Pornography on Family values', *Journal of Family Issues*, 1988, 9, 518–44.

19 Dolf Zillmann and Jennings Bryant, 'Pornography's Impact on Sexual Satisfaction', *Journal of Applied Social Psychology*, 1988, 18, 438–53.

20 James Weaver et al., 'Effect of Erotica on Young Men's Aesthetic Perception of their Female Sexual Partners', *Perceptual and Motor Skills*, 1984, 58, 929–30.

21 D.T. Kenrick, 'Influence of Popular Erotica on Judgements of Strangers and Mates', *Journal of Experimental Social Psychology*, 1980, 25, 159–67.

22 Nigel Williams, *False Images – Telling the Truth About Pornography*, (Kingsway, 1992), p. 46.

23 Peter Dalley, op. cit., 320.

24 *Final Report of The Attorney General's Commission on Pornography*, (Rutledge Hill Press, Nashville, 1986).

25 Bill Seals, 'Controlling Sexual Assault', (Minneapolis Hearings), op. cit.

26 Floyd Winecoff, quoted by Michael Laslett, 'Men's Fantasies and Actions Controlled by Pornography' (Minneapolis Hearings), op. cit.

27 Ray Wyre, 'Pornography and Sexual Violence', in Catherine Itzin, op, cit., p. 236.

28 Interview with Ted Bundy by Dr James Dobson, Associated Press, 25 January 1989. Video avaiable from CARE, 53 Romney Street, London SW1P.

29 Dolf Zillmann, 'Effects of Repeated Exposure to Nonviolent Pornography', in *Final Report of The Attorney General's Commission on Pornography*, op. cit.

30 Diana Russell, 'Pornography and Rape: A Causal Model', in Catherine Itzin, op. cit., p. 349.

31 Dennis Howitt and Guy Cumberbatch, 'Pornography: Impacts and Influences', 1990, Home Office Research and Planning Unit.

32 John Court, 'Pornography Update', *Br J Sex Med*, May 1981, p. 29.

33 Ray Wyre, op. cit., p. 243.

34 Christopher Bignell, 'Improving The Sexual Health of the Nation', *BMJ*, 1993, 307, 145–6.

35 Roy McCloughry, op. cit.

36 John Court, 1984, op. cit., p. 82.

CHAPTER 23: CHILD ABUSE

1 Diana Russell, 'The Incidence and Prevalence of Intrafamilial and Extrafamilial Sexual Abuse of Female Children', *Child Abuse and Neglect*, 1983, 7, 137.

2 Anon., 'Stop, Look, Listen', *BMJ*, 1992, 305, 838.

3 Diana Riley, ed., *Sexual Abuse of Children – Understanding, Intervention and Prevention*, (Radcliffe Press, 1991).

4 Anon., 'Female Sexual Abusers Are Not Rare', *BMJ*, 1992.

5 Ray Wyre, quoted by Tim Tate, 'The Child Pornography

Industry', in Catherine Itzin, ed., *Pornography*, (OUP, 1992) p. 211.

6 Anon., in Childline – The Second Annual Report.

7 Sylvia Frazer, *My Father's House: A Memoir of Incest and Healing*, (Virago, 1987).

8 Christopher Clulow and Janet Mattinson, *Marriage Matters*, (Penguin, 1989), p. 98.

9 Susan Forward and Craig Buck, *Betrayal of Innocence*, (Penguin, 1988).

10 Charlotte Vale Allen, *Daddy's Girl*, (McClelland & Stewart, 1980), p. 92.

11 Peter Baker, 'Maintaining Male Power', in Catherine Itzin, op. cit.

12 Karin Meiselman, *Incest: A Psychological Study*, (Jossey-Bass, 1978), p. 188.

13 Blair Justice and Rita Justice, *The Broken Taboo. Sex in The Family*, (Human Sciences Press, 1979), p. 187.

14 Philip G. Ney, 'Transgenerational Child Abuse', *Child Psychiatry and Human Development*, 1988, 18, p. 159.

15 Clifford Penner and Joyce Penner, *A Gift For All Ages*, (Word 1986), p. 239.

CHAPTER 24: AIDS

1 Michael Merson, 'Cases of AIDS Increase by A Fifth', *BMJ*, 1993, 306, 1562.

2 Christina M. De Wind, 'A Tale of One City', *BMJ*, 1992, 305, 260.

3 Peter Pallot, 'Most Aids Information Picked Up From TV', *Daily Telegraph*, 11 July 1992.

4 David Widgery, 'AIDS Farewells', *BMJ*, 1992, 305, 590.

5 B.G. Evans et al., 'Sexually Transmitted Diseases and HIV-1 Infection Among Homosexual Men In England and Wales', *BMJ*, 1993, 306, 426–8.

6 WHO Statement for World AIDS Day, 1 December 1991.

7 Emma Thompson, quoted in the *Daily Express*, 16 February 1993.

8   Claire Rayner, *Safe Sex*, quoted by Caroline Collier, in *Twentieth Century Plague*, (Lion, 1987), p. 51.

9   L.C. Rodrigues et al., 'Heterosexual Transmission of HIV', *BMJ*, 1992, 305, 364.

10 Robert Parsons, personal communication.

11 R.J. Kirkman et al., 'User Experience: Mates vs Nuforms', *British Journal of Family Planning*, 1990, 15, 107–11.

12 R.J. Kirkman, 'Condom Use and Failure', *Lancet*, 1990, 336, 1009.

13 Gregory Gardner, 'Promoting Sexual Health', *BMJ*, 1992, 305, 586.

14 Celia Haddon and Thomson Prentice, *Stronger Love, Safer Sex*, (Papermac, 1989), p. 76.

15 op. cit., p. 80.

16 op. cit., p. 98.

17 Patrick Dixon, *The Truth About AIDS*, (Kingsway, 1990), p. 114.

18 Kholoud Porter et al., 'Factors Associated with Lack of Awareness of HIV Infection before diagnosis of AIDS', *BMJ*, 1993, 307, 22.

19 David Morgan, 'AIDS Stigma in Insurance Market', *BMJ*, 1989, 299, 1536.

20 Jonathan Grimshaw, 'Being HIV Antibody-Positive', in Michael Adler (ed.), 'ABC of AIDS', *BMJ*, 1988, p. 47.

21 A.R. Moss and P. Bacchetti, 'Natural History of HIV Infection', *AIDS*, 1989, 3, 55–61.

22 Terry Madeley, 'Having AIDS', in 'ABC of AIDS', op. cit., p. 50.

23 Patrick Dixon, op. cit., p. 164.

24 Roy McCloughry and Carol Bebawi, *AIDS: A Christian Response*, (Grove Booklets, 1987), p. 24.

POSTSCRIPT

1   John Stott, *Issues Facing Christians Today*, (Marshalls, 1984), p. 311.

INDEX